THE HARDINESS OF PLANTS

Agronomy

A Series of Monographs Prepared under the Auspices of

THE AMERICAN SOCIETY OF AGRONOMY

General Editor

A. G. NORMAN

I. C. EDMUND MARSHALL: The Colloid Chemistry of the Silicate Minerals, 1949

II. BYRON T. SHAW, Editor: Soil Physical Conditions and Plant Growth, 1952

III. K. D. JACOB, Editor: Fertilizer Technology and Resources in the United States, 1953

IV. W. H. PIERRE and A. G. NORMAN, Editors: Soil and Fertilizer Phosphorus in Crop Nutrition, 1953

V. GEORGE F. SPRAGUE, Editor: Corn and Corn Improvement, 1955.

VI. J. LEVITT: The Hardiness of Plants, 1956

THE HARDINESS
OF PLANTS

J. LEVITT

Department of Botany
University of Missouri
Columbia, Missouri

ACADEMIC PRESS INC., PUBLISHERS
NEW YORK, N. Y.
1956

Preface

One of the oldest problems in the whole field of plant science is the extraordinary ability of some plants to withstand extremes of moisture and temperature, in contrast to the great sensitivity of others. Naturalists, physiologists, agronomists, horticulturists, geneticists have all been absorbed, at one time or another, with this apparent paradox. Sometimes the problem is forgotten by all for a decade or so until rudely awakened by the destruction of a "test year." The crop breeder seldom forgets it for long and is constantly trying to improve the hardiness of the plant he is developing. But since the genetics of hardiness has not been worked out, he is, unfortunately, still forced to use purely empirical methods. The purpose of this book is (a) to bring together the known facts on hardiness in a single volume which is intended not only for those involved in basic plant physiological studies but also for workers concerned with the many agronomic and horticultural problems that involve crop responses to environment and (b) to stimulate further research by presenting hypotheses that are based on the known facts but that must be tested by experiment.

Both objectives require the inclusion of old as well as new literature. This is in contrast to many fields of science, in which a review of the older literature serves no useful purpose—for instance, the essentiality of elements. In the earlier work, the importance of the trace elements was not known and the salts used were impure; therefore effects supposedly due to an added element may have been caused by an essential trace element present as an impurity. Temperature and water measurements, however, are quite reliable even in the older literature, since the past century has seen no basic improvements of biological importance in the techniques used. Sometimes, indeed, the older experiments may have been performed more carefully than some of the newer ones. Furthermore, due to a waning interest in the subject, some of the older work has not been repeated in recent years and therefore serves as our sole source of information. Consequently, an understanding of the hardiness of plants requires a thorough examination of the old as well as the new investigations.

The author earlier (1941) published a review of the work on frost injury and hardiness. This was planned as a guide to the research worker, and therefore consisted of a series of brief abstracts followed by a short analysis of the results. Since the third and last printing of this review has been exhausted for some time, it appeared that others besides the few who are working directly in this field of research are interested in the subject. The author, therefore, decided to rewrite the book in a more readable form. This required reworking the literature as well as bringing it up to date, and presentation of much of the data in more readily assimilated tables, graphs, and photographs. Much of the exact information should in this way become available to the reader without his having to consult the original literature. In order to orient the subject more clearly in the field of plant science, work on other kinds of hardiness has also been included. The aim is to achieve a more general concept of the hardiness problem by use of information culled from all kinds of hardiness.

A reappraisal of the subject seems, at this time, particularly justified, since the great burst of energy and the intense interest shown by plant physiologists during the first four decades of this century have given way to a lack of interest or experimental work in all but a very few laboratories. Even the rare papers that are appearing show frequently such a complete lack of familiarity with the earlier work that the conclusions arrived at are erroneous and merely add confusion to the problem. Reviews have continued to appear (Ullrich, 1943; Scarth, 1944; Chandler, 1945; Levitt, 1951), but these are all too brief to do the subject justice. It is the author's hope that a thorough reappraisal of the known facts should lead to a renewed interest. When this is coupled with the use of new methods, a successful attack on the still unanswered questions can be anticipated.

The author would like to express his appreciation to the John Simon Guggenheim Memorial Foundation for the grant of a fellowship that made this work possible during a sabbatical year spent in Europe. He would also like to acknowledge his debt to his many colleagues who freely granted use of their institutions to him: Dr. A. Däniker of the Zurich Botanical Gardens, Dr. T. C. van den Honert of the Botany Department, University of Leyden, and Dr. H. Burström of the Botanical Laboratories, University of Lund. Most of the work was done at the last mentioned institution. The author is, therefore, particularly grateful to the University of Lund, to the botanical librarian, Mrs. A. Almestrand, and to the many other university librarians who were so helpful at all times. Thanks are also due to the American Philosophical Society for a grant to cover the cost of photographing plates and figures from original papers.

May, 1956   J. LEVITT

Contents

Part I. Low Temperature Hardiness

Chapter

Part II. Low Moisture or Drought Hardiness

Part III. High Temperature Hardiness

Introduction

The ability of a plant to survive excesses or deficiencies of an environmental factor has been referred to indiscriminately as its resistance or hardiness toward the factor. This has led to some confusion of a purely semantic nature. It must, therefore, be clearly understood at the outset what is meant by these terms. Resistance to an environmental factor may be logically interpreted as the ability of an organism to prevent that factor from invading it. Cold resistance could, therefore, imply the ability of an organism to remain warm in a cold environment. Yet, in analogy with pathological terminology, resistance is also used in the sense of a tolerance of such a factor when it does invade the organism. This ambiguity can be completely avoided by the use of the long-accepted term "hardiness," which implies a certain toughness of the organism, or its ability to survive the full impact of the unfavorable environment without any protective barrier. Thus, the environmental resistance of a plant is here taken to imply its ability to survive an unfavorable external environment. Hardiness is its ability to survive an unfavorable internal environment, and is one specific aspect of the more general resistance. Cold hardiness can, therefore, mean only one thing—the ability of the organism to survive being cooled. This distinction between the two terms will be maintained for all environmental factors. Ephemerals, succulents, and deep-rooted plants, for instance, being adapted to dry climates, are drought-resistant. But the living cells of these plants are not exposed to the drought and may therefore be completely lacking in drought hardiness.

Only the more specific concept—hardiness—will be dealt with in this book. The plant's reactions will be classified according to the unfavorable environmental condition that it is subjected to:

1. Low-temperature hardiness. There are three distinct types—hardiness to extreme low temperatures, to chilling, and to frost.
2. Low moisture or drought hardiness.
3. High temperature or heat hardiness.
4. Hardiness to miscellaneous unfavorable factors.

PART I.
LOW TEMPERATURE HARDINESS

"Seldom does the opportunity occur to observe such pronounced changes in nature as after a sudden first frost. Plants that were previously bursting with life now offer a picture of complete destruction; everywhere are leaves and young shoots limp and blackened as though burnt by the frost. Tender shoots lie on the ground robbed of their turgor. Flowers have become wilted, their lively colors replaced by brown and dirty shades. Within this melancholy picture, there stand out plants that are better able to resist the frost. Not only may they fail to show any injury, but they may actually continue to bloom and produce new shoots until the falling snow hides them from the eyes. This perennially repeated picture gives rise to the following questions: Why is the frost destructive? How can some plants be more resistant than others though they differ from the others in no obvious manner?"

—MAXIMOV (1914)

Chapter I.

The Limits of Low Temperature Hardiness

Since different physiologic processes are affected by temperature in different ways (Belehradek, 1935), a drop in temperature—if sufficiently severe—may be expected to upset the balance and to produce pronounced changes in the plant, perhaps leading to injury. The early philosophers expressed this concept by saying that life cannot exist without its "natural heat" (Aristotle). Theophrastus stated that "the myrtle tree is without heat and therefore freezes rapidly; the laurel, on the other hand, is resistant as long as it retains its heat." Heat, in fact, was at one time thought of as a substance called "caloric."

The first experiments were based on such concepts, which may perhaps be referred to as the "caloric theory." Hunter (1775) froze many kinds of plants (bean seedlings, tulip bulbs, fir seedlings, oat and bean roots). On thawing, they were all dead and could then be frozen more readily. Touching frozen plants with unfrozen shoots produced local thawing. He concluded that the plants must die before they can freeze and that living plants have the ability to generate heat, by means of which they oppose this tendency. His later (1779) temperature measurements inside tree trunks showed these to be nearly always warmer than the surrounding air. He also observed that the sap obtained from tree trunks froze at a higher temperature than the trunk itself. From such evidence, Hunter concluded that all frozen trees are dead trees. Schöpf (1788) went a step further and suggested that the living plant possesses a "specific or bound heat" which is unchangeable and a "free or unbound heat" which may increase or decrease. Others (Hermbstädt, 1808; Schulz, 1823; Reum, 1835; Schacht, 1856) expressed similar views and this "caloric theory" became the prevalent one accepted and expounded by textbooks of that time (Uslar, 1794; Darwin, 1800; Willdenow, 1805).

The prevalence of this theory did not prevent more enlightened heretics from publishing experimental results in disagreement with it. As early as 1741, Duhamel completely discredited the caloric theory by reporting the freezing of apples for two months without injury. Nau (1809) showed that some of the experimental results obtained by Hunter with living plants could be duplicated with dead objects. Du Petit-Thouars (1817) actually observed ice inside plants that proved to be alive on thawing. Göppert (1830), and Le Conte (1852), published

5

detailed observations of freezing in uninjured plants. These observations have since been confirmed by many investigators (see Chapter 3), and some proceeded to ask if there is any limit to the low temperature that plants can attain without injury.

This question can now be answered on the basis of many tests by numerous investigators. Protoplasm can survive long exposures to the lowest temperatures attainable (Table 1). But in the case of the higher

TABLE 1

Survival of very low temperatures by plants. All were able to grow after the low temperature exposure. (See also Luyet and Gehenio, 1938.) (—190°C means liquid air was used, —250°C, liquid hydrogen).

Plant or plant part	Temperature	Exposure time	Observer
Seeds	—100°C	4 days	de Candolle, 1895
Seeds	—190°C	110 hr	Brown and Escombe, 1897
Seeds	—250°C	6 hr	Thiselton-Dyer, 1899
Bacteria and yeast	—190°C	6 months	Macfayden, 1900
Seeds	—190°C	130 hr	Becquerel, 1907
Fungi and algae	—190°C	13 hr	Karcher, 1931
Seeds	—190°C	60 days	Lipman and Lewis, 1934
Mosses (protonema)	—190°C	50 hr	Lipman, 1936
Seeds and spores	1–4°K	44 hr	Lipman, 1936a
Fungus mycelium and bacteria	—190°C	48 hr	Lipman, 1937
Spores and pollen grains	—273°C (within a few thousandths of a degree)	2 hr	Becquerel, 1954

and even some of the lower plants, this is true only of protoplasm in the dry state. The very seeds and other plant parts that survive the lowest temperatures are readily killed by them if first allowed to take up water (Table 2). In this hydrated state they freeze; in the dry state they remain unaltered (Schumacher, 1875; Schander and Schaffnit, 1919; Stuckey and Curtis, 1938). Even buds may have a low enough water content (20 to 30%) to prevent freezing at temperatures of —18 to —26°C (Wiegand, 1906). In many of the above cases the uptake of water occurred so rapidly (1 to 4 hr. Lockett and Luyet, 1951; Ivanoff, 1951) that the tremendous rise in killing temperature could not be due to growth.

Observations in nature had earlier revealed that normally hydrated protoplasm varies greatly in its tolerance of low temperatures (see Hunter above and Table 3). Frost injury (Fig. 1) has, of course, been

TABLE 2

Survival of low temperatures by dry and hydrated plants

Plant	Low temperature treatment	Survival		Observer
		Dry	Hydrated	
Seeds	−25 to −40°C for 15 hrs.	all germinated	none germinated	Göppert, 1830
Seeds	−190°C for 130 hrs.	all germinated	none germinated	Becquerel, 1907
Corn kernels	32 to 28°F	(25% moisture) all germinated	(75–85% moisture) none germinated	Kiesselbach and Ratcliff, 1918[*]
Yeast	−113°C	unaffected	vacuolate cells all killed; young (nonvacuolate) uninjured	Schumacher, 1875
Ranunculus tubers	−190°C for 18 days	(9% moisture) all survived	(30–50% moisture) all killed	Becquerel, 1932a
Wheat seed	−190°C for 2 mins.	(10.6% H_2O) all germinated	(25.1% H_2O) none germinated	Locket and Luyet, 1951
Alfalfa seed	−20°C for 1 day	90% germinated	none germinated	Tysdal and Pieters, 1934

[*] Similar results were obtained by Jensen, 1925; Steinbauer, 1926; Stuckey and Curtis, 1938; McRostie, 1939.

TABLE 3

Early observations of Low-temperature injury in different plants
(For more recent observations see Table 81.)

Plant	Killing temperature	Observer
Roses, etc.	freezing temperatures (not measured)	De Candolle, 1838
Circaea lutetiana Solanum Cucurbita spp.	—1 to —2°R	Krasan, 1869
Sedum,Sempervivum, maize, etc.	—3 to —8°C	Haberlandt, 1876
Roots of *Helleborus niger* and *H. viridis*	—15°R	quoted by Göppert, 1871
Roots of *Cicuta virosa*	—10°R	quoted by Göppert, 1871
Trees above snow line in the arctic, and lichens, mosses, and fungi on them	uninjured by —40 to —47°R	quoted by Göppert, 1871
Potato	—1.9 to —2.25°C	Maximov, 1914

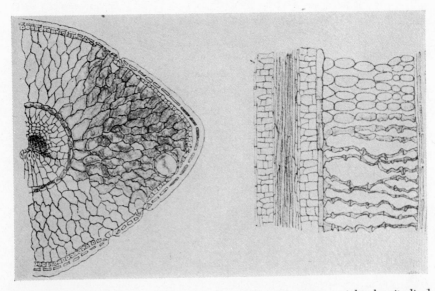

FIG. 1.   Frost injury in a spruce needle. Left, cross section; right, longitudinal section. Injured cells dark or collapsed (from Däniker, 1923).

observed by nearly everyone living in temperate zones, and many types have been described (Sorauer, 1884, 1906, 1907, 1936; Däniker, 1923). Since this injury occurs at different temperatures for different plants (Table 3), Mez (1905) suggested that for each plant there is a specific minimum temperature below which its protoplasm cannot survive. In view of the above evidence (Table 2), it must be assumed that he refers to plants in the hydrated state. Even in this form, however, his hypothesis was soon disproved. His own student (Voigtländer, 1909) showed that many plants can survive a much lower temperature if undercooled than if permitted to freeze (Table 4). Müller-Thurgau (1880) and

TABLE 4

Survival of low temperatures by cells in the undercooled vs. the frozen state
(from Voigtländer, 1909)

Species	Frost killing temperatures (°C)	Lowest temperature to which undercooled (without injury) (°C)
Agave americana	—5.5	—8.37
Escheveria leopoldiana	—3.4	—9.11
Tradescantia virginica	—5.2	—7.14
Ricinus communis	—5.5	—7.4
Tropaeolum majus	—4.0	—8.96

Molisch (1897) had earlier found the same thing. That very pronounced undercooling may also occur under natural conditions has been shown by many others (Table 5). In some cases, at least, freezing resulted in death at higher temperatures. Modern workers have begun to reinvestigate this fact (Mäde and Ullrich, 1941; Seemann, 1942). In the case of some fungi, however, injury may apparently occur even in the undercooled state (Lindner, 1915), but this is presumably a case of chilling injury (see Chapter 4).

Still more emphatic evidence against Mez's hypothesis was produced by Bartetzko (1909) and Maximov (1912). The former showed that even if ice formation is permitted, the killing temperature for *Aspergillus niger* varies inversely with the concentration of dextrose used in the culture medium (Table 6). Maximov went a step further and showed that simply immersing fully grown cells of higher plants in solutions protected them from low temperature injury (Table 7). This was true of all the plants tested—even the frost-sensitive *Tradescantia discolor*. Other solutes besides sugars were effective provided they were nontoxic. Repetition of these experiments by other investigators has brought full confirmation of Maximov's results (Åkerman, 1927; Tetley, 1931; Fukuda, 1932; Iljin, 1933, 1934; Chandler and Hildreth, 1935; Wilhelm, 1935). Kylin (1917) and Carrick (1920) failed to obtain protection, but this can be explained by the toxic nature of the solute used (some of the

TABLE 5

Undercooling under natural conditions

Plant part	Undercooling temp.	Other observations	Observer
Tree buds (8 species)	—18 to —26.5°C		Wiegand, 1906
Pyrola leaves	—32.14°C	(froze at —3.5°C when dead)	Lewis and Tuttle, 1920
Peach buds	—6 to —8°C		Johnston, 1922, 1923
Flower buds of plums	—21°F		Dorsey and Strausbaugh, 1923
Caragana	—21.3°C		Novikov, 1928
Hedera helix	—20°C	killed by —12 to —13°C if frozen	Iljin, 1934
Grain roots	—11°C	killed if frozen at several degrees higher	Zacharowa, 1926
Fir needles	—21°F		Clements, 1938

TABLE 6

Frost killing of *Aspergillus niger* grown in dextrose solutions of different concentrations (from Bartetzko, 1909)

Conc. of dextrose (%)	Frost killing point (°C)	Isotonic NaNO$_3$ (%)	Freezing point of NaNO$_3$ (°C)
1	—2	9	—3.3
10	—4	16	—5.6
20	—9	24	—8.2
30	—14	30.5	—10.2
40	—22	36.5	—11.9
50	living at —26	38.5	—12.5

algae were killed by Kylin's solutions even in the absence of freezing) or by lack of penetration (Carrick). It should be emphasized that protection occurs only if the solutions plasmolyze the cells (Åkerman, 1927).

Iljin went a step further. He was able to protect cabbage sections that were frozen in dry ice, even though he did not apply the protective solutions until the temperature was brought back to —7.8°C. Maximov had tried this method without success, and it now seems certain that Iljin's results do not involve true survival, for he was unable to obtain complete deplasmolysis and may therefore have been dealing only with tonoplast survival (Stuckey and Curtis, 1938). Siminovitch (unpublished) corroborated Iljin's results but showed that the deplasmolysis was always followed eventually by cell bursting.

TABLE 7

Frost killing of red cabbage when frozen in glucose solutions of different concentrations (from Maximov 1912)

Freezing temperature (°C)	Percent alive in glucose solutions of given molarities						
	0.0 (H₂O)	0.06	0.13	0.25	0.50	1.0	2.0
—5.2	50	100	100	100	100	100	100
—7.8	0	few	25	100	100	100	100
—11.1	0	0	few	50	100	100	100
—17.3	0	0	0	few	25	100	100
—22.0	0	0	0	0	few	100	100
—32.0	0	0	0	0	0	few	50

These results are of particular importance in formulating a general concept of low-temperature hardiness. It would appear that even hydrated protoplasm that is normally injured by moderately low temperatures can, under suitable conditions, have its hardiness markedly increased. The most extreme examples of this have been provided by Lipman (1937) using actively growing bacteria and fungi, and by Luyet and his co-workers. Luyet and Thoennes (1938a) were able to maintain strips of onion epidermis in the living state at the temperature of liquid air, though the tissue is normally killed by slight freezing. This was possible only when the rates of freezing and thawing were sufficiently great to prevent any observable crystallization of the water (less than $\frac{1}{1 \times 10^{-5}}$ sec per degree, Luyet, 1937). In the same way, Goetz and Goetz (1938) reduced the death rate of yeast cells exposed to —185°C from 75% to 3% by speeding up the cooling from 1 to 10^4 degrees/sec. Many other tissues (both plant and animal) have since been similarly exposed to liquid air without injury (Becquerel, 1949; Luyet, 1951). It has even been possible to freeze pollen grains of orchids rapidly and then dry them in the frozen state, in this way maintaining them alive much longer than if not so treated (Svihla and Osterman, 1943). True, Scholander *et al.* (1953) were able to kill arctic twigs that had previously stood —60°C by immersing them in liquid oxygen, but this may have been due to the relatively slow freezing and thawing of such bulky organs, and it does not detract from the clear-cut positive results obtained at will by Luyet.

From all these results the following hypothesis emerges:

All protoplasm is able to survive the lowest temperatures under suitable conditions.

Corollary: Only hydrated protoplasm can be injured by low temperatures.

Chapter 2.

The Temperatures of Plants Exposed to Freezing

The fact that ice can form in living plants led many early workers to a quantitative investigation of the temperature changes during the freezing process. Modern methods of plant temperature measurement with thermocouples are described by Ullrich and Mäde (1940), Eggert (1946), Rogers (1949). Most of the early measurements were made with thermometers inserted into tree trunks. Due to the bulk of these organs, the attainment of temperature equilibrium is slowed down, but exact determinations are much easier to obtain than in the case of thinner organs such as leaves. It was soon shown that, though the temperature difference between tree trunks and the surrounding air may be as much as 5 to 10°C, it is often much less, and the tissues can freeze quite readily (Table 8). Sometimes the tree temperature was even lower than the air temperature, and ice crystals were actually isolated from the frozen but uninjured trees (Göppert, 1830; De Candolle, 1838). Many showed no further drop in temperature for some time on reaching —1°C, though the air temperature was much lower (Göppert, 1830). This was attributed to the heat released on freezing (Nägeli, 1861).

The actual course of the temperature drop in plants exposed to subzero temperatures was determined by later investigators. Mez (1905) describes it as follows. There is almost a vertical drop to the freezing point, followed by a horizontal course until all the surplus water is frozen. This is succeeded by a shorter temperature fall to the eutectic point. As long as solidification of the solute continues, a horizontal path is followed. In the absence of any more solute, all the water freezes. Finally, there occurs a precipitate vertical drop toward the temperature of the freezing bath, indicating that no more heat of crystallization is liberated. Mez therefore concluded that no more ice occurs in the plant at —30°C than at —6°C (the supposed eutectic point). It is not clear whether his description is based on theory or experiment, for it was not until a few years later that his students (Apelt, 1907; Rein, 1908; Voigtländer, 1909) published evidence purporting to support Mez's concept.

Mez's description and explanation of the freezing curves of plants have since been opposed by all investigators, (Table 9) both for theoretical

TABLE 8

Comparison of tree temperatures with air temperatures during winter. Thermometer bulb near center of trunk.

Species	Trunk diameter	Air temperature	Tree temperature	Condition of tree	Observer
White ash	1 ft.	41°F	51°F		Schöpf, 1788
Beech	3 in.	35	35		Schöpf, 1788
Chestnut	3 ft.	22	36		Schöpf, 1788
Red cedar	1 ft.	34	38		Schöpf, 1788
	3 in.	24	30		Schöpf, 1788
White ash	3 ft.	32	34		Schöpf, 1788
	50 cm.	2–20°C	9–19°C		Solomé, 1803
Maple, sumach		—20°R		sap unfrozen	Schulz, 1823
Elm, red fir		—13 to —15°R	—12 to —14°R	no injury	Schübler, 1827
		—2.0	—0.1		Schübler, 1827
		—2.5	—0.5		Schübler, 1827
		—15.2	—14		Schübler, 1827
General	6–8 in.		1–2°R difference		Schübler, 1827
	2 ft.		5–7°R difference		Schübler, 1827

reasons (Fischer, 1911; Maximov, 1914; Luyet and Gehenio, 1937), and because the temperature curves they obtained do not agree with his description of the process.

That two plateaus may be observed in the freezing curves of plant tissues has been pointed out by Luyet and Gehenio (1937), both from

TABLE 9

Evidence against a eutectic point in plants

Material frozen	Results obtained	Observer
Partially evaporated peach twig sap (1/6 to 1/8 of original volume)	Unfrozen at —22°C	Chandler, 1913
Physiological salt (0.7% NaCl)	Inhibition of temperature drop almost indetectable at the eutectic point (—22°C)	Fischer and Jensen (See Maximov, 1914)
Living or dead red beet	Slower temperature drop at —8°C when frozen than when undercooled	Maximov, 1914
Red cabbage	Decrease in volume of unfrozen sap below —6°C	Schander and Schaffnit, 1919
Grain seedlings	No sign of a double freezing pt.	Zacharowa, 1926
Potato cylinders (dead)	No sign of a double freezing pt.	Luyet and Gehenio, 1937
Clover	Ice formation continued below —20°C	Greathouse, 1935
Rhododendron leaves	Maximum frost curvature at —15 to —20°C	Fukuda, 1933

their own results and from those of earlier investigators (Fig. 2). This may have been the basis of Mez's theory. But since this "double freezing point" appears only in living tissue (Fig. 3), it cannot be due to a eutectic point. Furthermore, it can be suppressed in living tissue by a preliminary surface drying, accentuated by soaking in water. Luyet and Gehenio suggest that the first freezing point is due to freezing of the extracellular water, the second due to freezing of intracellular water. The latter may conceivably occur either after exosmosis of water from the cells or while it is still in the vacuoles. The final death blow to the theory of a eutectic point was the evidence that ice formation continues in plant tissues at temperatures well below the supposed eutectic point, e.g. below —30°C (Greathouse, 1935; Scholander et al., 1953; Fig. 4).

Presumably, most if not all the solutes remain in solution below their eutectic points due to protection by substances, such as hexoses, that are difficult to crystallize.

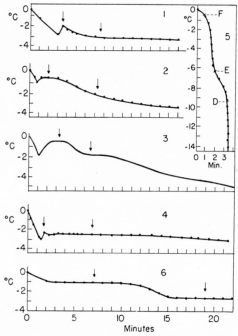

FIG. 2. The double freezing point as obtained by various workers (from Luyet and Gehenio, 1937).

Though no eutectic point can be detected for plant tissues, a freezing point can be readily determined. But the plant's temperature nearly always drops below this point before freezing occurs (Fig. 2). There is therefore also an undercooling point (Table 10) which may vary much more than the freezing point. It may even be altered by mechanical shocks (Luyet and Hodapp, 1938). The freezing point itself is not constant. It is lower in living than in dead tissues (Table 11), and varies somewhat with the rate of temperature drop (Maximov, 1914; Walter and Weismann, 1935; Luyet and Gehenio, 1937). In fact, if the cooling rate is slow enough, the freezing point of the living tissue is identical with that of dead tissue (Luyet and Galos, 1940).

All these results are a little difficult to explain. Since the intercellular water of a living (but not a dead) plant is nearly pure, one would expect it to freeze at a higher temperature in living than in dead tissues; and if Luyet and Gehenio's explanation of the "double freezing point" is correct, it would seem logical for the freezing point of dead tissue to fall somewhere between these two freezing points of living tissue, instead

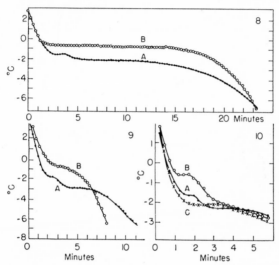

FIG. 3. Freezing curves for potato tissues. The "double freezing point" in curves 8A and 9A obtained with living tissues, the single freezing point in curves 8B and 9B with dead tissues. Accentuation of the "double freezing point" by presoaking for 4 hr (10B). Elimination of the "double freezing point" by drying in air for 4¾ hr before freezing (10C) (from Luyet and Gehenio, 1938).

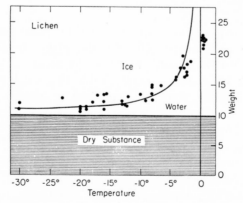

FIG. 4. Progressive ice formation with temperature drop to —30°C in the lichen *Cetraria richardsonii* (from original of figure 5, P. F. Scholander *et al.*, *J. Cellular Comp. Physiol.* **42**: 22, 1953).

of above both of them, as is actually the case. On the other hand, even though the intercellular water is nearly pure, its freezing point must be lower than that of pure water, because it is mainly imbibition water in the cell wall. Due to its close proximity to the cell contents, it must be practically in vapor pressure equilibrium with the water inside the cell. Consequently, the first freezing point should essentially represent that of the tissue as a whole. But what can we expect this freezing point to be? Since the tissue is living, it possesses turgor. At full turgor (e.g. after presoaking in water) the freezing point should be practically that of pure water. Therefore, the freezing point of living, turgid tissue should be *above* rather than below that of dead tissue.

TABLE 10

Undercooling and freezing points of some tissues

Plant	Undercooling point	Freezing point	Observer
Potatoes	—6.1°C	—0.98	Müller-Thurgau, 1880
Aspergillus niger			
in 1% dextrose	—6	—0.29	Bartetzko, 1909
in 20% dextrose	—8	—2.89	Bartetzko, 1909
in 50% dextrose	—14	—8.9	Bartetzko, 1909
Red beet root	—6.83	—1.88	Maximov, 1914
Tussilago farfara	—2.70	—1.83	Maximov, 1914
Potato tuber	—1.60 to —2.42	—0.85 to —1.57	Maximov, 1914

Unfortunately, the experimental difficulties in determining the true freezing point for a living tissue are such that theory and experiment cannot usually be expected to agree. Initial crystal formation in a slowly cooled, fully turgid plant would soon come to a stop. If, for instance, 1% of the plant's water froze, the cell sap concentration would increase slightly, causing the freezing-point lowering to drop by about 0.01°C in a plant with a freezing point of —1.0°C. Such a drop would not be significant. But this loss of 1% of its total water would reduce the cell's turgor by 10 to 20%, since a loss of 5 to 10% of its total water is usually sufficient to convert a turgid cell into a flaccid one. The freezing point of the above plant would, therefore, be lowered by 0.1 to 0.2°C, and this would be easily detected on the freezing curve as a "double freezing point." In complete conformity with this explanation, Luyet and Gehenio (1937) were able to accentuate the double freezing point by soaking the tissue (thus raising its turgor pressure) in advance of freezing, and to eliminate it by allowing the tissue to dry for a few hours in air before freezing (Fig. 3, curves 10A–C). Quantitatively, the difference between the two

TABLE 11

The freezing points of living and dead tissues (°C)

Plant	Living	Dead	Observer
Phaseolus leaves	—1.1	—0.5	Müller-Thurgau, 1880
Cypripedium leaves	—2.0	—0.5	Müller-Thurgau, 1880
Red beet roots	—2.15 to —2.55	—1.25	Maximov, 1914
Tussilago farfara	—2.03 to —3.35	—0.97	Maximov, 1914
Helleborus viridis	—4.07 to —5.88	—2.07 to —2.15	Maximov, 1914
Potato tubers	—1.0	—0.5	Müller-Thurgau, 1880
	—1.22	—0.63	Maximov, 1914
	—0.87 to —2.00	—0.69 to 0.80	Walter and Weismann, 1935
	—1.2 to —2.0	—0.5 to —0.75	Luyet and Gehenio, 1937

freezing points sometimes seems too large to be accounted for by this loss in turgor. But it must be realized that the plant juices cannot be stirred to maintain a uniform mixture, such as in the case of a solution freezing in a test tube. Therefore, further ice formation might not occur in significant amounts when the temperature dropped the 0.1 to 0.2°C to the true second freezing point; for undercooling could still occur in all except the regions in the immediate vicinity of the first few ice masses. The relatively slow rate of ice propagation through the intercellular spaces would not be sufficient to raise the tissue temperature above this undercooling point but would simply prevent a further drop in temperature. In the case of dead tissues, such a gradual propagation of crystal formation cannot occur, since the ice can spread directly through the cells instead of being confined to the intercellular spaces as in living tissues (see next chapter).

The above facts lead to the conclusion that even most determinations of the first freezing point yield too low a value; for the small amount of heat liberated on freezing 1% of the plant's water is usually not enough to counteract completely the effect of the cooling mixture. The results of Luyet and Galos (1940) are in complete conformity with this reasoning. Not only did slow cooling raise the freezing point of living tissue to that of dead tissues, but in the slowest cooling used, the freezing point of living tissue was actually higher than that of dead tissue.

On the basis of all these results, Mez's incorrect description of the temperature in a plant exposed to freezing must be replaced by the following. The initial temperature drop is steady and continues below the freezing point of the tissues. At some point that varies markedly with the conditions, there is a sudden rise in temperature. This first variable minimum is the undercooling point; the maximum that the temperature subsequently rises to is the freezing point of the tissues. This freezing point of the tissues is also variable and must not be confused with the freezing point of the expressed juice, which is constant as long as the concentration is unaltered. The temperature remains constant at the freezing point for some time, provided the rate of cooling is not too rapid, forming a plateau in the freezing curve. As ice continues to form in the tissue, the temperature begins to drop again. A second plateau may be formed in living but not in dead tissue. The subsequent temperature drop is rapid again. Ice formation in the plant does not cease abruptly but continues at a progressively decreasing rate, even at —30°C. In brief, the freezing plant exhibits an undercooling point, which varies greatly, a freezing point which varies less markedly, sometimes a "second freezing point," but no eutectic point.

Chapter 3.

Ice Formation in the Plant

Even during the era of the caloric theory of low-temperature injury, the freezing of plants was already being studied. The frost splitting of trees, which occurs with a "crack like that of a gun," led to the belief that the plant tissues expand on freezing and may ultimately rupture because of the expansion (Bobart, 1684; Chomel, 1710; Du Hamel and de Buffon, 1737; Stromer, 1749; Thouin, 1806; Hermbstädt, 1808). But Schübler (1827) pointed out that this splitting occurs only in thick trees (1½ to 2 ft in diameter), not at all in thin ones (a few inches in diameter), though the temperature drops much lower in the latter. He further states that when a tree is split in this way, no significant injury occurs; on the other hand, it is the youngest twigs that are injured first, though they never suffer such splits. Nevertheless, even the limpness of thawed herbaceous plants was thought to be due to rupture (Senebier, 1800; Thouin, 1806; Hermbstädt, 1808). Plants that survive freezing were believed able to prevent such expansion or even to contract due to the presence of oils that shrink on freezing (Bobart, 1684; Du Hamel and de Buffon, 1737; Stromer, 1749; Reum, 1835).

This "rupture theory" has been accepted even relatively recently (Goodale, 1885; Kerner and Oliver, 1894; West and Edlefsen, 1917; Goetz and Goetz, 1938; Bugaevsky, 1939a), perhaps because it is based on the sound physical fact that water expands on freezing. Since the plant consists mostly of water, the assumption that it, too, expands on freezing was a logical one. But others besides Schübler began to doubt the theory. Du Petit-Thouars (1817) found it difficult to believe that some plants could survive such expansion, yet he knew that many survive freezing. Soon after, Göppert (1830) examined literally thousands of plants microscopically in search of cell rupture. In agreement with previous observations, he found that the juice could be easily squeezed out of frost-injured leaves; but he was unable to find any torn cell walls, though the cells were somewhat collapsed. Others confirmed his observations (Morren, 1838; Lindley, 1842; Schacht, 1856; Martens, 1872—see Prillieux, 1872; Schumacher, 1875). Nägeli (1861a) pointed out, in fact, that cell walls can stretch much more than the small amount that would occur even if all the cell's water froze. He also showed that frost-killed Spirogyra cells will collapse if transferred to glycerin after thawing. This

21

could not happen if there were any tears in the wall. But the final death blow to the rupture theory was the discovery that tissues actually contract, instead of expanding, on freezing (Table 12). Even frost splitting of trees can be explained by an asymmetrical contraction (Caspary, 1857).

The explanation of plant contraction during freezing required direct microscopic examination of frozen tissues. This showed that the rupture theory was unsound at the outset, for instead of the ice forming inside

TABLE 12

Volume changes on freezing of plant tissues (see also Müller-Thurgau, 1880)

Plant part	Percent change in volume	Observer
Leaves	—25	Hoffmann, 1857
Petioles and midribs	—1 to —3½ (length)	Sachs, 1860
Beet root and pumpkin fruit	0	Sachs, 1860
Bark of twigs	—13.5	Wiegand, 1906
Wood of twigs	— 2.5	Wiegand, 1906
Yeast cells	—10	Molisch, 1897
Spirogyra cells	diameter reduced to 1/3	Molisch, 1897
Cladophora cells	diameter reduced by 20%	Molisch, 1897

the cell, as had been tacitly assumed, it normally occurs outside it—in the intercellular spaces or on the surface of the tissues (Table 13; Fig. 5). Many attempts have been made to explain the location of the first crystals in the intercellular spaces (Sachs, 1860; Müller-Thurgau, 1886; Kerner, 1894; Cavallero, 1888, 1891; Wiegand, 1906a; Åkerman, 1927; Bugaevsky, 1939, 1939a; Ullrich and Mäde, 1940). These explanations usually assume either vapor pressure gradients or a preliminary exudation of cell water into the intercellular spaces. But neither of these can provide the explanation, since the vapor pressure gradients would normally be in the wrong direction—from a maximum in the cell sap to a minimum in the surrounding air; and the exudation that has been observed is a result of freezing. It is a simple fact, however, that a layer of oil favors the undercooling of water. Even immersing a whole plant in oil has been shown to produce this effect (Mez, 1905). The protoplasts are therefore very well adapted to undercooling, for not only are they small (and this also favors undercooling), but they are surrounded by a lipid layer—the plasma membrane. The water outside the protoplast (in the wall and intercellular spaces) is not so protected and therefore freezes after a relatively slight undercooling. The lipid layer around the protoplast serves a double purpose, for even after ice crystals form outside it, they cannot penetrate the lipid layer and therefore are unable to "seed" the aqueous phase of the protoplast (Chambers and Hale, 1932). This is not surprising, since even nonliving membranes that are freely permeable to liquids may be completely impermeable to growing ice crystals (Lusena and Cook, 1953). Once ice forms in the intercellular spaces, the vapor pressure drops below that of the protoplast, and water diffuses from the protoplast through the permeable

TABLE 13

Observations of extracellular ice formation in the plant

Plant	Observer	Plant	Observer
Daphne, Hydrangea, Iris, Fritillaria	Du Petit-Thouars, 1817	Twigs of *Acer negundo*	Dalmer, 1895
Many	Göppert, 1830	Algae, Agave, Aloe, beet	Molisch, 1897
Exotic plants	Caspary, 1854	Algae, potatoes, beets	Wiegand, 1906,
Potatoes, beets	Schacht, 1856	Tree twigs, buds	Wiegand, 1906a
Pumpkin slices	Sachs, 1860	Cabbage, fungi	Schander and Schaffnit, 1919
Iris germanica, etc.	Prillieux, 1869	Fucaceae	Kylin, 1917
Nitella syncarpa	Kunisch, 1880	*Buxus sempervirens*	Steiner, 1933
Roots and tubers	Müller-Thurgau, 1880	Peach buds	Dorsey, 1934
		Cortical cells of trees	Siminovitch and Scarth, 1938

plasma membrane to the regions of crystallization. In this way, the cell sap concentration increases steadily and ice formation inside it is avoided even at very low temperatures.

The ice crystals grow to masses larger than the cells (Fig. 5), and the cells contract and even collapse (Fig. 6; Table 12). This contraction may be so severe that, in the case of the epidermal cells with colored vacuoles, the opposite sides of the cell can be seen to come in contact with each other (Iljin, 1933, 1934; Siminovitch and Scarth, 1938; Fig. 7). Since the cells are firmly connected with each other, this results in a contraction of the tissues and of the organ as a whole; at the same time, the air from the intercellular spaces is squeezed out (Lindley, 1842; Wiegand, 1906a). The ice crystals may be confined to certain regions, forming such large masses (as much as 1000 times the size of a cell—Müller-Thurgau, 1886) that tissues are pushed apart (Caspary, 1854; Schacht, 1856; Fig. 5). On thawing, the intercellular ice is converted to water, leaving the

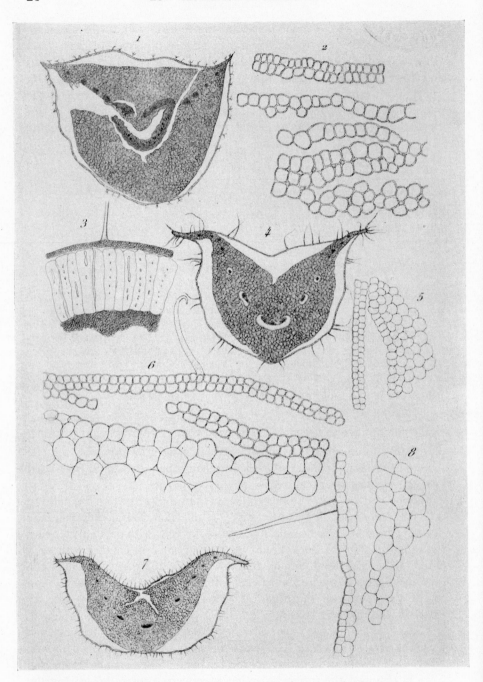

Fig. 5. Contraction of internal tissues from epidermis, and other tissue separations caused by ice masses formed between the tissues. Actual ice masses shown diagrammatically in 3 (from Prillieux, 1869).

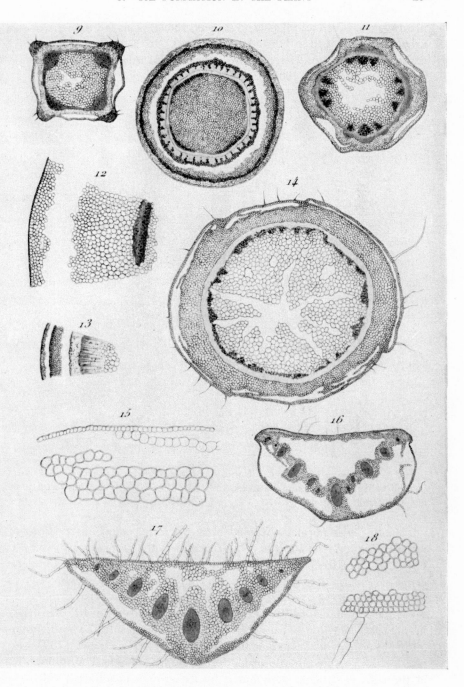

plant water-soaked and flaccid (Prillieux, 1869). This led earlier workers to believe that cell rupture had occurred. In the case of uninjured tissues, the cells rapidly reabsorb the water, but injured cells are unable to do this (Wiegand, 1906a).

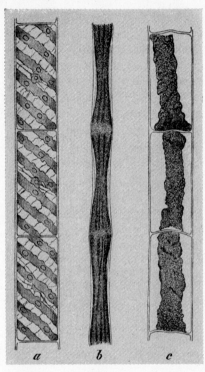

FIG. 6.   Spirogyra (X300): (a) Normal state. (b) Frozen and lying in ice, showing cell collapse without any ice inside the cell. (c) Thawed, showing "frost plasmolysis" (from Molisch, 1897).

Though ice is normally formed extracellularly, many observations of intracellular ice formation have been made in the laboratory (Table 14; Fig. 7, 8). The freezing occurs in sudden flashes in one cell at a time, the crystals appearing to be both within and outside the vacuole (e.g. in onion epidermis—Chambers and Hale, 1932). When freezing is relatively slow, the ice may form between the wall and the tonoplast. This may be the same phenomenon as the "thin hull of ice inside the wall" previously described by Schander and Schaffnit (1919). Onoda (1937) explains this exceptional type of ice formation as follows. The protoplasm of the cells is strongly dehydrated by ice growth in adjacent cells. As a result, it separates from the wall. The space formed becomes filled with ice, resulting in pseudoplasmolytic freezing. But this description is not in accord with the cell collapse observed by Iljin and others. Ice formation between the wall and the protoplasm in Nitella had previ-

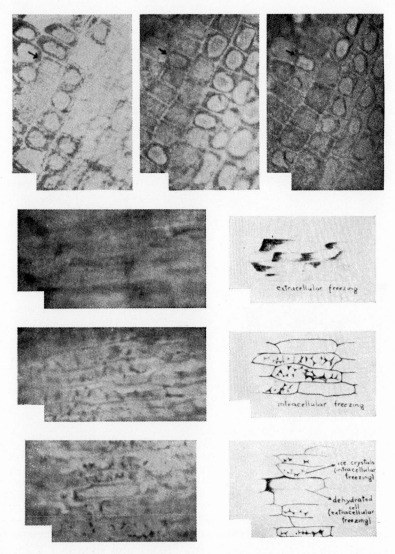

FIG. 7. Ice formation in cortical tissues of Cornus twigs (upper three) and red cabbage epidermis. Extracellular and intracellular freezing shown diagrammatically at right (from Siminovitch and Scarth, 1938).

ously been described by Cohn, 1871, and in *Conferva fracta* by Göppert, 1883. In cortical cells of trees, with thick protoplasm layers, Siminovitch and Scarth (1938) saw the ice form first at one end of the protoplasm, from where it spread around each side of the vacuole to the other end.

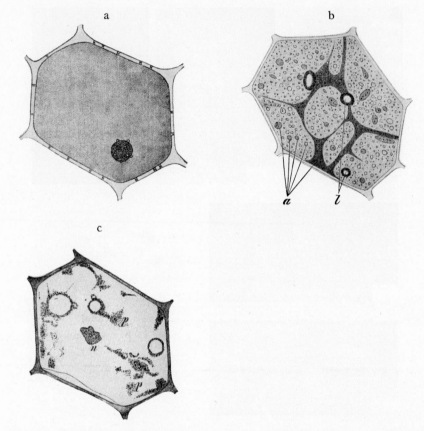

FIG. 8. Epidermal cell of *Tradescantia discolor* (X300). (a) Normal cell filled with red cell sap. (b) Frozen intracellularly. Most of sap converted to ice, concentrated unfrozen sap at *a*, air bubbles at *1*. (c) Thawed. Wall and nucleus stained red, coagulated cytoplasm at *p* (from Molisch, 1897).

Only when the freezing of the protoplasm was complete did the vacuole freeze. In one case, in fact, the protoplasm froze but the vacuole remained unfrozen. Stuckey and Curtis (1938) also state that the cytoplasm appears to freeze before the vacuole. The flashlike, cell-by-cell freezing that occurs when ice forms intracellularly has been strikingly recorded in recent years by the moving picture camera (Luyet, Modli-bowska).

In nearly all cases, the intracellular ice formation was brought about by rapid freezing (Table 14)—e.g. by supercooling well below the freezing point of the tissue and then inducing or waiting for ice formation. Not only was freezing more rapid than normally occurs in nature, but, to facilitate observation, sections of tissues were used. That intracellular

TABLE 14

Observations of intracellular ice formation in the plant

Plant	Temperature at which frozen	Observer
Apple		Morren, 1838
Pumpkin	—12 to —20°R	Sachs, 1860
Nitella syncarpa	—3 to —4°C	Cohn, 1871
Roots and tubers	—10°C	Müller-Thurgau, 1880
Conferva fracta		Göppert, 1883
Codium bursa	—11°C	Molisch, 1897
Tradescantia crassula (staminal hairs)	—6.5°C	Molisch, 1897
Agave, Aloe, beet	Rapid cooling	Molisch, 1897
Tradescantia discolor and *T. guianensis*	Slow freezing	Molisch, 1897
Tradescantia and *Vallisneria spiralis*	—4 to —5°C	Schaffnit, 1910
Cabbage	—5°C	Schander and Schaffnit, 1919
Fungi	Rapid freezing	Schander and Schaffnit, 1919
Cabbage, tree cortex	—12°C	Siminovitch and Scarth, 1938

ice formation is not due to sectioning was shown by Siminovitch and Scarth (1938), who observed it in whole potted plants cooled from 0°C to —10°C in half an hour. But though this type of freezing can be obtained at will in the laboratory, the question is whether or not it occurs under natural conditions. The only available evidence is from painstaking observations of normally frozen tissues in the open. In all such cases, only extracellular ice has been found (Table 13). Nonetheless, the conditions suitable for intracellular freezing do occur in nature. Cambium temperatures on the south side of a tree can rise to as much as 50 to 55°F above those on the north side (Eggert, 1944). This must certainly be followed by very rapid freezing as soon as the south side is shaded, and may conceivably lead to "sun scald." Whether or not this type of injury is due to intracellular freezing cannot be decided until careful microscopic observations are made.

Chapter 4.

Chilling Injury

As early as 1778, Bierkander reported on some eight species that were killed at 1 to 2° above the freezing point (Molisch, 1896). Goeppert (1830) obtained similar results. Of 56 species of tropical plants tested by Hardy (1844), some 25 were killed at 1 to 5°C (Molisch, 1896). Molisch (1897) suggested that low temperature damage in the absence of freezing should be called chilling injury (*Erkältung*) as opposed to frost injury (*Erfrieren*). That the two are different follows from the fact that frost injury can occur at temperatures that are fully tolerated by the same plants in the absence of freezing (Table 4). Exceptional plants, such as fungi, may be killed even in the undercooled state (Lindner, 1915; Onoda, 1937).

The explanations usually given for chilling injury involve a disturbance of the balance between physiological processes (Molisch, 1897). The following are some possibilities:

(a)   an excess of transpiration over water absorption.

(b)   an excess of respiration over photosynthesis, or a disturbance within the former.

(c)   an excess of protein breakdown over synthesis.

(a)   This is a case of injury by desiccation. That it may occur at low temperatures was first indicated by Sachs (1865, see Molisch, 1896). He found that plants such as tobacco and cucumber begin to wilt if their roots are cooled to temperatures just above zero. This may lead, eventually, to death by desiccation. Molisch (1896) confirmed these results. But he also covered some plants with bell-jars containing large pieces of wet filter paper before cooling them, and immersed the leaves of others in snow and ice water. In these ways he was able to expose the plants to temperatures just above freezing in the absence of transpiration. Even under these conditions chilling injury occurred (Table 15). Above 60°C no injury was produced even after 1 to 2 weeks.

Under natural conditions, winter injury due to desiccation has frequently been reported or inferred from the lower transpiration rates of the more northerly distributed species (Bates, 1923; Iwanoff, 1924; Walter, 1929; Thren, 1934; Michaelis, 1934; Rouschal, 1939). It has even been suggested that the higher concentration of the cell sap in alpine plants than in individuals of the same species from the plains indicates a better ability to remove water from the soil (Senn, 1922). But direct determinations have failed to produce any evidence of winter injury due to desiccation in cold climates (Hildreth, 1926). Twigs do not dry out appreciably at temperatures below 41°F, and above this temperature the rate of water transfer to the twigs is quite adequate to prevent injury from the transpirational loss (Wilner, 1952).

TABLE 15

Chilling injury in plants from warm climates. Exposed continuously to 1.4 to 3.7°C in diffuse light and covered to prevent transpiration. From 28 species listed by Molisch (1897)

Species	Time for first injury to appear	Time for complete killing (days)
Episcia bicolor Hook.	18 hr	5
Sciadocalyx warscewitzii Regel	24 hr	5
Eranthemum tricolor Nichols	48 hr	4–5
Eranthemum couperi Hook.	3–5 days	10
Boehmeria argentea Linden	8 days	20
Iresine acuminata	11 days	19
Uhdea bipinnatifida Kunth	15 days	16
Eranthemum nervosum R.Br.	20 days	30–35

(b) This would imply injury due to starvation. But it would require weeks for the reserves to be used up at chilling temperatures (0–5°C). Other kinds of metabolic disturbances seem to occur in fruits (Pentzer and Heinze, 1954). In green tomatoes and bananas, the ratio of CO_2 evolution in N_2 to that in air was 0.7 at 13°C, but it rose to 1.3 to 1.4 at 5 to 6°C (Banga 1936). Plank (see Smith, 1954) has explained injury by the accumulation of a cell toxin due to disturbances in the normal balance of biochemical processes. Injury would then depend on whether the rate of accumulation of the toxin exceeds the rate of its dispersal. In plums, the evidence is in agreement with this concept (Smith, 1954). Thus, injury due to 21 days' storage at 31°F was prevented if the fruit were warmed to 65°F for 1 to 2 days at about the seventeenth day. Furthermore, the rate of injury was more rapid at 40°F than at 34°F. Similar results have been obtained by others (Pentzer and Heinze, 1954).

(c) Wilhelm (1935a) found an increase in soluble nitrogen as a result of exposure to low temperature and therefore favored a disturbance in the nitrogen metabolism as the explanation of chilling injury. But Seible (1939) showed that this was true only when chilled plants were compared with the light controls. In the dark controls there was an even greater increase in soluble nitrogen (Table 16).

In many cases (e.g. fruit—see above), chilling injury is a slow process, and may be explained by a rather gradual metabolic disturbance. Yet many crop plants native to warm climates show such injury after 24 to 48 hr at 0.5 to 5°C (Sellschop and Salmon, 1928), and this seems too short a time for marked metabolic disturbances to occur at such low

TABLE 16

Protein breakdown in Solanum plants exposed to low temperatures
(from Seible, 1939.)

Days treated	Ratio of protein N to soluble N		
	Light controls	Cold room plants	Dark controls
2	15.9	9.7	8.2
4	19.8	9.2	6.7
7	16.9	8.2	4.6
11		13.35	1.95

temperatures. Other cases of still more rapid injury have been reported (Table 17). Möbius' results are particularly significant since the 1 to 2 minute exposures are certainly far too brief to permit any harmful disruption in the plant's metabolism. Yet injury was obvious a few hours after transfer to the greenhouse. Seible (1939) divides plants that suffer chilling injury into two types according to the speed of the reaction. The first type (e.g. Episcia, Achimenes, Gloxinia) show injured spots after hours or at the latest after a day, due to death of the protoplasm and infiltration of the intercellular spaces. The second type (e.g. Tradescantia, Solanum, Coleus) are more resistant. They remain perfectly normal and turgid for a full day but become soft and wilted only after 5 to 6 days' chilling. Many fruits would fit into Seible's second type. Some apples, for instance, are injured by prolonged storage at temperatures below 36 to 40°C; but the fruit of tropical plants is much more sensitive—bananas may be injured by a few hours at temperatures below 55°C (Pentzer and Heinze, 1954). Seible was forced to conclude that nothing is known of the cause of chilling injury. The same, of course, must be said about chilling hardiness. Apparently, it is possessed by all plants of temperate climates (except their fruit), since chilling injury has never been observed in them. Recent results (Spranger, 1941) indicate that greenhouse plants normally susceptible to chilling injury when grown at 17°C may become hardy if grown at 12°C for 2 months.

Direct observations under the microscope have revealed pseudoplas-

TABLE 17
Rapid chilling injury

Plant	Plant temp.	Air temp.	Exposure time	Injury	Observer
Begonia metallica		−5°C	1–2 min	older leaves died	Möbius, 1907
	6°C app.	−10	1–2 min	leaves fell off	Möbius, 1907
Tradescantia zebrina	6°C app.	−10	1–2 min	wilted	Möbius, 1907
Fittonia argyroneura	6°C app.	−10	1–2 min	wilted	Möbius, 1907
Callisia repens	2½°C app.	−10	1½ min	wilted	Möbius, 1907
Aspergillus niger	−2°C		2 hr	killed	Bartetzko, 1909
Sea algae	1 to 2°C		12–72 hr	killed	Biebl, 1939
	−2°C		12 hr (no ice formation)	killed	Biebl, 1939

molysis at chilling temperatures (Molisch, 1897; Greeley, 1901; Livingston, 1903). This may be a cause of the injury and has been explained by a rapid, injurious increase in permeability. Why such a change should occur, however, no one has attempted to explain. Gehenio and Luyet (1939) suggest that the chilling death of myxomycete plasmodia may be due to syneresis of the protoplasm.

Chapter 5.

Frost Injury

RELATION TO CONDITIONS OF FREEZING AND THAWING

In contrast to chilling injury, which is most common in tropical and subtropical plants, frost injury may occur in all plants. It is, therefore, far more prevalent and has been more intensively studied. Many descriptions of it are found in the literature (see quotation p. 2 and Figs. 1, 6, 8). Those plants that are subject to chilling injury (as well as some that are not) are usually killed by the first touch of frost (Molisch, 1897). On the other hand, some that are native to cold climates may be frozen solid at the lowest temperatures without injury (Scholander *et al.*, 1953). Between these two extremes all gradations occur (Tables 3 and 81). Even for a single plant the range of frost killing temperatures may be large, depending on its physiological state (Table 81). And when in the same physiological state, the frost killing temperature still depends on the following conditions of freezing and thawing.

1. RATE OF FREEZING.

Killing may occur at higher temperatures if the freezing is rapid than if it is gradual (Table 18). Similarly, if the same freezing temperature is used, those frozen rapidly may show more injury than those frozen slowly. This has been shown for roots of horticultural plants (Carrick, 1920; Potter, 1924), apple twigs (Hildreth, 1926), wheat seedlings (Anderson and Kiesselbach, 1934), raspberry buds (Schwartze, 1937), and trees (Day and Peace, 1937). Negative results have been obtained in plants whose killing temperatures are so close to their freezing points that no real difference in freezing rate can be obtained, and no appreciably higher frost killing temperature is possible (Chandler, 1913; Pfeiffer, 1933; Levitt, 1939).

2. RATE OF THAWING.

Greater injury may occur if thawing is rapid than if it is gradual (Table 19). But rate of thawing has no effect on injury under any of the following conditions (Table 20). (a) The plants are already killed by rapid freezing (see above). (b) They are killed at temperatures so close to their freezing points, even when thawed slowly, that no detectable rise in the frost killing point is possible. This is true of all tender

35

plants, as can be seen by the relatively high freezing temperatures in Table 20 as compared with Table 19. (c) They are killed at temperatures so far below their frost killing temperatures that rate of thawing (or

TABLE 18
Effect of rate of freezing on killing temperature

Plant	Killing temperature		Observer
	Frozen rapidly	Frozen slowly	
Twigs of several trees	—22°C	lower than —30°C	Winkler, 1913
Apple twigs	4½° higher than when frozen slowly		Chandler, 1913
	—10°F	—25 to —40°F	Beach and Allen, 1915
Apple trunk	—20°C	lower than —28°C	Mix, 1916
Pine shoots	—22°C	—33°C	Pfeiffer, 1933
Cabbage	—5.6°C	—6.8°C	Levitt, 1939

TABLE 19
Reports of increased injury with increased rate of thawing

Plant	Freezing temperature	Observer
Leafy twigs	—10 to —20°R	Hoffman, 1857
Yeast	—20°C	Schumacher, 1875
Apples and pears		Müller-Thurgau, 1894
Wheat seedlings	—17°C	Wright, 1890
Agave americana	— 7°C	Molisch, 1897
Mature apples	—5°C (sometimes)	Chandler, 1913
Winter wheat leaves	— 9°C	Hedlund, 1917
Red cabbage	— 7°C	Åkerman, 1919
Aucuba japonica	—10°C	Åkerman, 1919
Plum twigs	—18°F	Dorsey and Strausbaugh, 1923
Apple twigs	—35°C	Hildreth, 1926
Wheat seedlings	—10°C	Åkerman, 1927
Wheat plants		Janssen, 1929a
Alfalfa plants	—18°C	Peltier and Tysdal, 1931
Pine twigs		Pfeiffer, 1933
Wheat	—18°C	Anderson and Kiesselbach, 1934
Grains		Wilhelm, 1935
Apples, potatoes, onions		Lutz, 1935
Trees	lower than —19°F	Day and Peace, 1937
Cabbage sections	—15 to —20°C	Levitt, 1939
Crab blossoms		Field, 1939
Potato	— 6°C	Wartenberg, 1941

freezing) can have no effect (Detmer, 1886; Åkerman, 1919). (d) They are so frost hardy that no injury occurs at any rate of thawing—e.g. in the case of native trees during winter (Moll, 1880; Göppert, 1883; Wiegand, 1906).

TABLE 20

Reports of no effect of thawing rate on injury

Plant	Freezing temperature	Observer
Bulbs and tubers	—1.4°C	Göppert, 1830
	—10.0	Göppert, 1830
Potato		Schacht, 1859
Evergreen leaves		Moll, 1880
Onions and potatoes	—2 to —7°C	Kunisch, 1880
Potato	—2°C	Müller-Thurgau, 1886
Leaves, fruit, apple twigs		Müller-Thurgau, 1886
Various plants	—5°C	Molisch, 1897
Potatoes	—2.4°C	Apelt, 1907
Fungi	—10 to —12°C*	Bartetzko, 1909;
		Lindner, 1915
Peach buds, young fruit		Chandler, 1913
Twigs		Winkler, 1913
Potato, Tradescantia zebrina	—2°C	Åkerman, 1919
Roots of fruit trees		Carrick, 1920
Apple roots	—8°C	Potter, 1924
Grains		Zacharowa, 1926
Alfalfa roots		Weimer, 1929
Wheat		Worzella, 1935
Raspberry buds		Schwartze, 1937
Cabbage plants	—2 to —6°C	Levitt, 1939
Fruit blossoms		Field, 1939

* Lindner froze his fungi submerged. Therefore he probably could not obtain really rapid thawing.

3. LENGTH OF TIME FROZEN.

Greater injury may occur after long-continued freezing than after short freezing periods at the same temperature (Table 21). Many of the earlier workers came to this conclusion from their observations but failed to support it with quantitative evidence (Schöpf, 1788; Meyen, 1841; Göppert, 1883; Oberdieck, 1872). Others gave the opposite view, again without quantitative evidence (Middendorff, see Göppert, 1883; Hoffman, 1857; Nägeli, 1861; Schumacher, 1875; Molisch, 1897). Kunisch (1880) suggested that the length of time frozen is important only insofar as evaporation is enhanced, but this is not in accord with experimental results (see Chapter 4). It is, of course, also true that much of the positive evidence (e.g. in Table 21) may simply be due to lack of attainment of equilibrium during the shorter periods of time—especially in the case of bulky material such as the potato tubers used by Hogetop (1930). It is also true that frost death can be very rapid (Molisch, 1897; Iljin, 1934; Day and Peace, 1937; Levitt, 1939). For that reason, it

TABLE 21
Effect of freezing time on frost killing

Plant part	Freezing time and injury	Observer
Roots	¼ hr, 27.5%; 4 hr, 31.5%; 17 hr, 43.5%	Potter, 1924
Apple twigs	More injury after 12 hr than 3 hr at —30°C	Hildreth, 1926
Grain seedlings	The same injury after either 24 hr at —11 to —13°C or 13–18 days at —6 to —7°C	Schaffnit and Wilhelm, 1932
Cabbage	The same injury after 9, 12, 16 hr at —5.6°C but injury increased from 1–8 days	Levitt, 1939
Wheat	More injury from 10–30 days at —7°C than 24 hr at —10°C to —13°C	Wilhelm, 1935

usually makes very little difference whether the plant remains frozen for one or several hours after equilibrium is reached. When the time is measured in days, however, the injury may increase with time (Table 21).

4. NUMBER OF TIMES FROZEN.

Injury may occur after two or more freezings at the same temperature that fails to injure in one freezing (Table 22). It is, of course, true that repeated freezing and thawing does not always cause injury (Hoffman, 1857; Wiegand, 1906; Dorsey, 1934). Day and Peace (1937) obtained greater killing only when the temperature used was slightly above the killing temperature for a single freezing. Oberdieck (1872) and Kunisch

TABLE 22
Effect of repeated freezings and thawings on killing temperature

| Plant | Killing temperature | | No. of freezings | Observer |
	Single freezing	Repeated freezings		
Euphorbia lathyris	below —4°C	—4°C	6x	Göppert, 1830
Potato	—2.33°C	—2.0°C	6x	Apelt, 1907
Hypnum aduncum	—15°C	above —10°C	3x	Irmscher, 1912
Acer pseudoplatanus (also other trees)	—21°C	—13°C	7x	Winkler, 1913

(1880) believe that repeated freezing and thawing causes injury only when the soil does not thaw out sufficiently to allow the uptake of water to replace that lost from the leaves during the thaw. This certainly cannot explain some of the above results, and especially the many obtained by Winkler (1913) with twigs that had been removed from the plant.

5. POST-THAWING TREATMENT.

Injury may increase after thawing, if the plant is exposed to unfavorable conditions. It has long been known that death may not occur until days or even weeks after freezing (Oberdieck, 1872; Russell, 1914; Lindner, 1915; Åkerman, 1927) and that the injury may be reversible (Ivanov, 1931). Since the frost-injured leaves lose water excessively (Göppert, 1830; Nägeli, 1861a; Prillieux, 1872; Kunisch, 1880), Müller-Thurgau (1894) recommends their removal immediately after thawing to save those not injured by the frost. But this loss of water cannot explain the greater injury obtained with Aspergillus cultures (Richter, 1910; Lindner, 1915) and with bulky organs like potatoes, apples, and onions (Lutz, 1935) when kept at higher temperatures after thawing, nor the results given in Table 23.

TABLE 23

Effect of post-thawing treatment on frost injury to cabbage cells (unpublished results)

Freezing temperature	Post-thawing solution	% Injury
	(a) Unhardened cells	
—5°C	0.25M $CaCl_2$	50
	H_2O	100
—4°C	0.25M $CaCl_2$	25
	H_2O	100
—5°C	0.30M $CaCl_2$	75
	H_2O	100
—4°C	0.30M $CaCl_2$	25
	H_2O	100
—3°C	0.30M $CaCl_2$	0
	H_2O	100
	(b) Hardened cells	
—11°C	0.40M $CaCl_2$	0
	H_2O	75
—16°C	0.40M $CaCl_2$	0
	H_2O	100
—13°C	0.40M $CaCl_2$	0
	H_2O	50
—12°C	0.40M $CaCl_2$	0
	H_2O	75

THE MOMENT OF INJURY

These effects of the treatment during and after freezing and thawing raise the question of when the frost injury occurs. In other words, what is the "moment of frost injury"? In answering this question, the mode of ice formation in the plant must first be taken into account. Though ice normally forms extracellularly, it may also arise inside the cell, at least under laboratory conditions (Chapter 3). Such intracellular ice formation is induced by rapid freezing (Chapter 3), and apparently always results in injury, though it is sometimes not immediately fatal (Table 24). The few cases of cells still capable of plasmolysis after intracellular freezing seem all to be due to tonoplast survival, the rest of the protoplasm being dead. When intracellular freezing obviously occurs throughout the cell (i.e. in the vacuole), tonoplast survival never occurs, though it may be seen following extracellular freezing (Levitt, unpublished). This would seem to indicate that the tonoplast is the last part of the protoplasm to be injured by extracellular freezing. Since there is no physical change during thawing like the cell expansion following extracellular freezing, the moment of injury in the case of intracellular freezing must be during the freezing process itself. The intracellular ice formation also explains why rapid freezing should cause injury at temperatures that the plant survives when frozen slowly.

Extracellular ice formation, however, may or may not result in injury (Table 25). If intracellular ice formation is always fatal, a plant that survives slow but not rapid thawing must have been frozen extracellularly. Such injury due to rapid thawing is usually taken as evidence that the moment of injury is during the thawing process. However, it is also conceivable that reversible changes may occur while frozen extracellularly that may lead to death during rapid thawing but to recovery during slow thawing. This may also explain the increased injury due to length of time frozen, repeated freezing and thawing, and unfavorable post-thawing conditions.

Not only is injury on rapid thawing no proof that it is initiated during the thawing process, but, as pointed out by Müller-Thurgau (1886), the converse is also true, and injury may conceivably occur during thawing no matter how slow it is. Consequently, it is necessary to obtain more direct evidence of the moment of injury. This was long ago attempted by observing the still frozen plant for signs of injury (Table 26). These observations of changes in color or odor have been rather conclusively shown to be categorical evidence of death (Molisch, 1897). There is, therefore, no doubt that frost injury can occur during the freezing process. It also seems likely, in view of the moderate freezing tempera-

TABLE 24

Effect of intracellular freezing on living tissues

Plant	Conditions and observations during freezing	Injury	Observer
Algae, epidermis of *Tradescantia discolor* and *T. guianensis*		dead	Molisch, 1897
Winter annuals		alive (plasmo-lyzed	Schaffnit, 1910
Tradescantia and *Vallisneria spiralis*		dead	Schaffnit, 1910
Cabbage	−5°C thin hull of ice inside cell	alive	Schander and Schaffnit, 1919
Rhoeo discolor	frozen in water	dead	Åkerman, 1927
Cabbage	−5.2°C	alive	Åkerman, 1927
Apple and onion		coagulation of protoplasm before vacuole froze	Tetley, 1931
Onion epidermis	−10°C	functional tonoplast, protoplasm dis-integrated	Chambers and Hale, 1932
Various species		dead	Onoda, 1937
Cabbage, hardy tree cells		dead (in one case tonoplast survival)	Siminovitch and Scarth, 1938

tures used, that extracellular ice formation was involved. Unfortunately, however, this has not been corroborated by direct observation. It has, therefore, not been proved conclusively that the injury due to extracellular ice formation can occur while the plant is still frozen.

Nevertheless, the above indirect evidence is supported by the many observations of frost-injured cells. Usually, these have shown only that the protoplasm was coagulated and contracted (Schacht, 1856; also see

TABLE 25
Observations of injury due to extracellular ice formation

Plant	Injury	Observer
Various plants	dead	Caspary, 1854
Beets	uninjured	Schacht, 1859
Iris, etc.	many uninjured	Prillieux, 1869
Roots and tubers	some still alive but some killed	Müller-Thurgau, 1880
Algae	dead	Molisch, 1897
Algae	alive or dead depending on freezing temperature	Kylin, 1917
Cabbage, fungi	injury in some cases	Schander and Schaffnit, 1919
Spirogyra, etc., epidermis of Tradescantia, etc.	alive after short freeze dead after longer freeze	Onoda, 1937
Hardy tree cells	alive	Siminovitch and Scarth, 1938
Nonhardy tree cells	dead	

Figs. 6, 8), or granular (Klemm, 1895), or that the cytoplasm was foamy and nuclei coarse (Matruchot and Molliard, 1900, 1901, 1902). The chloroplasts may lose their pigment and become vacuolated (Haberlandt, 1876). Even the more recent statement that the frost-coagulated protoplasm is less rigid than that of heat-coagulated cells (Luyet and Grell, 1936) is not much help. But one characteristic of frost-killed cells—the contraction of the protoplasm—is so typical that it has been called "frostplasmolysis."

This phenomenon was mentioned by several of the early investigators and studied carefully by Buhlert (1906). But the observations of "frostplasmolysis" were always made on dead cells after they were thawed (Fig. 6). The term is, therefore, an unfortunate one, since it has led many to believe that this "plasmolysis" is supposed to occur while the cell is frozen (Becquerel, 1949). Actually, it is due to the cell contraction during extracellular ice formation and the inability of the dead protoplast to reabsorb the water formed in the intercellular spaces on thawing of the extracellular ice. As a result, the cell wall expands back to nearly its original shape, while the dead protoplast remains contracted, giving a false appearance of plasmolysis. This would seem to indicate that the injury had already occurred during the freezing process and the cells were nonfunctional by the time the ice began to thaw.

TABLE 26
Direct observations of injury during the freezing process

Plant	Observation	Observer
Tradescantia staminal hairs	Protoplasm clumping seen as soon as enough ice thawed to permit observation	Kühne, 1864
Calanthe and Phajus white flowers	Turned blue while still frozen	Göppert, 1871*; Kunisch, 1880; Müller-Thurgau, 1886; Molisch, 1897
Begonia manicata	Changed from green to yellow while frozen	Detmer, 1886
Nitophyllum and other red algae	Changed from red to orange while frozen	Molisch, 1897; Kylin, 1917
Ageratum mexicanum	Exuded odor of coumarin while frozen	Molisch, 1897

* Prillieux (1872) was unable to corroborate these results but this was due to insufficiently long freezing according to Müller-Thurgau.

The following are the suggested interrelationships between (1) frost injury, (2) the conditions of freezing, thawing, and post-thawing, and (3) the mode of ice formation in the plant.

1. Intracellular ice formation always or nearly always results in death. Freezing that is rapid enough to occur intracellularly is therefore fatal. Exceptions occur only under artificial conditions, when the freezing is so extremely rapid that the ice crystals are too small to be seen with the microscope (see Chapter 1).

2. Extracellular ice formation may or may not result in death.

3. At some intermediate point between irreversible injury and no injury, extracellular ice formation produces changes that progress to death (a) if thawing is too rapid, (b) if post-thawing conditions are unfavorable, (c) if the frozen state is maintained too long, or (d) if the plant is frozen and thawed repeatedly. These changes may be reversed, permitting survival if the four conditions are favorable.

Chapter 6.

The Measurement and Meaning of Frost Hardiness

For many years, the *winter hardiness* of plants (i.e. their ability to survive the severities of winter) has been determined by field survival. This always requires years of observation, since *test winters*—winters severe enough to damage all but the fully hardy—occur only about once in 10 years (Macoun, 1908). Such a method of measurement is too slow and may conceivably involve several factors other than the ability of a plant to survive freezing. Consequently, in the past two or three decades, much use has been made of artificial freezing tests under controlled conditions. Pioneers in the use of this method were the University of Minnesota in the United States (Hildreth, 1926) and the Plant Breeding Station at Svalöf in Sweden (Åkerman, 1927). Many other research institutions in countries throughout the world have since adopted the method. A description of freezing chambers is given by Peltier (1931). After freezing the plants at a known temperature, they are usually left for one to two weeks to recuperate in the greenhouse, and the percent injury is then estimated. Good agreement is usually obtained between the rating by such freezing tests and by field survival (Åkerman, 1927; Worzella and Cutler, 1941; Weibel and Quisenberry, 1941; Kneen and Blish, 1941; Meader *et al.*, 1945; Scott and Cullinan, 1946; Straib, 1946), though there are some exceptions (Åkerman *et al.*, 1935).

As shown above (Chapter 3), the frost killing temperature of a plant can be varied by changing the conditions of freezing and thawing. Any comparison of the frost hardiness of different plants therefore requires a rigid control of these conditions as follows:

1. The plants must be actually frozen, not merely undercooled. This is frequently induced by a moving current of air.

2. Freezing must be at a standard rate (e.g. a temperature drop of 2°C per hour).

3. A single freeze must be used for a standard length of time.

4. Thawing must be at a standard rate. This may be controlled by the next standardization.

5. The conditions after thawing must be standardized—e.g. by returning the plants to the hardening chamber (5°C) for 24 hours.

Under the above standardized conditions, it is possible to obtain a relatively constant frost killing temperature for any one variety in a specific physiological state (see Chapters 7 and 8). In practice, arbitrary methods of expressing the results are usually adequate. In order to obtain a numerical value that increases with hardiness, Åkerman (1927) and his students give a value of 1 to plants that are completely killed, a value of 5 or 10 to those completely uninjured under the same conditions of freezing and thawing. Intermediate values vary inversely with the degree of injury. Averages of large numbers of tests can in this way give duplicable numerical values for hardiness. Åkerman's method has found wide use in evaluating varieties, as it is far superior to the older, crude arrangement of plants as "very hardy, hardy, less hardy, tender." An ingenious method of speeding up the measurement and of making the numerical rating objective, has been developed by Dexter *et al.* (1930, 1932). After exposure to frost, the tissues are placed in water for a standard time. The quantity of electrolytes which has diffused out is measured by conductivity tests and is proportional to the injury. Megee (1935), Stuart (1938), Wilner (1952), and others have corroborated the value of this method.

But there are disadvantages to Åkerman's and Dexter's methods. Since different freezing temperatures must be used for plants differing markedly in hardiness, it is not possible to list plants in a continuous numerical series by either method, as can be done with frost killing temperatures (Table 27). Nor is it often possible to compare the results of different

TABLE 27

Frost hardiness of some winter annuals (From Tumanov and Borodin, 1930)

Species	Frost killing temperatures in winter (°C)
Rape	— 9
Oats	—10
Peas	—10
Lucerne	—11
Barley	—12
Rye (southern region)	—13
Vetch	—15

workers numerically, since they may have used different arbitrary freezing temperatures. Perhaps the most important objection is the fact that neither method permits the theoretical treatment (see below) that is possible with absolute measurements of frost killing temperatures—i.e. temperatures producing 50% killing. It would therefore be preferable if all arbitrary evaluations of frost hardiness were dropped in favor of absolute numerical values.

In order to obtain an exact numerical value for frost hardiness, the following definition will be used:

The frost hardiness of a plant is the number of degrees (°C) below its freezing point at which it must be frozen in order to produce 50% killing.

The difference between the value so obtained and the more commonly used frost-killing point is usually too small to be of practical importance. In theory, however, the above more exact definition is very useful (see Chapter 15), and it has the added advantages of (a) giving positive values that are directly proportional to frost hardiness, and (b) assigning a value of zero to all plants that are killed by the "first touch of frost," no matter what their freezing points. Thus, if frost killing points are used for hardiness, a plant must be said to become hardier if its cell sap concentration increases, even if it is still killed as soon as it freezes. Its true frost hardiness, however, as defined above, remains zero.

It may be asked whether the standardization of conditions given above permits an adequate measurement of frost hardiness. Is it not possible, for instance, that a rapid freezing would yield a different order of hardiness among several varieties or species? Though this possibility has not yet been sufficiently investigated, there is apparently no such thing as survival of intracellular ice formation (see Chapter 5), so it might seem reasonable to eliminate this type of injury by inducing slow freezing. Some results have indicated, however, that plants may differ in their abilities to avoid intracellular freezing (Siminovitch and Scarth, 1938), and this difference would be completely overlooked by measurements made under the above standard rate of freezing. The same is true of the other standardized conditions. Consequently, the frost hardiness that is measured under these conditions is of a specific type—hardiness toward the injurious effects of a single extracellular freezing when maintained for a period of a few hours and followed by a slow thawing and by relatively low temperatures after thawing. In at least some cases, however, varying the standard conditions of freezing and thawing has failed to alter the relative frost hardiness of different varieties (Åkerman, 1927).

Measurements of frost hardiness have generally been made for the following three purposes:

1. To determine the effects of environmental conditions on the hardiness of a plant.

2. To compare the hardiness of different species or varieties of a

species. (When this is done, they must all be in the hardened state—see Chapter 7.)

3. To determine which properties of the plant are associated with hardiness.

Many geneticists have shown that crosses between varieties differing in frost hardiness may result in progeny that is either hardier or less hardy than either parent (Nilsson-Ehle, 1913; Hayes and Garber, 1919; Åkerman, 1923; Quisenberry and Clark, 1929; Andersson, 1935; Kovpak, 1939; Saltykovsky and Sapriguina, 1939; Worzella, 1942). They explain these results by the existence of two or more hardiness factors. This must be accepted by the physiologist as a warning of the complexity of the problem.

Chapter 7.

Variations in Frost Hardiness with Environment

TEMPERATURE

The marked seasonal changes in frost hardiness have been shown repeatedly by investigators in many countries. Even plants that survive the most extreme freezing during midwinter may be killed by very slight freezing during spring (Fig. 9). That these changes are related to the

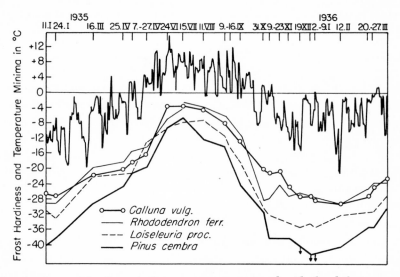

Fɪɢ. 9. Seasonal hardiness in four evergreens compared with the daily temperature minima (from Ulmer, 1937).

temperature is indicated by the parallelism between the curves. A decrease in frost hardiness during winter occurs when the plants are exposed to warm weather for two weeks (Göppert, 1830) or even a few hours (mosses, Irmscher, 1912; evergreen trees, Pisek, 1950); an increase in frost hardiness, when they are exposed to low temperatures (Haberlandt, 1875; Schaffnit, 1910; Irmscher, 1912; Chandler, 1913; Gassner and Grimme, 1913; etc.). It is now standard procedure to "harden off" plants by exposing them for a week or two to temperatures a few degrees above the freezing point (Table 28). The "threshhold temperature" above which hardening does not occur is usually 5 to 10°C (Harvey, 1922).

Some results have indicated that alternating warm and cold temperatures are at least as effective as constant low temperatures (Harvey, 1918, 1930a; Tumanov, 1931; Tysdal, 1933; Angelo *et al.*, 1939). Others have failed to obtain as hardy plants with alternating temperatures (Peltier

TABLE 28

Relation of frost hardiness to temperature treatment

| Plant | Killing temperature | | Observer |
	After growth at warm temp.	After exposure to low temp.	
Cabbage	—3°C	< —3°C	Harvey, 1918
Wheat (Minhardi)	—10°C	< —15°C	Tumanov and Borodin, 1930
Alfalfa	—13.6°C	< —17.0°C	Peltier and Tysdal, 1932
Alfalfa	—9°C	< —13.7°C	Tysdal, 1933
Cabbage	—2.1°C	—5.6° C	Levitt, 1939

and Kiesselbach, 1934; Suneson and Peltier, 1934; Day and Peace, 1937). Suneson and Peltier (1938) seem to have resolved these differences, for they obtained maximum resistance by exposure to alternating temperatures during November and December, followed by sustained low temperature for three weeks. The high temperature had to be during the daytime and accompanied by high radiation. Obviously, the effect of temperature on frost hardiness depends on interactions with other environmental factors.

MOISTURE

The early investigators recognized an inverse relation between environmental moisture and frost hardiness (Du Hamel and Buffon, 1737; Van Mons, 1838; Oberdieck, 1872; Müller-Thurgau, 1886). Many more recent workers went a step further and actually increased frost hardiness by withholding water from the plant (Table 29). Certain complicating factors must, however, be recognized. Klages (1926), for instance, points out that the temperature drop is slower in moist than in dry soil. It is, therefore, necessary to exclude such differences in order to obtain a true picture of the effect on hardiness. When soil moistures were equalized immediately before the freezing test, Tysdal (1933) found little difference in the hardiness of alfalfa plants after two weeks' exposure to different soil moistures at 5°C. The same results were obtained by Day and Peace (1937a) for trees, and Platt (1937) for grains.

But these results, clear as they are, do not eliminate moisture as a factor in frost hardiness. In the author's experience, when cabbage plants are grown at greenhouse temperatures with low moisture supply, their growth is retarded and they become somewhat hardier than others grown alongside them with high moisture. They are also able to harden much more than the high moisture plants on exposure to low temperature. But once they are at the low temperature, as Tysdal and others found,

TABLE 29

Reports of an inverse relation between frost hardiness and moisture supply

Plant	Observer
Cabbage	Chandler, 1913; Rosa, 1921; Levitt and Scarth, 1936
Wheat	Sinz, 1914; Martin, 1927; Janssen, 1929; Steele, Waldo, and Brown, 1934; Suneson and Peltier, 1938; Kabanov, 1938
Vegetable plants	Chandler, 1913; Rosa, 1921
Strawberries	Angelo et al., 1939

the moisture supply no longer has any effect on hardening off. Thus, just as in the case of temperature, the effect of moisture supply on frost hardiness depends on interactions with other factors.

LIGHT

The hardening of plants when alternating low and high temperatures are used has been shown to occur only if the light is supplied during the high-temperature period (Dexter, 1933; Tysdal, 1933). Even continuous low temperatures in the absence of light are incapable of inducing hardiness in winter annuals (Tumanov, 1931; Dexter, 1933; Pfeiffer, 1933; Constantinescu, 1933; Andersson, 1944; Table 30). Many have also found a reduction in hardiness as a result of darkening the plant (Lidforss, 1907; Weimer, 1929; Angelo et al., 1939). Furthermore, if the

TABLE 30

Frost hardiness of wheat hardened with and without light (from Andersson, 1944)

5 = undamaged,   1 = killed

Temperature exposed to (°C)	Frost hardiness			
		After hardening		
	Before hardening	10 hr light per day	5 hr light per day	Darkness
—12	1.4	4.1	3.9	1.1
—16	1.0	2.1	1.3	1.0
—20	1.0	1.7	1.0	1.0

leaves are chlorotic, the plants are unable to harden even when exposed to light, though when allowed to become green by spraying with ferrous sulfate, they harden normally (Rosa, 1921). Similarly, if exposed to CO_2-free air, hardening does not occur even in the light (Dexter, 1933). Plants with abundant organic reserves are exceptions, for they harden markedly at 0°C even in the dark (Dexter, 1933).

All these results strongly indicate that light is needed during the hardening period to permit photosynthetic accumulation of reserves. Direct evidence of active photosynthesis during hardening at low temperatures has also been produced (Andersson, 1944), showing that the sugar accumulation is quantitatively accounted for by photosynthesis (see Chapter 12).

MINERAL NUTRITION

Nitrogen has almost invariably been found to reduce hardiness (Table 31), and similar results obtained with complete fertilizer or manure (Ellet and Wolfe, 1921; Worzella and Cutler, 1941; Livingston and Swinbank, 1950) may be ascribed to the nitrogen. One or two of the recorded cases do not really involve frost hardiness, since the species used are incapable of hardening and the plants therefore merely escaped freezing. This is also true of one of the two exceptional cases of increases in resistance with nitrogen application (Table 31).

Potassium and phosphorus applications, in contrast to nitrogen, have generally been found to increase hardiness (Table 32), and those cases of increases due to complete fertilizers (Müller-Thurgau, 1886; Schribaux, 1929; Strahov and Tiunova, 1937; Brown and Potter, 1949) may be due to them. But negative results have also been obtained, and in some cases the positive results were even reversed by excessive applications (Dorsey and Bushnell, 1920; Christoff, 1939). Even the positive results are frequently more apparent than real, since they were obtained with plants incapable of developing true frost hardiness (potatoes, corn, tomatoes). Increases in hardiness have also been related to calcium applications (Oberdieck, 1872; Skinner and Reed, 1925; Levitt, 1933). It seems obvious from the above results that the effect of mineral nutrition on frost hardiness varies with the conditions. This is usually explained by assuming that the treatments producing excessive growth (primarily nitrogen) reduce frost hardiness, perhaps due to the sugar loss (Lidforss, 1907); those that retard growth increase it. Increases in hardiness due to mineral nutrition have also been attributed to the effect on reserves, due to increases in the rate of photosynthesis (Baumann, 1902; Yasuda, 1927). Increases in hydration (Fuchs, 1935; Wilhelm,

TABLE 31

Effect of nitrogen on frost hardiness

Plant	Observer	Plant	Observer
		(a) Resistance reduced by nitrogen	
Wheat	Müller-Thurgau, 1886	Cabbage	Levitt, 1933
Wheat	Sinz, 1914	Grains and cabbage	Dexter, 1935
Cabbage	Hedlund, 1917	Kentucky blue grass	Carroll and Welton, 1939
Chick pea, beans	Harvey, 1918		
Coffee	Pantanelli, 1920	Winter wheats	Kuksa, 1939
Cabbage	Camargo, 1921	Winter grains	Christoff, 1939
Brambles	Boswell, 1925	Apple trees	Collison and Harlan, 1934,
Herbaceous plants	Lott, 1926		Tingley *et al.*, 1939,
Herbaceous plants	Kimball, 1927		Smith and Tingley, 1940,
	Arland, 1931, 1932		Sudds and Marsh, 1943
Potatoes and tomatoes	Schaffnit and Wilhelm, 1932	Cherry trees	Kennard, 1949
		(b) Resistance increased by nitrogen	
Corn	Magistad and Truog, 1925		
Peach trees	Knowlton and Dorsey, 1927		
		(c) No effect of nitrogen	
Grapes	Gladwin, 1917		
Cabbage	Dunn, 1937		
Strawberry	Angelo *et al.*, 1939		

TABLE 32

Effects of potassium and phosphorus on frost hardiness

Potassium		Phosphorus	
Plant	Observer	Plant	Observer
(a) Increased hardiness			
Potato	Baumann, 1902	Wheat	Hedlund, 1917
	Wartenberg, 1929	Chick pea, bean	Pantanelli, 1920
	Lacis, 1930	Coffee	Camargo, 1921
Various crops	Couturier, 1903	Pecans	Skinner and Reed, 1925
Cabbage, tobacco (in sand cultures)	Chandler, 1913	Corn	Magistad and Truog, 1925
Wheat	Hedlund, 1917		
Coffee	Camargo, 1921	Clover	Koperzinskii, 1939
Corn	Magistad and Truog, 1925	Wheat, wheat-rye hybrids	Saveljev, 1939
Onions	Wallace, 1926	Winter wheat	Kuksa, 1939
Barley	Yasuda, 1927		
Winter rye	Arland, 1931, 1932		
Potatoes and tomatoes	Schaffnit and Wilhelm, 1932		
Grains, spinach, rape	Wilhelm, 1935		
Clover	Koperzinskii, 1939		
Wheat, wheat-rye hybrids	Saveljev, 1939		
Winter wheat	Kuksa, 1939		
Winter grains	Christoff, 1939		
(b) No effect or decreased hardiness			
Fruit trees, cabbage, and tobacco	Chandler, 1913	Grapes	Gladwin, 1917
		Cabbage	Dunn, 1937
Wheat	Sinz, 1914		
Grapes	Gladwin, 1917	Wheat	Ellet and Wolfe, 1921
Cabbage	Levitt, 1933		Sergeyev and Sergeyeva, 1939a
	Dunn, 1937		
Strawberries	Angelo et al., 1939	Grains, spinach, rape	Wilhelm, 1935

1935) and post-thawing recuperation (Wohack, 1930) have also been suggested as factors.

All these effects of environment on frost resistance point to another standardization that must be adopted when varieties are compared. They must be grown under standard conditions of light, temperature, moisture, and mineral nutrition, then hardened by exposure to low temperature for a standard time before testing. Otherwise the results are meaningless, for even the most frost-hardy species or variety may be completely without hardiness at certain times of the year or when grown under certain conditions.

Chapter 8.

The Relation of Frost Hardiness to Growth and Development

All the hardiness responses of the plant to environment (Chapter 7) depend on the developmental stage it is in. Low-temperature treatment, for instance, fails to harden newly formed buds of evergreens which may survive —30°C during winter (Winkler, 1913); and the actual changes in hardiness may not follow the temperature changes at certain times of the year (Ulmer, 1937). This is clearly shown by the effects of exposures to low and high temperatures for one day, on the hardiness of the plant at different times of the year (Pisek, 1953; see Fig. 10).

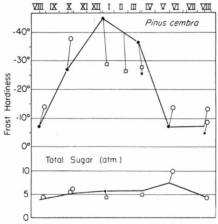

Fɪɢ. 10. Effect of one-day exposure to low (circle) or to room (square) temperature on hardiness of pine at different times of the year (upper curve). Seasonal sugar change shows very little change with hardiness (lower curve) (from Pisek, 1953).

A further complication arises from the effect of the environmental factor on the developmental stage itself. Light, for instance, has been found to favor hardening (Chapter 7). Yet increasing the length of day, which of course alters the developmental stage, actually reduces the plant's ability to harden (Table 33); though adequate hardening may sometimes still occur (Kneen and Blish, 1941). At the same time as the hardiness decreases, the length of the embryonic spike increases (Sestakov and Smiranova, 1936; Sestakov and Sergeev, 1937) and the plant passes through the "second stage of development." Vernalization has also been found to decrease the plant's ability to become frost hardy (Table 34). But since the low temperature used to vernalize plants does induce some hardening, the vernalized plants may be more hardy than

TABLE 33
Reports of greater frost hardening following shorter photoperiods

Plant	Observer
Cereal grains	Dexter, 1933; Timofejeva, 1935; Saprygina, 1935; Saltykovskij and Saprygina, 1935; Sestakov, 1936; Rudorf, 1938; Suneson and Peltier, 1938
Alfalfa (at some temperatures)	Tysdal, 1933
Cauliflower	Frischenschlager, 1937
Woody plants (intermediate day best)	Moschkov, 1935
Pine	Bogdanov, 1935
Abelia grandiflora	Kramer, 1937
Sweet clover	Smith, 1942

TABLE 34
Reports of a relation between frost hardiness and vernalization

Plant	Observer
(a) *Reduction in hardiness with vernalization*	
Cereals	Vasilijev, 1934
Wheat and barley	Rudorf, 1938
Winter wheat	Kostjucenko, 1939; Kuksa, 1940
(b) *Parallelism between length of vernalization period required and frost hardiness of varieties*	
Summer and winter rye	Gassner, 1918
Various grains	Tavcar, 1930; Kuckuck, 1933; Saltykovskij and Saprygina, 1935; Saprygina, 1935; Martin, 1932; Quisenberry and Bayles, 1939; Saltykovskii, 1939

the nonvernalized if these have not been subjected to hardening temperatures (Saltykovskij and Saprygina, 1935; Timofejeva, 1935; Vetuhova, 1936a). If both are exposed to hardening temperatures, the nonvernalized always become more frost hardy than the vernalized (Vetuhova, 1936a, 1938, 1939a). In many cases, those varieties that require the longest cold treatment for vernalization are the most hardy (Table 34), though there are many exceptions (Hayes and Aamodt, 1927; Martin, 1932; Quisenberry and Bayles, 1939; Saltykovskij and Saprygina, 1935; Straib, 1946).

This reduction in frost hardening capacity due to photoperiodic treatment and vernalization is related to the later stages of development—the transition from the vegetative to the reproductive stage. The same relation, however, has been found during the early stages of growth and development. Buds have long been known to lose their frost hardiness as they develop (West and Edlefsen, 1917, 1921; Roberts, 1922; Knowlton and Dorsey, 1927; Field, 1939; Geslin, 1939). Similarly, the hardiness of winter annuals is inversely related to rate of growth in the fall (Buhlert, 1906; Schaffnit, 1910; Hedlund, 1917; Klages, 1926; Worzella, 1932; Mark, 1936; Kolomycev, 1936; Vasiliev, 1939). It is generally found, in fact, that if plants are growing rapidly, they cannot be frost hardened (Rivera and Corneli, 1931; Dexter, Tottingham, and Graber, 1932), whereas treatments that retard growth increase hardening (Chandler, 1913; Harvey, 1918; Rosa, 1921; Collison and Harlan, 1934; Shmelev, 1935; Kessler and Ruhland, 1938), though exceptions may occur (Kuksa, 1940).

Another aspect of the same phenomenon is the relation between hardiness and rest period (also called dormancy), maturity, or ripening, particularly in the case of woody plants such as fruit trees (Senebier, 1800; Treviranus, 1838; Lindley, 1842; van Mohl, 1848; Oberdieck, 1872; Halsted, 1889; Chandler, 1913; Dorsey and Bushnell, 1920; Strausbaugh, 1921; Bradford and Cardinell, 1922; Pojarkova, 1924; Knowlton and Dorsey, 1927; Wilson, 1929, 1930; Day and Peace, 1934; Schwartze, 1937; Horsfall and Vinson, 1938; Oknina and Markovich, 1951), though this relation may hold for some plants but not for others (Pojarkova, 1924). Similarly, the reduction in frost hardiness of plants brought indoors during winter occurs only if they are no longer in their rest period (Lidforss, 1907; Meyer, 1932; Kessler, 1935). This relationship applies only to plants capable of developing hardiness; others may be dormant yet possess no frost hardiness (Clements, 1938); on the other hand, some plants have no winter rest period (Walter, 1949). In many cases, the importance of this period is in preventing the loss of frost hardiness during winter warm spells which would lead to injury during subsequent hard freezes (Brierley and Landon, 1946). Recent attempts to improve frost hardiness by the use of substances that prevent breaking of the rest period or that induce recovery, have not been successful (Oknina and Markovich, 1951; Moretti, 1953), perhaps due to secondary effects of these substances. Kessler and Ruhland (1942), however, were able to reduce frost hardiness by inducing growth with heteroauxin and ethylene.

Many attempts have been made to relate the age of a plant to its frost hardiness. Among the early workers, some considered young plants more tender than older ones (Du Hamel, 1741; Schöpf, 1788; Senebier, 1800; Treviranus, 1838), others held the opposite view (DuPetit-Thouars, 1817; Göppert, 1830; Schumacher, 1875), and still others concluded that the relationship varies (Thouin, 1806; Hoffman, 1857). Müller-Thurgau (1886) states that young leaves are more tender than old ones, but the very young suffer least. But he points out that the uninjured may merely avoid freezing. Recent results are just as evenly divided (Table 35).

TABLE 35
Relation between age and frost hardiness

Plant	Observation	Observer
(a)	Evidence of greater hardiness in younger tissues	
Evergreens	Younger leaves more resistant	Winkler, 1913
Peach trees	Less frost injury in younger trees	Chandler, 1919
Wheat seedlings	Hardier at 1 wk than at 2–4 wk	Klages, 1926
Wheat and oat	Younger tissue hardier	Crépin et al., 1929
Wheat	Younger leaves hardier	Crescini and Tettamanzi, 1929
Pine	1-yr harden better than 2-yr twigs	Pfeiffer, 1933
Wheat	Younger seedlings harden better than older ones	Worzella, 1935
Alfalfa	5-day seedlings hardier than 10-day	Peltier and Tysdal, 1931
Lespedeza	Maximum hardiness at 2 wk, decreased until 8 wk	Tysdal and Pieters, 1934
Cabbage	Younger leaves harden better	Levitt and Scarth, 1936
Flax	Younger tissues are more hardy	Dillman, 1941
Juniper	Juvenile branches are more hardy	Gardner, 1944
(b)	Evidence of minimum hardiness at intermediate age	
Fruit (e.g. peach)		Garcia and Rigney, 1914
Clover	Least resistant at 21 days	Steinbauer, 1926
Grain seedlings	Least resistant at 2- and 3-leaf stage	Peltier and Kiesselbach, 1934; Suneson and Peltier, 1934
Alfalfa	Least hardy after 5 days' soaking	Tysdal and Pieters, 1934
Helianthus annuus	Middle leaves most damaged	Gicklhorn, 1936
Grasses and legumes	Least able to harden at 2–4 wk, improved hardening at 4–9 wk	Arakeri and Schmid, 1949

TABLE 35 (*continued*)

Plant	Observation	Observer
	(*c*) *Evidence of greater hardiness in older tissues*	
Fungi	Increases from 24–48 hr	Lindner, 1915
Cabbage	Older leaves harden more readily (but see Levitt and Scarth above)	Harvey, 1918
Walnut	Older trees dormant earlier, hardier toward early frosts	Batchelor, 1922
Olives, grapes, peaches	Greater injury in youngest succulent tissues	Rivera and Corneli, 1931
Strawberry	More injury in hardened young plants	Angelo *et al.*, 1939
Pine	Young seedlings suffer more frost injury	Münch and Liske, 1926
Fir needles	Increase in resistance through first 3 yr	Clements, 1938
Wheat	Seedlings increased in hardiness from 1-leaf to 2–4 leaf, to 5–15 leaf stage	Worzella and Cutler, 1941
	(*d*) *Miscellaneous results*	
Fruit trees, succulents	Sometimes young growth hardier, sometimes less hardy	Chandler, 1913
Pears (fruit)	Hard ripe more hardy than immature or fully ripe	Hawkins, 1922
Pine	Sometimes oldest needles most injured, sometimes youngest	Münch, 1928
Winter grains	Intermediate sowing most hardy	Janssen, 1929
Strawberry plants	Oldest daughter plants recovered more rapidly than mother or younger daughter plants	Steele, Waldo, and Brown, 1934
Pine needles	Current needles less hardy early in winter, more hardy later	Clements, 1938
Wheat	Age had no effect on hardiness in first phase, resistance increased later with age	Golicinskii, 1939

This is not surprising, since so many other factors may introduce complications. The hardiness response of a plant to developmental stage may be potential and may not show up until hardened by low temperature. On the other hand, unfavorable environmental conditions (such as high N) may lead to an exhaustion of reserves and therefore counteract the favorable effect of a developmental stage. Furthermore, tissues that are young to one worker may be old to another. Actually, it is the physiological rather than the chronological age that should be considered.

In spite of all these complications, certain generalizations follow from the recorded results. It has been shown that the dry seed tolerates the lowest temperatures but possesses no true frost hardiness, since it is readily killed by freezing if in the hydrated state (Chapter 1). The plant, therefore, begins its life with a minimum of hardiness. This is followed by a rise in hardiness with development. In the case of seedlings with insufficient reserves, an exhaustion of these may lead to a second minimum followed by a second maximum due to photosynthesis. On transition from the vegetative to the reproductive stage, hardiness drops again (Tables 32 and 34). The series of changes may be shown diagrammatically (Fig. 11). All the results recorded in Table 35 can be

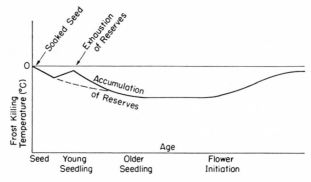

Fɪɢ. 11.   Diagrammatic representation of changes in frost hardiness with age.

found in this diagram, at least in the case of winter annuals, if it is assumed that different species reach the minima and maxima at different ages (e.g. wheat vs. lespedeza). A similar cycle of changes in frost hardiness seems to occur in developing buds. The unfolded leaves of a bud were early recognized to be completely tender, whereas the buds from which they develop and the leaves they develop into are more hardy (Hoffman, 1857). In evergreens, very young leaves are most sensitive (Winkler, 1913; Däniker, 1923). Yet the young but fully developed are hardier than the older ones. The age of tree tissues also seems important in relation to the rate and depth of entrance into the rest period.

Chapter 9.

Morphological Factors Associated with Hardiness

The greater part of the work on frost hardiness consists of a search for factors correlated with it. The purpose of the search has been twofold: (1) to find a "measuring-stick" that can be used quickly and quantitatively to help select hardy varieties, and (2) to learn something about the mechanism of frost hardiness. These results must be accepted with some caution, since the test of hardiness in many cases has been field survival. This may sometimes involve factors other than frost hardiness. Both morphological and physiological factors have been investigated.

Since the morphological factors are so readily observed, even the early investigators recognized that there is not much connection between structure and frost hardiness (Lindley, 1842; Halsted, 1889). Many have found some correlation (Table 36), others have failed to find any (Table 37). Even those who succeeded frequently indicated that there are

TABLE 36

Reports of morphological factors associated with frost hardiness

Plant	Factor	Observer
Wheat	Darker green, smaller, harder, more cuticularized leaves	Sinz, 1914
Winter grains	Greater ratio of root length to leaf area	Salmon, 1933
Wheat	Smaller leaf area and leaf width	Klages, 1926a
Winter rye	Roots more extensible and higher tensile strength	Kokkonen, 1927
Wheat, barley, oats	Growing points deeper in soil	Tavcar, 1930
Alfalfa	Growing points deeper in soil	Blinn, 1911
Winter wheats	Roots less horizontal, less top growth	Worzella, 1932
Wheat	Smaller first internode and leaf	Kolomycev, 1936
Cabbage	Thicker leaves covered with bloom	Harvey, 1918; Rosa, 1921
Chinese cabbage	Tougher cuticle, less succulent leaves	Harvey, 1922
Apple	harder twigs (some exceptions)	Beach and Allen, 1915
Plums	More lenticels	Strausbaugh, 1921
Flax	Branched vs. erect habit	Dillman, 1941

exceptions and that no one structural characteristic is sufficient as a measuring stick of hardiness (e.g. Beach and Allen, 1915).

Cell size has received more attention than any other factor. Molisch (1897) and D'Arsonval (1901) suggest that small cell size might protect a plant by favoring undercooling. Wiegand (1906)) obtained direct evidence of this in 20 species of trees. But most of the work has consisted of attempts to show a relation between small cell size and true

TABLE 37
Investigations showing no relation between structure and frost hardiness

Plant	Factor	Observer
Grain varieties	Leaf width, length, and thickness	Schaffnit, 1910
Wheat	Various morphological factors	Nilsson-Ehle, 1913
Wheat	Width of leaf	Sinz, 1914
Winter grains	Cell structure, epidermal covering	Salmon, 1917
Winter wheat	Morphological characters	Barulina, 1923; Crépin et al., 1929

TABLE 38
Cytological characters associated with hardiness

Plant or plant part	Character	Observer
Twigs	Thicker cell walls	Schübler, 1827
Evergreen leaves, twigs	Aggregation of chloroplasts in winter	Kraus, 1875; Haberlandt, 1875; D'Arbaumant, 1901; Lewis and Tuttle, 1923; Scarth and Levitt, 1937; Vetuhova, 1936
	Smaller cells	de Candolle (see Treviranus, 1838)
Various plants (watering with solutions)	Smaller cells	Chandler, 1913; Harvey, 1918
Grape vine	Greater cell wall thickness	Gladwin, 1917
Leaves	Smaller cell size	Rosa, 1921
Citrus species	Lower stomatal density	Hirano, 1931
Apples	Diploids (smaller cell size) hardier	Anonymous, 1935
Rape	Diploids (smaller cell size) hardier	Schlosser, 1936
Trees (cortex)	Smaller cell size	Levitt and Scarth, 1936
Many species	Polyploids more northern distribution than related diploids	Muntzing, 1936; Fischer and Schwanitz, 1936 (see Granhall, 1943)

frost hardiness. A positive relation has been found by so many investigators (Table 38) that it cannot be ignored. In fact, the several
cases of a relation between smaller plant size and frost hardiness recorded above (Table 36) are readily explained by the small cell size
of the hardy plants. On the other hand, there are many clear-cut cases
of hardier plants having larger cells (Table 39) and there is no question

TABLE 39

Investigations showing no relation between cytological characters and
frost resistance

Plant	Character	Observer
Sedum and Sempervivum vs. mulberry and myrtle	Cell size (the former are more resistant yet have larger cells)	Treviranus, 1838
Numerous species	Cell size	Rein, 1908
Wheats	Cell size	Barulina, 1923
100 species	Diploids vs. polyploids	Bowden, 1940
Apples	Diploids vs. polyploids	Granhall, 1943, 1950

but that plants can be hardened though their cells are unable to shrink
in size. It must, therefore, be concluded that cell size is a factor, but only
a secondary one, in frost hardiness. For the primary factor, it is necessary to investigate the physiological properties of the plant.

Chapter 10.

The Relation of Total and Bound Water Content to Frost Hardiness

Frost injury, by definition, is due to solidification of water. Low water content is therefore the most obvious factor to investigate in relation to frost hardiness, and many claims of such a relation have been made (Bobart, 1684; Du Hamel and de Buffon, 1737; Senebier, 1800; Schübler, 1827, 1829; De Candolle, 1838; Lindley, 1842; Sachs, 1873; Göppert, 1883; Frank, 1895; Gladwin, 1917). Air-dry plants have already been shown to survive the lowest temperatures obtainable, but this is not due to frost hardiness (Chapter 1). Low moisture supply during growth enhances the ability of plants to harden, though it has no effect during the hardening period itself (Chapter 7). But it was early recognized that water content may give no indication of frost hardiness, for instance in the case of some very succulent but hardy Crassulaceae (Hoffman, 1857; Müller-Thurgau, 1886).

More recent investigations have attempted to test the importance of water content by quantitative determinations on a number of varieties differing in frost hardiness. Shutt (1903) was able to obtain a very good correlation in the case of apple varieties (Table 40). Similar results have since been obtained by many others (Table 41), though many failures have also been recorded (Table 42). One possible source of

TABLE 40

Hardiness and water content of apple varieties (from Shutt, 1903)

Variety	Hardiness	Water content (%)
McMahon White		45.79
Yellow Transparent	hardiest	45.82
Duchess		46.00
Wealthy	less hardy	48.06
Scott's Winter		48.21
Scarlet Pippin	still less hardy	48.23
Walworth Pippin		46.58
Boy's Delight		46.75
Hebble White	least hardy	49.74
Blenheim Pippin		50.01

TABLE 41

Investigations showing an inverse relation between moisture content and hardiness

Plant	Observer
Peach buds	Johnston, 1919, 1922, 1923
Apples	Hooker, 1920; Bakke, Radspinner, and Maney, 1920; Hildreth, 1926; Traub, 1927
Raspberry	Schwarze, 1937
Apple roots	Stuart, 1938
Wheat (also barley, oats)	Seelhorst, 1910; Schaffnit, 1913; Sinz, 1914; Hedlund, 1917; Newton, 1924a; Newton and Brown, 1926; Åkerman, 1927; Martin, 1927; Starkov, 1931; Tavcar, 1930; Roemer, Rudorf, and Lueg, 1928 (one exception); Lueg, 1929; Fuchs, 1930; Tumanov and Borodin, 1930; Mudra, 1932; Ebiko and Watanabe, 1935; Vasiljev, 1934; Starkov, 1931; Laude, 1937; Christoff, 1939; Potapov, 1939
Clover	Greathouse and Stuart, 1934
Kentucky bluegrass	Carroll and Welton, 1939
Alfalfa	Peltier and Tysdal, 1931; Megee, 1935
Cabbage, kale	Harvey, 1918; Rosa, 1921; Carolus, 1930
Evergreens	Meyer, 1928; Rigg and Cain, 1929; Langlet, 1934; Ulmer, 1937

TABLE 42

Investigations showing no relation between moisture content and hardiness

Plant	Observer
Apple	Chandler, 1913; Hildreth, 1926; Traub, 1927; Thomas, 1927; Stark, 1936; Field, 1939
Peach	Chandler, 1913
Brambles	Lott, 1926
Citrus	Ivanov, 1939
Evergreens (complications due to transpiration)	Rigg and Cain, 1929; Goldsmith and Smith, 1926; Pisek, Sohm, and Cartellieri, 1935; Clements, 1938
Wheat	Newton, 1922 (succeeded later—see Table 42); Crescini and Tettamanzi, 1929; Balde, 1930; Gassner and Goeze, 1931
Rye, barley, etc.	Martin, 1927; Fuch, 1930; Tumanov, 1931; Constantinescu, 1933; Andersson, 1935; Wilhelm, 1935; Christoff, 1939; Laude, 1937
Spinach, rape	Wilhelm, 1935
Alfalfa	Peltier and Tysdal, 1931; Megee, 1935; Weimer, 1929; Dexter, 1935a

error was indicated by Beach and Allen (1915). Though hardy apple varieties had a slightly lower moisture content during summer, they conserved their supply better during winter. Consequently, after some time their moisture content was higher than that of the tender varieties. These results were corroborated by Strausbaugh (1921) for plums, by Hildreth (1926) for apples, and by Sinz (1914), Newton (1924), Werman (Arland, 1931), and Starkov (1931) for wheat. The fluctuations in water content were far less in the more hardy than in the less hardy varieties during winter. Similarly, in the case of evergreens the moisture content decreases during fall and winter, though the change is small and is complicated by a passive loss due to transpiration. Ulmer (1937) was able to relate the hardiness change to this "active" decrease in moisture content but found no relation to the "passive" (transpirational) decrease. This, then, may account for some of the negative results obtained (Table 42).

It must, therefore, be concluded that if differences in transpirational loss are excluded, the hardening process involves a reduction in the percent water, and that, frequently, the greater the degree of hardiness developed the greater is this reduction. The most striking example is wheat, which has given a good correlation in the hands of some twenty independent workers in many countries, a lack of correlation in only three or four investigations (Tables 41 and 42). On the other hand, barley has almost uniformly failed to yield such a correlation. In the case of woody fruit plants, the results have been as often negative as positive. The marked reduction in water content under conditions preventing transpirational loss was shown by digging up rhizomes of plants growing in the Arctic (Table 43). Unfortunately, even this may be partly due to distillation of water from the rhizomes to the external ice.

Several investigators have attempted to improve the frost hardiness of plants by artificially reducing their water content. In a vast number of tests, Chandler (1913) was never successful, though in all cases the wilting was sufficient to give the tissues a limp appearance. If, however, water supply was reduced over a long period of time (1½ months), a definite increase in frost hardiness occurred. The results of Tysdal (1933) and other workers are in full agreement with Chandler. Some (Müller-Thurgau, 1880; Carrick, 1920; Potter, 1924; Iljin, 1934) have found a very slight increase in frost hardiness due to wilting, others (Ulmer, 1937) none at all.

These contradictory results suggest that perhaps it is not the total water content, but only a certain portion of it that is important in frost hardiness—the portion held by the dry matter in equilibrium with a definite low vapor pressure. This has been called *bound water*. But there are two main types of water binding—one by osmotically active (i.e. molecularly dissolved) the other by colloidal substances. The former depends on the solute content, which can be determined much more simply and accurately by direct measurements of freezing-point lowerings or of plasmolytic values (see Chapter 11). The colloidal content and its water binding properties, on the other hand, cannot be determined either quantitatively or qualitatively in any other way than by measuring colloidally bound water.

TABLE 43

Winter water content as percent of summer water content in rhizomes of plants growing in the Arctic[*]

Species	Winter water content as percent of summer water content
Poa artica R. Br.	36
Luzula nivalis (Laest.) Beurl.	60
Eriophorum polystachyum Honck.	64
Salix rotundifolia Trautv.	47
Papaver radicatum Laest.	104
Potentilla emarginata Pursh.	74
Pedicularis sudetica Willd.	77
Petasites frigidus (L) Fries.	26

[*] From original of table 5, P. F. Scholander *et al.*, *J. Cellular Comp. Physiol.* **42**: 9, 1953.

Indirect evidence led many investigators to postulate an increased water-binding power in frost-hardy plants. The many reports of a slower water loss mentioned above have been interpreted in this way, though others have explained it by structural differences—e.g. stronger cutinization, white bloom, etc. (Sinz, 1914). In evergreens, differences in water loss may be unaccompanied by any difference in frost hardiness (Doyle and Clinch, 1926), because they depend on physical protection by the outer layers of cells. Similarly, hardy and nonhardy alfalfa varieties do not differ in rates of water loss (Megee, 1935). Kessler and Ruhland (1938) removed the upper epidermis and found either a greater water loss from the hardier leaves or no difference between leaves differing in hardiness. Boon-Long (1941) obtained similar results with cabbage. The re-uptake of water by air-dried leaves has failed to show any difference

TABLE 44

Bound water determinations showing a correlation with frost hardiness

Plant and method	Observer
1. Dye absorption apple	Dunn and Bakke, 1926; Dunn, 1930, 1933, 1935, 1937
2. Resistance to freezing at about —20 to —30°C *Caragana arborescens* pine fir needles	Novikov, 1928 Clements, 1938
3. Pressure cereal leaves pitch pine needles Digitalis, Arctostaphylos Kentucky bluegrass	Newton, 1922, 1924, 1924a; Martin, 1927; Laude, 1937 Meyer, 1928 Rigg and Cain, 1929 Carroll and Welton, 1939
4. Dilatometer (—5 to —10°C) cabbage brambles wheat alfalfa	Rosa, 1921 Lott, 1926 Bobko and Popowa, 1929; Lebdeincev, 1930 Grandfield, 1943
5. Cryoscopic wheat cabbage	Newton, 1924, 1924a; Martin, 1927; Gortner and Gortner, 1934; Chandler, 1941 Greathouse, 1932
6. Calorimetric clover grains alfalfa apple Kentucky bluegrass cabbage (—5.6°C) (nonosmotically bound)	Greathouse and Stuart, 1934; Greathouse, 1935 Dexter, 1934; Christoff, 1939 Dexter, 1935a Stark, 1936 Carroll and Welton, 1939 Levitt, 1939
7. Refractometric wheat	Briginec and Tregubenco, 1939; Vetukhova, 1939
8. Plasmometric cortical cells of trees	Levitt and Scarth, 1936
9. Decreased "dry weight" at high temperatures *Aspergillus niger*	Todd and Levitt, 1951

between wheats differing in hardiness (Newton, 1924a); in the case of clover a correlation has been obtained (Greathouse and Stuart, 1936a).

Attempts to measure bound water more directly have yielded contradictory results (Tables 44 and 45) and therefore require careful analysis. The dye adsorption method may sometimes measure colloidal content, and indirectly bound water if the colloids happen to be hydrophilic, but in no sense can it be considered a reliable method. The pressure method measures destruction of semipermeability by frost injury

TABLE 45

Bound water determinations showing no correlation with frost hardiness

Method and plant	Observer
1. Dye absorption	
cabbage	Levitt, 1933
	Dunn, 1937a
2. Pressure	
alfalfa	Steinmetz, 1926
Kentucky bluegrass	Carroll and Welton, 1939
3. Cryoscopic	
alfalfa	Steinmetz, 1926
wheat	Martin, 1927; Chandler, 1941
cabbage, cauliflower	Kimball, 1927
4. Calorimetric	
apple (—10°C to —20°C)	Maney, 1931; Stark, 1936
pitch pine needles (—20°C)	Meyer, 1932
wheat	Van Doren, 1937
5. Plasmometric	
cabbage	Levitt and Scarth, 1936

if the tissues have been allowed to freeze before exposure to the pressure. When the tissues have not been frozen, it measures the injury produced by the pressure itself. In neither case does it measure bound water. The unfrozen state of many plant tissues at low, subzero temperatures has also been attributed to bound water (Novikov, 1928; Lipman, 1937; Clements, 1938), though the tissues may simply have been undercooled (Table 5, Chapter 1). The cryoscopic method is open to many errors and is, at best, merely an indirect measurement of solute content (Chandler, 1941).

The dilatometric and calorimetric methods give measurements of a combination of osmotically and colloidally bound water at temperatures not far below the freezing point, though the colloidally bound can be calculated (Lebedincev, 1930; Levitt, 1939). At —20°C or lower, they measure colloidally bound water nearly exclusively. Both positive and negative results have been obtained, but the variations between individual results are frequently far too great to permit detection of the differences that may exist (e.g. Stark, 1936).

Most of the positive results can be explained by increases in osmotically active rather than colloidally active substances. Some are due to incorrect methods of calculation—e.g. expressing the results on a fresh-weight instead of a dry-weight basis (see Meyer, 1932; Levitt, 1939). Others are due to calculations based on ideal solutions (Weismann, 1938). The deviations of sucrose from the laws of ideal solutions are sufficient to result in large but spurious estimates of colloidally bound water. When corrections are made for these deviations, Lebedincev's results are completely accounted for by the osmotic behavior of the solutes (Table 46). On the other hand, if an increase in colloidally bound water should

TABLE 46

Bound water determinations of Lebedincev recalculated on the basis of true freezing point lowerings of sucrose (from Weismann, 1938)

Winter wheat variety	Percent bound water at —3.8°C				
	According to Lebedincev			According to Weismann	
	Total	Osmotic	Colloidal	Osmotic	Colloidal
Hostianum	42	37	5	41	1
Erythrospermum "Durable"	42	36	6	41	1
Erythrospermum "Zemka"	36	33	3	36	0

occur solely in the protoplasm, determinations on whole pieces of tissues that are usually more than 90% nonprotoplasmic could not possibly reveal the changes. The opposite result might actually be obtained from such gross measurements, due to an accumulation of sugars which increase the total dry matter without adding any colloidally bound water. This may explain the failure to find an increase in colloidal content or quality on hardening as a percent of the total dry matter (Newton, 1924a; Megee, 1935; Vetuhova, 1936a, 1939a), for it could be easily hidden due to a greater increase in sugars.

In view of these complications, methods capable of measuring colloidally bound water in protoplasm have been sought. One of these is the plasmometric method. It measures the nonsolvent space in living cells. A progressive reduction in this space with progressive osmotic dehydration of the cell can be explained if part of it is due to bound water. Because of the low sensitivity of the method, no nonsolvent space (and therefore no bound water) could be detected in the highly vacuolate cabbage cells (Levitt and Scarth, 1936). In the highly protoplasmic cortical cells of trees, however, both nonsolvent space and bound water were large, in the vacuole as well as in the protoplasm. More bound water seemed to occur in the hardier cells, but due to the large margin of error of the method, these results are not conclusive. The colloidal content was apparently correlated with hardiness, and the nonsolvent space decreased with loss of hardiness much more rapidly than did the cell sap concentration (Table 47). Here again, however, complications due to the behavior of sucrose must be taken into account.

TABLE 47

Decrease in nonsolvent space of cortical cells with loss in hardiness
(from Levitt and Scarth, 1936)

Date	Catalpa		Liriodendron	
	Osmotic potential (atm)	Nonsolvent space (%)	Osmotic potential (atm)	Nonsolvent space (%)
March 12	22.6	42	25.2	37
March 31	21.9	40	21.9	36
April 20	23.2	52	19.3	24
May 11	14.3	20	17.4	21
June 1	12.4	29	13.0	6
June 22	9.4	13	14.3	16

More conclusive evidence was obtained with the highly protoplasmic mycelium of Aspergillus niger (Todd and Levitt, 1951). Unlike the higher plants, this fungus contains only living cells (at least in young cultures) and each cell is thin-walled and filled with protoplasm containing only a few small vacuoles. Bartetzko (1909) had earlier shown that the frost hardiness of this organism can be increased by increasing the osmotic concentration of the medium in which it is grown (Table 6). The bound water of such cultures was therefore measured, using the very simple method of determining the decrease in "dry" weight with rise in temperature. This decrease is due to removal of bound water which

is held by the colloids at lower temperatures (Gortner, 1938). The
results show a steady increase in the water bound by the mycelium with
increase in osmotic concentration of the medium, and therefore with
increase in frost hardiness (Fig. 12).

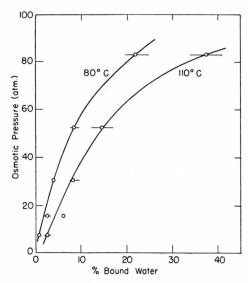

Fig. 12.   Bound water in mycelium of *Aspergillus niger*. The quantity increases
with the concentration (in atm) of the medium in which it is grown (from Todd
and Levitt, 1951).

Chapter 11.

The Relation of Cell Sap Concentration and Sugars to Frost Hardiness

CELL SAP CONCENTRATION

Most of the results showing a correlation between bound water and hardiness have been due to osmotically bound water (Chapter 10). They indicate, therefore, a higher concentration of solutes in hardy than in nonhardy plants. A vast number of direct determinations of solute concentration have in general shown the same thing (Figs. 13, 14; Tables 48

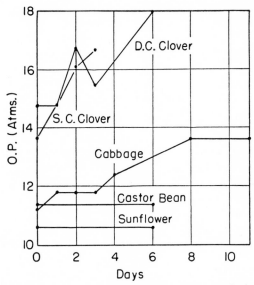

FIG. 13. The increase in osmotic potential of cabbage and clover leaf cells during hardening at 5°C. Castor bean and sunflower kept at the same temperature fail to show a rise in either osmotic potential or frost hardiness (from Levitt and Scarth, 1936).

49). The correlation with frost hardiness involves both an increase in solutes during hardening and a parallelism between the solute concentration and the hardiness of different varieties (Table 48). In a few cases (Magistad and Truog, 1925; Civinsky, 1934) frost hardiness is not involved, since the plants are killed by very slight freezes and the so-called "hardier" variety is simply better able to avoid freezing by virtue of a lower freezing point. But such tender plants are usually incapable of undergoing any increase in solutes on exposure to hardening temperatures (Rein, 1908; Pantanelli, 1918; Rosa, 1921; Meindl, 1934; Schlosser, 1936), unlike frost-hardy plants (Fig. 13). Potato tubers are

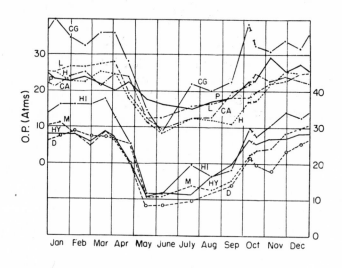

Fig. 14. Seasonal changes in osmotic potential of hardy woody plants, determined on cortical cells of current growth, October, 1934–October, 1935. Lower chart, average weekly temperature (from Levitt and Scarth, 1936). *Upper curves:* CG = *Caragana arborescens,* L = *Liriodendron tulipifera,* CA = *Catalpa hybrida,* H = *Hydrangea paniculata,* P = *Picea pungens.*

Lower curves (apple varieties): HI = Hibernal and HY = Hyslop (hardy); M = Milwaukee, and D = Delicious (less hardy than above).

exceptions, for though unable to harden, they show a marked increase in solutes at hardening temperatures (Müller-Thurgau, 1882; Apelt, 1907). The negative results (Table 49) have been obtained primarily when comparing varieties, both the more hardy and the less hardy varieties showing the same increase in solute concentration with hardening. Some of the negative results may be due to the same factor as

complicated the determination of moisture contents (Chapter 10)—i.e.
a passive loss of water (Grahle, 1933; Pisek, Sohm, and Cartellieri, 1935).
But this can be true only when freezing-point determinations are used.

TABLE 48
Investigations showing a positive relation between solute concentration and frost
hardiness (f = freezing point method, p = plasmolytic method)

Plant	Observer
Cabbage, rape (f p)	Harvey, 1918; Rosa, 1921; Greathouse, 1932; Levitt and Scarth, 1936; Schlösser, 1936
Garden plants (f) Vegetables	Chandler, 1913, 1914; Onodera and Takasaki, 1930
Persea americana (f)	Harris and Popenoe, 1916
Citrus trees (f)	Haas and Halma, 1928, 1931
Grains (p f)	Buhlert, 1906; Newton, 1922; Barulina, 1923; Govorov, 1923; Martin, 1927; Mudra, 1932; Newton, 1924; Tumanov and Borodin, 1930; Lueg, 1929; Fuchs, 1935a; Eibl, 1926; Mader, 1927; Åkerman, 1927; Janssen, 1929; Christoff, 1939; Tysdal and Salmon, 1926 (viscosity); Fuchs, 1930; Granhall, 1943
Clover, lucerne (p f)	Eibl, 1927; Greathouse and Stuart, 1934
Fruit trees (f p)	Chandler, 1914; Bakke, Radspinner, and Maney, 1920; Carrick, 1920; Johnston, 1922; Levitt and Scarth, 1936
Evergreens (p f)	Buhlert, 1906; Lidforss, 1907; Dixon and Atkins, 1912, 1915; Winkler, 1913; Korstian, 1924; Gail, 1926; Meyer, 1928; Preising, 1930; Pfeiffer, 1933; Steiner, 1933; Grahle, 1933; Pisek, Sohm, and Cartellieri, 1935
Broadleaf trees (f p) etc.	Winkler, 1913; Levitt and Scarth, 1936; Arrhenius and Söderberg, 1917; Fukuda, 1932, 1933
Mosses (p)	Irmscher, 1912
Succulents (f)	Kessler, 1935

TABLE 49
Investigations showing lack of a relation between solute concentration and frost
hardiness (f = freezing-point method, p = plasmolytic method)

Plant	Observer
Grains (f)	Sinz, 1914; Salmon and Fleming, 1918; Newton, 1922; Barulina, 1923; Janssen, 1929; Onodera and Takasaki, 1930; Arland, 1931; Christoff, 1939
Clover, alfalfa (f)	Koperzinskii, 1939; Steinmetz, 1926; Weimer, 1929; Megee, 1935
Mosses (p)	Irmscher, 1912
Evergreens (f)	Korstian, 1924*; Michaelis, 1934a
Succulents (f)	Kessler, 1935

* Negative results due to method according to Meyer, 1928.

The fact that even the plasmolytic method may fail to show a correlation with varietal hardiness (Fig. 14) proves that there are some real exceptions. Furthermore, the very investigators who have succeeded in demonstrating the most striking correlations when some varieties are compared, have completely failed in the case of others. Wheat varieties, for instance, usually give excellent results (except when originating in different countries); barley varieties usually show no correlation between frost hardiness and solute concentration. And some of the hardiest evergreens (e.g. Picea, Fig. 14) show relatively little change in cell sap concentration though their hardiness varies from one extreme to the other.

Some attempts have been made to find out whether the relation between cell sap concentration and frost hardiness is a direct one. It is easy to show that growing plants in high concentrations of solutes markedly increases hardiness (Table 6; Maximov, 1908; Chandler, 1913). But this certainly produces other changes besides the increase in cell sap concentration (Todd and Levitt, 1951). When rapidly penetrating substances (e.g. glycerine, urea, ethyl alcohol) are used, such secondary changes are presumably avoided and a small but definite lowering of

TABLE 50
Effect of solute uptake on frost hardiness (from Chandler, 1913)

Plant	Treatment	Δ of solu- tion used (°C)	Δ of sap after solute uptake (°C)	Killing
Cabbage	none		0.780	80% at —4°C
	KCl	0.775	1.145	40
	glycerine	2.82	1.780	20
	NH₄Cl	0.360	0.950	100
Cowpeas	sucrose	1.570	1.230	0.0 at —3°C
	glucose	1.740	1.250	49.9
	glycerine	1.575	1.160	0.0
	KCl	0.730	1.130	66.6
	NH₄Cl	0.725	1.140	41.6
	water	0.00	0.870	66.6

the frost killing point occurs (Table 50, Åkerman, 1927; Iljin, 1935). In the case of succulents, however, there was little or no increase in frost hardiness (Kessler, 1935). The absorption of considerable quantities of sugar from solution resulted in only slight increase in the frost hardiness of cabbage leaves (Dexter, 1935). On the other hand, it is possible to lower frost hardiness very markedly by chloroform treatment without affecting the cell sap concentration (Kessler, 1935; Ulmer, 1937).

It seems obvious from these results that the increase in cell sap concentration is unable by itself to account for all the increase in frost hardiness that normally accompanies it. Furthermore, plants with concentrations as high as 30 atm. may be killed by light frosts (Walter, 1931). Consequently, this factor has been examined for other possible explanations.

SUGARS

The sweetening of plants on exposure to low temperatures has long been known. Pliny mentions rape as an example. The evidence that has accumulated from exact analyses leaves no doubt that this sugar accumulation is the cause of the increased cell sap concentration on hardening. Total electrolytes remain constant in various plants (Dixon and Atkins, 1915; Lewis and Tuttle, 1920; Newton, 1922), while sugars which account for only 4 to 8% of the osmotic effect in unhardened wheat are responsible for 10 to 40% in the hardened (Mudra, 1932; Newton, 1922). In evergreens the relation is similar (Table 51).

TABLE 51

Average percent of osmotic values due to sugars in summer and winter
(from Steiner, 1933)

| Species | Percent of osmotic value due to sugars | |
	Summer	Winter
Ilex aquifolium	34.4	56.0
Hedera helix	34.9	48.5
Pinus silvestris	33.1	45.9
Taxus baccata	24.5	33.1

Indirect evidence of the importance of carbohydrates is the fact that a reduction in carbohydrate reserves, whatever the cause, leads to reduced frost hardiness (Oberdieck, 1872; Müller-Thurgau, 1880; Chandler, 1919; Chapter 7). This fact has long been recognized by horticulturists. But the most important evidence comes from determinations of sugar and starch content during the hardening period. It has long been known that starch decreases to a winter minimum in woody plants (Table 52) while sugars increase to a maximum (Table 53). This is uniformly true in the bark of all trees and in the leaves of evergreens. But it is true only of the above-ground portion of the plant. Even here, however, the starch in the wood fails to show more than a partial disappearance, though this is more nearly complete in softwoods than in hardwoods. No such change occurs (a) in submerged plants (Lidforss, 1896), (b) in roots under natural conditions (Sinnott, 1918, etc.), except in the free-lying roots which contain less starch than the subterranean ones (Weber, 1909), (c) in the inner regions of rhizomes (Lidforss, 1896). It has been shown that the tissues in which the starch conversion does not occur are the least frost hardy (Steinmetz and Hillborn, 1937).

TABLE 52

a. Reports of a winter starch minimum in at least the bark tissues of various trees

Russia:

Famintzen and Borodin, 1867
Russow, 1883, 1884
Grebnitzky, 1884

France

Mer, 1879, 1891, 1898
D'Arbaumont, 1901
Leclerc du Sablon, 1904
Michel-Durand, 1919

United States:

Halsted, 1889
Preston and Phillips, 1911
Price, 1916
Sinnott, 1918
Hooker, 1920
Mitra, 1921
Korstian, 1924
Hildreth, 1926
Rigg and Cain, 1929
Jones and Bradlee, 1933
Siminovitch *et al.*, 1953

Germany:

Schulz, 1888
Fischer, 1891
Tischler, 1905
Schellenberg, 1905
Niklewski, 1906
Fabricius, 1906
Winkler, 1913
Kirchhoff, 1915
Ulmer, 1937

Sweden:
Antevs, 1916

Japan:
Ishibe, 1935

Canada:
Tuttle, 1919
Gibbs, 1940

England:
Swarbrick, 1927
Cockerham, 1930
Wight, 1933

b. Reports of a winter starch minimum in evergreen leaves

France:

Mer, 1876

Germany:

Lidforss, 1896
Overton, 1899
Guttenberg, 1907, 1927

United States:
Ehlers, 1915
Clements, 1938

Sweden:
Lidforss, 1907
Badalla, 1911

Ireland:
Doyle and Clinch, 1927

Though most of the earlier observations of a starch minimum in winter were unaccompanied by sugar determinations, some of them and most of the later ones also showed a sugar maximum during winter (Table 53). That these changes are temperature-controlled was proved by transferring twigs to room temperature during winter (Czapek, 1901; Niklewski, 1906; Lidforss, 1907; Korstian, 1924). In a short time sugar disappeared and was replaced by starch. This agrees with the observa-

TABLE 53

Observations of a sugar maximum in winter

Plant	Observer
Evergreens (including conifers)	Mer, 1876; Lidforss, 1896; Leclerc du Sablon, 1906; Michel-Durand, 1919; Preising, 1930; Geffken, 1936; Ulmer, 1937; Meyer, 1928; Langlet, 1934
Betula	Niklewski, 1906; Sosa and Sosa Bourdouil, 1936
Apple trees	Hooker, 1920b; Hildreth, 1926; Traub, 1927

tion that at any time during winter the cell sap concentration may be greater at lower temperatures (Ursprung and Blum, 1916). The relation to temperature is further shown by (a) the more extensive starch loss during winter from evergreens in the colder northern regions of Japan than in the warmer southern part (Miyake, 1902); (b) the greater sugar increase at higher altitudes during winter in the case of spruce (Goldsmith and Smith, 1926); (c) the lack of starch → sugar conversion in pear trees overwintered in the greenhouse, though it occurred in others stored at —2°C (Gardner, 1929). But not all the results show such a clear-cut relation between the seasonal development of hardiness at low temperatures and starch → sugar conversion. Some investigators have failed to find a starch minimum in winter, e.g. in the case of *Gnetum gnemon* (Schulz, 1888), grapevine and Aristolochia (D'Arbaumont, 1901) and some evergreens (Leclerc du Sablon, 1906). On the other hand, Sinnott (1918) found it in all 300 tree species examined by him, though some were growing in the frostless Gulf of Mexico.

These results are not really contradictory but merely show that both temperature and season are involved in the carbohydrate change; sometimes the one is the controlling factor, sometimes the other. This was very clearly shown by Weber (1909). Tilia was always able to regenerate starch at room temperatures during winter. The starch again disappeared when the twigs were returned to the open. Yet maintaining branches at winter temperatures (—10 to + 2°C) failed to prevent the spring regeneration of starch; conversely 0 to —4°C failed to cause its disappearance during early summer (July-August). In late summer (August–September), however, the low temperature treatment did succeed in causing starch to disappear, reaching its minimum 2 months ahead of time. In fall (October), whole trees were removed indoors (15–20°C) and kept there throughout the winter. No starch decrease occurred at these temperatures except such as could be accounted for by respiration. Notter (1903—see Antevs, 1916) and Lewis and Tuttle (1920, 1923) observed a similar interaction between the effects of season and temperature on the starch $\leftrightharpoons$ sugar change.

More recent investigations of the relation between carbohydrates and frost hardiness have been mainly concerned with winter annuals. In all, or nearly all, cases, the hardening process was accompanied by an increase in sugars, and a comparison of the varieties of a species has also in most cases shown a greater sugar content in the hardier varieties (Tables 54 and 55). This relationship is sometimes astonishingly close (Table 56). But striking as the parallelism may be, there definitely is a limit; for if different grains are compared, or even varieties from different countries, the relation breaks down (Table 55). This is not simply due to differences in technique, for in several cases the same investigator has obtained a good correlation with some varieties or

TABLE 54

Reports of a relation between sugar content and frost hardiness

Plant	Observer
Cabbage, kale	Harvey, 1918; Rosa, 1921; Carolus, 1930
Crop plants	Schander and Schaffnit, 1919; Kreutz, 1930
Grains (leaves, crown)	Gassner and Grimme, 1913; Sinz, 1914; Gassner, 1918; Newton, 1922, 1924; Newton and Brown, 1926; Yasuda, 1926; Åkerman, 1927; Rikhter, 1927; Janssen, 1929; Balde, 1930; Fuchs, 1930; Hauser, 1930; Tumanov, 1931; Tottigham, Shands, and Delwicke, 1931; Mudra, 1932; Novikov, 1934; Vasiljev, 1934; Andersson, 1935, 1944; Fuchs, 1935a; Timofejeva, 1935; Vetuhova, 1938; Christoff, 1939; Kuksa, 1939a; Saveljev, 1939; Kneen and Blish, 1941; Granhall, 1943
Kentucky bluegrass	Carroll and Welton, 1939
Woody plants (shrubs)	Pojarkova, 1924; Schwarze, 1937
Alfalfa, clover	Steinmetz 1926; Greathouse and Stuart, 1934; Ireland, 1939
Coffee	Camargo, 1921
Apple roots	Stuart, 1938
Orange, mandarin	Ivanov, 1939
Evergreens	Pisek, 1950

TABLE 55

Reports failing to show a relation between sugar content and frost hardiness

Plant	Observer
Vetch, clover, alfalfa	Tumanov, 1931; Koperzinskii, 1939a; Mark, 1936
Brambles, shrubs	Lott, 1926; Pojarkova, 1924
Orange, mandarin, lemon	Ivanov, 1939b
Grains	Saveljev, 1939; Balde, 1930; Tumanov, 1931; Novikov, 1934; Constantinescu, 1933; Christoff, 1939
Apple	Hildreth, 1926

TABLE 56

Relation between sugar content and frost hardiness in wheat (from Åkerman, 1927)

Variety	Relative sugar content	Relative frost hardiness (I = highest)
Sammet	100	I
Svea II	87	II
Thule II	67	IV
Standard	66	IV
Sol II	65	IV
Pansar II	48	V
Extra Squarehead II	44	VI
Danish small wheat	41	VII
Wilhelmina	39	VIII
Perl summer-wheat	29	IX
Halland summer-wheat	22	X

conditions but not with others (Tables 54 and 55). Thus, *vulgare* wheats show an excellent correlation between sugars and hardiness, but when compared with *turgidum* varieties the relationship does not hold well (Granhall, 1943). Similarly, only the alpine evergreens of intermediate hardiness markedly accumulate sugars on hardening (Table 57; Fig. 10). The sugar increase is about as small in the hardiest conifers as in the least hardy evergreens.

The increase in sugars on hardening is due to starch conversion in trees and some herbaceous plants. In grains, however, it is directly due to photosynthesis during the hardening period; and the sugars accumulated can be accounted for quantitatively by the photosynthetic rate (Fig. 15). Furthermore, the temperature coefficient is very low for photosynthesis (1–2), high for respiration (2–3). Consequently, no such accumulation can occur at high temperatures.

A hydrolysis of disaccharides to monosaccharides during hardening has also been suggested (Müller-Thurgau, 1882; Niklewski, 1906; Rikhter, 1927; Steiner, 1933). On the other hand, it is frequently the disaccharides that accumulate (Mudra, 1932; Fuchs, 1935b; Kneen and Blish, 1941; Hylmö, 1942). In some cases, their accumulation is secondary both in time and quantity (Mudra, 1932; Kneen and Blish, 1941; Andersson, 1944); in others, the disaccharide may be the main sugar accumulated (Siminovitch and Briggs, 1954). It has recently been stated that even where monosaccharides have been found, this is due to hydrolysis of disaccharides during the determinations (Roberts, 1950).

TABLE 57

Frost-hardiness and sugar contents of alpine plants (from Ulmer, 1937)

Species	Midwinter killing temp. $(-°C)$	Yearly amplitude in frost hardiness $(°C)$	Yearly amplitude in total sugars (partial osmotic potential in atm)
Pinus cembra	<38.7	>28	2.9
Picea excelsa	<38	>29	3.6
Pinus montana	34.9	28.9	6.0
Loiseleuria procumbens	34.9	25.9	5.6
Juniperus communis-nana	34.0	25.0	6.1
Arctostaphylos uva ursi	29.2	20.4	8.7
Calluna vulgaris	28.0	23.0	12.0
Rhododendron ferrugineum	27.3	22.3	6.3
Erica carnea	18.5	14.0	11.4
Saxifraga aizoon	18.5	14.0	4.3
Homogyne alpina	18.0	14.5	9.3
Globularia nudicaulis	18.2	13.5	2.9
Veronica tournefortii	10.8	6.5	3.1
Stellaria media	9.7	7.2	1.0

It is obvious that these basic carbohydrate changes are not the sole reason for frost hardiness, since there are so many exceptions (Table 55). Further evidence of this is the now well-known fact that the major starch ⇌ sugar changes in the fall and in the spring do not occur at the same rate or time as the major frost hardiness changes (Notter, 1903; Chandler, 1913; Levitt, 1941; Siminovitch and Briggs, 1949; Pisek, 1950). On the other hand, as mentioned above, exposure to hardening temperatures in the summer brings the sugar content up to the winter maximum without producing much of an increase in frost hardiness. Similarly, it has long been known that there is a marked starch → sugar conversion in potato tubers at low temperatures (Einhof, see Göppert,

1830; Morren, 1838; Payen, 1838; Lindley, 1842; Schacht, 1856; Müller-Thurgau, 1882; Wright, 1932). Even though the tubers fail to become frost hardy, more sugar accumulates than in very hardy apple twigs during winter (Hildreth, 1926).

Direct attempts to prove the importance of sugars have been made by sugar feeding. In most cases there is no evidence that the sugars were taken up in appreciable amounts (Ewart, 1898; Bartetzko, 1909; Maximov, 1908; Åkerman, 1927; Iljin, 1935; Angelo *et al.*, 1939). When absorption was proved (Lidforss, 1907; Chandler, 1913; Dexter, 1935), the increase in hardiness was slight—far less than accompanied a much smaller sugar accumulation at hardening temperatures.

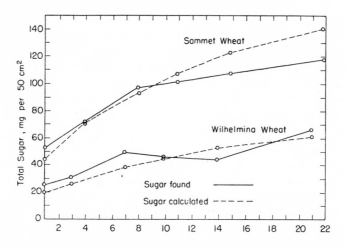

FIG. 15. Sugar content of wheat plants during hardening. Measured values compared with values calculated from rate of photosynthesis (from Andersson, 1944). Abscissa = no. days hardened.

Little evidence is available for the cause of the starch → sugar conversion at low temperatures. One logical suggestion is an activation of the hydrolytic enzymes, but early attempts to prove this ended in failure (Müller-Thurgau, 1882). On the contrary, tulip bulbs kept in the cold form sugars less rapidly on transfer to warm temperatures than do those kept at warm temperatures (Algera, 1936). Müller-Thurgau (1882) ascribed the sugar accumulation to a marked reduction in the respiration rate at the low temperature, without as marked a drop in activity of the hydrolytic enzymes. But the sugar accumulation is greater at 0°C than at 3°C even though the respiration rate is minimal at 3°C and rises at 0°C (Hopkins, 1924; Schander *et al.*, 1931—see

Snell, 1932; Wright, 1932). One complication, however, is the very effect of the sugar increase on respiration rate (Snell, 1932). In any case, the respiratory utilization of sugars could not possibly account for the decreased sugar content at high temperatures, for at this rate, all the reserves of the tuber would be used up in a very short time; and, as shown above, the sugar loss is actually due to starch formation. Several other suggestions have been made without any evidence to back them, e.g. a weakening of the synthetic mechanism (Michel-Durand, 1919; Doyle and Clinch, 1927); a dependence of starch synthesis on the temperature, of starch solution on the time of the year (Weber, 1909); an increased permeability of the starch "membrane" to the enzyme (Coville, 1920); a pH control (Mitra, 1921—but this could not be confirmed by Hopkins, 1924); a hormone control (Lewis and Tuttle, 1923).

The most widely held concept is a shift in the starch $\leftrightharpoons$ sugar equilibrium caused by the temperature drop (Overton, 1899; Czapek, 1901; Rosa, 1921; Fuchs, 1935; Algera, 1936). According to the laws of thermodynamics, since hydrolysis of starch is an exothermic process, the concentration of sugars must increase at low temperatures. Direct evidence of this is the fact that when leaves are floated on 2–5% sugar solutions, rich starch accumulation occurs at 16 to 18°C but little or none at 0 to 2°C (Czapek, 1901). The sugar must be increased to 7% before some starch forms at 0°C. Unfortunately, the sugar formation directly due to the temperature drop would be relatively slight (Algera, 1936). Furthermore, if this were the complete explanation, all plants (whether frost tender or frost hardy), would show the same sugar accumulation at low temperatures, and it would happen equally at all times of the year. Since neither of these predictions agrees with the facts, it seems certain that an enzyme activation of some sort must be involved (Siminovitch et al., 1953), even though older attempts to discover it have failed. Recent work, has, in fact, shown that such a change does occur in potato tubers (Arreguin and Bonner, 1949). Ewart et al. (1953) found both amylase and phosphorylase in the bark of black locust, and they suggest that a differential sensitivity to natural sulfhydryl reagents may control the seasonal changes. But later evidence indicated that phosphorylase was not involved in the starch synthesis (Ewart et al., 1953).

One unanswered question is why does the starch → sugar conversion go to completion in bark but not in wood cells? This may perhaps be related to the less active metabolism of the latter. But it may also be due to the more severe and rapid temperature changes that the externally located bark cells are exposed to. Fluctuating temperatures might conceivably be important in bringing about starch hydrolysis. But there is direct evidence against this at least in the case of herbaceous plants (potato tubers, cabbage leaves, etc.). The starch to sugar conversion occurs as readily at constant low temperatures as at fluctuating ones. A more likely suggestion is a relation between starch hydrolysis and oxidation-reduction potential, for where oxygen is deficient (e.g. in roots, submerged plants, internal tissues of rhizomes, or woody tissues of twigs), the hydrolysis occurs only partially or not at all.

The changes in moisture, solute, and carbohydrate contents so commonly though not invariably associated with hardiness can now be assembled in one general scheme. When the plant is subjected to hardening conditions, there is usually an accumulation of sugars, due either to starch conversion or to photosynthesis. In the latter case there is a marked increase in dry matter, a decrease in total water content, an increase in solutes, an increase in crystalloidally bound water. Any one of these factors may then be closely correlated with frost hardiness in plants such as grains. When sugar accumulation is due to starch conversion, however, though solutes and crystalloidally bound water both markedly increase, total moisture content cannot be perceptibly changed, since total carbohydrate content is unchanged. The major moisture decrease in such cases must occur during the earlier accumulation of starch.

Chapter 12.

Miscellaneous Factors Investigated in Relation to Frost Hardiness

In the search for the cause of frost hardiness, many factors other than those already discussed have been investigated. These can be divided into seven groups: (a) nitrogenous substances, (b) lipids, (c) tannins and anthocyanins, (d) pentosans and pectins, (e) acidity, (f) salts, and (g) metabolic processes.

NITROGENOUS SUBSTANCES

Most of the investigations of nitrogenous substances have attempted to show a relation between soluble, nonprotein, or amino nitrogen and hardiness (Table 58). The mere fact that the first report of an increase in these substances at low temperatures was in the nonhardy potato

TABLE 58
Relation between nonprotein (or amino) nitrogen and frost hardiness

Plant	Observer
(a) *Reports of a direct relation*	
Cabbage	Harvey, 1918; Schaffnit and Lüdtke, 1931
Wheat	Schander and Schaffnit, 1919; Newton, 1922, 1924; Janssen, 1929; Schaffnit and Lüdtke, 1931; Tottingham, Shands, and Delwicke, 1931; Christoff, 1939
Clover	Koperzinskii, 1939a
(b) *Negative reports*	
Wheat	Sinz, 1914; Newton, 1924; Newton and Brown, 1926; Mudra, 1932
Alfalfa	Tottingham, Shands, and Delwicke, 1931; Mark, 1936
Bartlett pear	Gardner, 1929
(c) *Reports of an inverse relation*	
Barley, oats, cabbage	Dexter, 1935
Apples	Hildreth, 1926; Thomas, 1927; Traub, 1927; Mulay, 1932

(Müller-Thurgau, 1882) might have thrown doubt on the usefulness of such investigations. Not only have different workers reported different results, but even the same investigator has found a correlation under some circumstances but not under others (Table 58). Mudra (1932), in fact, was able to reverse the results by lowering the temperature to

86

different degrees. The impossibility of relating soluble nitrogen to frost hardiness follows from the fact that both frost precipitation (Newton, Brown, and Anderson, 1931) and chilling injury (Wilhelm, 1935) may produce an increase. In fact, it has long been known that merely starving a plant in the dark results in a conversion of protein to amides (Chibnall, 1939), yet such treatment reduces hardiness (Chapter 7).

Others have attempted to relate total or protein N to hardiness (Mudra, 1932; Greathouse and Stuart, 1934; Megee, 1935; Lott, 1926; Christoff, 1939), though just as many failed to obtain such a relation (Wilhelm, 1935; Smirnova and Sestakov, 1938; Carroll and Welton, 1939; Sattler, 1929; Clements, 1938). These efforts were again doomed to failure from the outset, since total nitrogen can be increased by nitrogen fertilization which reduces frost hardiness.

The failure of the above attempts must not be interpreted as meaning that there is no relation between nitrogenous substances and frost hardiness. They simply indicate that the methods used were too crude to obtain results of value. It is necessary to analyze for individual nitrogenous substances rather than haphazard mixed groups of them. Recent attempts along these lines have been made by Siminovitch and Briggs (1949, 1953a). Of the nitrogen fractions determined, only the water-soluble proteins were found to increase with hardiness in the bark of locust trees during fall, and to decrease with hardiness during spring. This correlation held even in tree stumps that failed to deharden when kept dormant during summer, though sugars disappeared as if dehardening were taking place. Electrophoretic analysis of these water-soluble proteins revealed five major constituents (Briggs and Siminovitch, 1949). Though the amounts of these, relative to each other, remained constant during the periods of greatest change in hardiness, a marked change in their relative proportions occurred in midsummer, prior to the hardening period, leading to a marked increase in the quantities of two of the components. This increase in soluble proteins with hardiness has recently been found in wheat (Johansson, 1954—personal communication). However, it should be pointed out that even the potato tuber, which is incapable of becoming frost hardy, may also show a marked rise in soluble proteins at $3°C$ (Levitt, 1954a).

LIPIDS

Though it is now known that starch disappearance in winter is due to sugar formation (Chapter 11), Hales (1727) thought that oils or fats were formed as hardiness increased and disappeared with loss of hardiness. Many observations of lipids in winter appeared to confirm this

(Table 59), but nearly as many attempts ended in failure (Table 60). Even those who observed fat during winter agreed with Fischer (1891) that there are "fat trees" and "starch trees," and that only in the former does any fat accumulate. Others believe that what has been identified as fat is in many cases tannin or something else that shows a similar staining reaction (Meyer, 1918).

TABLE 59

Reports of a maximum oil content during winter or paralleling hardiness

Plant	Observer
Linden, birch, poplar, Caragana	Famintzin and Borodin, 1867; Baranetzky (see Grebnitzky, 1884); Suroz, 1891
Various native trees	Russow, 1884; Fischer, 1891; Schmidt, 1909; D'Arbaumont, 1901; Notter, 1903; Preston and Phillips, 1911; Antevs, 1916; Sinnott, 1918; Tuttle, 1919, 1921; Ishibe, 1935
Mulberry	Taguchi, 1940
Conifers	Fischer, 1891; Lewis and Tuttle, 1920, 1923
Evergreen leaves	Mer, 1876, 1877; Haberlandt, 1882; Schulz, 1888; Lidforss, 1896, 1907; Leclerc du Sablon, 1906; Tuttle, 1919, 1921; Korstian, 1924; Clements, 1938
Plum	Dorsey and Strausbaugh, 1923
Barley	Wilhelm, 1936

TABLE 60

Reports of no oil or of no winter maximum or correlation with frost hardiness

Plant	Observer
"Starch trees" (Tilia, Betula, etc.)	Fischer, 1891; Tischler, 1905; Niklewski, 1906; Weber, 1909; Gibbs, 1940
Conifers and broadleaved evergreens (nonfoliar parts)	Leclerc du Sablon, 1906; Fabricius, 1906; Meyer, 1918; Doyle and Clinch, 1927; Malhotra, 1931
Pear shoots	Gardner, 1929
Winter wheat	Newton and Brown, 1926
Alfalfa	Megee, 1935

TANNINS AND ANTHOCYANINS

Accumulation of these substances during winter has frequently been reported (Mer, 1877, 1898; Russow, 1883; Schulz, 1888; D'Arbaumont, 1901; Tischler, 1905; Kirchhoff, 1915; Schander and Schaffnit, 1919; Goldsmith and Smith, 1926). Some have even found larger amounts in more hardy species or varieties (Tischler, 1905; Harvey, 1922; Crépin *et al.*, 1929). But this is certainly not a general phenomenon, since many very hardy plants contain little or none of these substances, and many very tender plants contain large amounts.

PENTOSANS AND PECTINS

A correlation between pentosans and hardiness was first reported by Hooker (1920a) and Rosa (1920, 1921). But later, better-performed analyses on the same species as well as many others revealed absolutely no relation between the two (De Long, 1924; Doyle and Clinch, 1926; Lott, 1926; Newton, 1924; Newton and Brown, 1926; Hildreth, 1926; Rigg and Cain, 1929). In alfalfa, clover, and bluegrass, some evidence of a relation has since been produced (Mark, 1936; Greathouse and Stuart, 1934, 1936a; Carroll and Welton, 1939). Pectins have been very little investigated and the results have been negative (Greathouse and Stuart, 1936a; Lott, 1926) except for an autumn increase in raspberries (Lott, 1926).

ACIDITY

A reduction in acidity (a pH rise of 0.2 to as much as 3.0) during the hardening of plants has been recorded by so many investigators (Table 61), that it must be a rather general phenomenon, in spite of

TABLE 61
Relation of acidity to frost hardiness

Plant	Observer
(a) *Observations of less acidity (higher pH) in hardier tissues*	
Apple, pear trees	Hooker, 1920; Mitra, 1921; Abbott, 1923; Anderssen, 1929
Wheat, barley	Newton, 1922; Constantinescu, 1933
Root tissues	Zacharowa, 1926
10 species (except pith and xylem)	Rea and Small, 1927
Cabbage	Levitt, 1933; Dexter, 1935
Clover	Greathouse and Stuart, 1934a, 1936
Evergreens	Kessler, 1935
(b) *Observations of no difference in acidity*	
Apple, apricot trees	Bakke, Radspinner, and Maney, 1920
Herbaceous crop plants	Rosa, 1921
Wheat	Newton, 1922
Alfalfa	Dexter, Tottingham, and Graber, 1930
Clover	Greathouse and Stuart, 1934
Conifer leaves	Goldsmith and Smith, 1926; Doyle and Clinch, 1926

the many unsuccessful attempts to discover it. But some of the same
investigators that showed this relation were unable to find any correlation
with varietal hardiness. Similarly, the fact that the same change may
occur in the nonhardy potato when subjected to "hardening" temperatures (Schaffnit and Wilhelm, 1932), seems to indicate that the pH
change is unrelated to hardiness. According to Wilhelm (1935), it is due
to the rise in soluble nitrogen, and this may be unrelated to hardiness
(see above).

Further evidence that the two are causally unrelated is evident from
attempts to alter frost hardiness by changing the pH of the plant. Though
earlier experiments seemed to indicate that low concentrations of acids
lowered frost hardiness and low concentrations of bases increased it
(Maximov, 1912; Zacharowa, 1926; Iljin, 1934), it is difficult to understand how the strong acids and bases used could produce any effect on
the pH of the cells, since protoplasm is impermeable to them. Raising
the pH of the plant by applying easily absorbed nitrogenous substances
failed to increase frost hardiness (Dexter, 1935; Kessler, 1935). Similarly,
easily penetrating ammonia and acetic acid failed to produce any effect
(Levitt and Scarth, 1936). All this seems to substantiate Pantanelli's
(1919) conclusion that frost hardiness is not related to acidity.

An increased buffering against pH on exposure of wheat to low tem-
peratures has been reported by Mudra (1932), though not found by
Janssen (1929). Cabbage fails to show any such change (Levitt, 1933;
Dexter, 1935).

SALTS

As pointed out by Lidforss (1907), hardening occurs under conditions
unfavorable to salt uptake or loss. It is not surprising, therefore, that so
many investigators have failed to find any change in salt content with
hardening (Dixon and Atkins, 1915; Lewis and Tuttle, 1923; Traub, 1927;
Rigg and Cain, 1929; Haas and Halma, 1931). The very increase in
carbohydrates that occurs in green plants at hardening low temperatures
would yield an apparent decrease in salt content, and this has repeatedly
been obtained (Gorke, 1906; Chandler, 1913; Rosa, 1921; Newton, 1922;
Fuchs, 1935). It is perhaps this apparent change that led Hales (1727)
to relate high salt content to frost tenderness. Even when species, varieties, or parts of a plant differing in hardiness have been compared, the
same relation has been found (Zacharowa, 1926; Dexter, 1934; Kessler
and Ruhland, 1938; Bakke, Radspinner, and Maney, 1920; Greathouse
and Stuart, 1934). Some, however, have failed to find any relation
between electrolytes and frost hardiness (Crescini and Tettamanzi, 1929;

Ibraginov, 1931; Dexter, 1935a; Megee, 1935; Sinz, 1914; Newton, 1922; Fuchs, 1930). Still others have reported a direct relation between the two (Constantinescu, 1933; Santaella, 1934—see Fuchs, 1935b; Nizenjkov, 1939; Saveljev, 1939). But since these results were based on conductivity measurements, they could easily have been due to increases in organic acid ions rather than inorganic salts (Fuchs, 1935a). On the other hand, such factors as adsorption, viscosity, ionization, etc., may also be involved (Greathouse, 1938). Direct determinations have failed to reveal any relation between calcium content and frost hardiness (Pisek, 1950).

METABOLISM

Winter annuals covered by snow have often been said to winterkill due to respiratory loss of carbohydrate reserves (Yasuda, 1929; Tumanov et al., 1935). That this loss may be significant over long periods of time is indicated by the measurable rates of respiration at —6 to —7°C (Zeller, 1951), —10°C (De Long et al., 1930), or even —30°C (Scholander et al., 1953). The killing is not believed to be due to smothering, since the oxygen content under the snow is sufficient (Tumanov et al., 1935). Even the high concentrations of CO_2 and the low concentrations of O_2 that may occur under a solid layer of ice can be withstood for weeks without serious injury (Brierley and Landon, 1939). Consequently, it has been suggested that those varieties survive whose respiratory rates are lower, since their reserves would last longer (Newton and Anderson, 1931; Dexter, 1933, 1933a). On the other hand, even 80 cm. below the snow, there may be enough light for some photosynthesis (Rubel, 1906). Again, the rate of the process might easily be a deciding factor in the survival of the plant.

Following up these suggestions, an inverse relation between respiration rate and frost hardiness has been reported by several investigators (Tables 62, 63), though others have failed to detect it (Table 63). That the relation may vary with the conditions has been shown by Martin (1927) and Andersson (1944). If, for instance, previously lighted plants are used, the respiration rate is greater in the hardier variety. Andersson explains this by the higher concentration of substrate exerting a mass action effect. After two days in the dark, however, the rate is lower in the hardier variety.

Fewer determinations have been made of photosynthesis in relation to frost hardiness. In winter wheats, it is much less affected by temperature than is respiration, and it may be higher in hardier varieties (Fig. 16). Therefore, sugar accumulates more rapidly at low temperatures (Andersson, 1944). Alpine plants have been found to assimilate more rapidly below 5°C than do plants from the plains (Henrici, see Senn, 1922). Assimilation is measurable even at —2 to —3°C (Zeller, 1951). Vetuhova (1936, 1938) observed less of a depression of photosynthesis with temperature drop in hardy varieties of wheat. Andersson (1944) showed greater assimilation rates in the hardier wheat and rye varieties and a

TABLE 62

CO_2 output of apple twigs from varieties differing in hardiness. Twigs collected Dec. 28, stored for a few days at —15°C, then transferred to 6°C. CO_2 output determined during the following six hours (from De Long et al., 1930)

		CO_2 output	
Variety	Serial order of hardiness	CO_2 per kg (mg)	Serial order
Hibernal	1 (most hardy)	106	2
Duchess	2	98	1
Patten	3	133	4
Haralson	4	146	7
Wealthy	5	138	6
McIntosh	6	137	5
Fameuse	7	126	3
Wolf River	8	154	8
Jonathan	9	175	9
Sugar Loaf	10	212	10

TABLE 63

Relation between respiration and frost hardiness

Plant	Observer
(1) Reports of an inverse relation between respiration and frost hardiness	
Cereals	Govorov, 1923; Martin, 1927; Newton and Anderson, 1931; Potapov, 1939, 1939a; Andersson, 1944
Apple	De Long et al., 1930
Strawberries	Brierley and Landon, 1938
(2) Reports of no relation or a direct one	
Wheat	Martin, 1927; Andersson, 1944
Alfalfa	Megee, 1935; Silkett, Megee, and Rather, 1937; Ibraginov, 1931

greater assimilation surplus in a hardier wheat variety. But even non-hardy, submerged plants become adapted to low temperatures and are then able to photosynthesize more rapidly at these low temperatures in weak light (Harder, 1925).

TABLE 64

Relation between enzymatic activity and frost hardiness

Enzyme	Plant	Observation	Investigator
		(a) Of carbohydrate metabolism	
Dextrinase Amylase Maltase	conifer leaves	less during winter	Doyle and Clinch, 1927
Emulsin, invertase	conifer leaves	constant	Doyle and Clinch, 1927
Diastase	alfalfa	more sugar formed by enzyme from hardy plants	Tysdal, 1934
Carbohydrases	wheat	greater activity in less hardy	Bereznickaja and Oveckin, 1936, 1936a
Starch active	clover	more hydrolysis by enzyme from non-hardy	Greathouse and Stuart, 1937
Invertase		more hydrolytic activity in non-hardy at high temp.	Sisakjan and Rubin, 1939
Invertase	grains	more synthesis in hardened	Morosov, 1939
		(b) Of fat metabolism	
Lipase	conifer leaves	always negative	Doyle and Clinch, 1927
		(c) Of protein metabolism	
Proteolytic enzymes	winter cereals	related to hardiness	Kling, 1931—see Tysdal, 1934
Proteolytic enzymes	wheat	greater activity in less hardy	Bereznickaja and Oveckin, 1936, 1936a
		(d) Oxidation-reduction	
Peroxidase	conifer leaves	related to starch	Doyle and Clinch, 1927
Catalase	wheat	direct correlation with hardiness	Newton and Brown, 1931
Catalase	Pinus sylvestris	direct correlation with hardiness	Langlet, 1934
Catalase	Citrus	no relation	Ivanov, 1939

Many suggestions have been made of a relation between frost injury or hardiness and enzyme activity (Schaffnit and Ludtke, 1931; Mitra, 1921; Pantanelli, 1920); but few have actually made the necessary measurements. Due to the frequently noted relation between carbo-

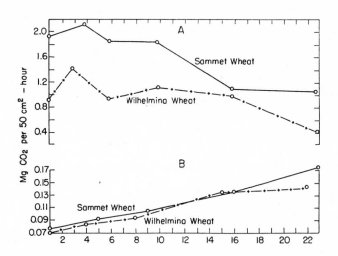

Fig. 16. Rates of assimilation (A) and respiration (B) in wheat varieties. Assimilation higher in hardier variety (Sammet) (from Andersson, 1944).
Abscissa = no. days hardened.

hydrates and frost hardiness, a few of the enzymes of carbohydrate metabolism as well as some others, have been investigated (Table 64). But the results are too few and contradictory to permit any conclusions. It is also unfortunate that the most interesting enzymes have not as yet been studied, though some beginnings have been made (Ewart et al., 1953).

Chapter 13.

The Relation of Protoplasmic Properties to Frost Hardiness

Though sugars and related substances are often strictly correlated with frost hardiness, there are also many clear-cut exceptions. It is obvious, therefore, that some other factor must also be involved, and since all the vacuolar properties have been investigated, this factor must be protoplasmic in nature. Protoplasmic properties are, of course, much more difficult to investigate than vacuolar properties since (1) the vacuole is present in much greater quantity than the protoplasm and is more easily extracted, and (2) protoplasm is altered as soon as cells are injured. It is necessary, therefore, to work with living cells if normal protoplasm is to be investigated.

PERMEABILITY

Since death or even injury, whatever the cause, always results in loss of semipermeability, this fact has been used to measure frost injury and therefore frost hardiness (Chapter 6). Such an injurious increase in permeability may occur even at suprazero temperatures in mandarin oranges (Pantanelli, 1919) and sometimes in potatoes (Bennett, 1934). A completely distinct phenomenon is the change in permeability of uninjured cells, associated with frost hardening. Such a change at low temperatures has, in the past, been proposed to account for chloroplast changes, starch hydrolysis, etc. (Haberlandt, 1878; Coville, 1920; Walter, 1931; Mudra, 1932). But the first experimental evidence was provided by Lidforss (1907). He noticed that mosses deplasmolyze rapidly in potassium nitrate solutions and suggested that their high frost hardiness may be related to this factor. Plasmolytic determinations have since shown conclusively that the permeability to polar substances increases at hardening temperatures, though only in the case of plants that actually increase in frost hardiness (Fig. 17). Permeability to apolar substances is unaltered (Levitt and Scarth, 1936). Confirmatory results have been obtained for celery (Whyte-Stevens, 1937), cabbage (Boon-Long, 1941), *Ranunculus repens* (Hofmeister, 1938), and wheat (Hirai et al., 1950); but tests with wheat varieties differing in hardiness failed to yield significant results (Granhall, 1943). It is interesting to note that earlier observations are in agreement with this relation. Thus stomatal cells are the most frost hardy (Molisch, 1897; Rikhter, 1927; Starkov, 1931) and also the most permeable of all leaf cells (Weber, 1930). On the other hand, water plants never develop true frost hardiness (Lidforss, 1907) and the aquatic leaves are less permeable to water and potassium salts than the aerial leaves (Wahry, 1936).

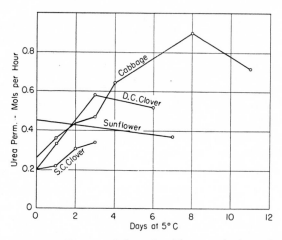

Fig. 17. Increase in cell permeability of cabbage and clover leaf cells during hardening at 5°C. No increase in sunflower which fails to harden at the same temperature (from Levitt and Scarth, 1936).

In apparent opposition to these results, Russian investigators have reported a lower permeability in frost hardy plants, on the basis of diffusion of electrolytes from the tissues (Ivanov, 1931; Golus, 1935, 1938; Cajlachjan, 1935; Sestakov and Sergeev, 1936, 1937; Sergeev and Lebedev, 1936; Sergeev and Sergeeva, 1939a). But, as in the case of the conductivity method used by Dexter *et al.* (see Chapter 6), it is apparently on frost-injured tissues that the measurements have been made. In any case, the electrical conductivity method is not a good measurement of the permeability of living cells, for the less hardy may have a higher salt content (see Chapter 12). Their own experiments show that less hardy grains absorb more salts (Sergeev and Lebedev 1936), and in many cases at least, no diffusion from uninjured cells into distilled water can be detected (Hoagland, 1940). In spite of these difficulties, even the electrical conductivity method has indicated a higher permeability associated with frost hardiness in succulents (Kessler and Ruhland, 1938).

PROTOPLASMIC CONSISTENCY OR VISCOSITY

According to Seifriz (1936), the term consistency stands for a combination of viscosity, elasticity, and even adhesiveness. Investigations have led to two conflicting conclusions: (1) that protoplasmic consistency increases with frost hardiness (Kessler, 1935; Kessler and Ruhland, 1938); (2) that it decreases with frost hardiness (Scarth and Levitt, 1937; Levitt and Siminovitch, 1940; Siminovitch and Levitt, 1941).

(1) The evidence for an increase in consistency with increasing frost hardiness is as follows:

a. When subjected to a centrifugal force, the plastids of hardy cells were less readily displaced than those of nonhardy cells (Kessler, 1935). This was also true when wheat varieties differing in hardiness were compared (Granhall, 1943).

b. When plasmolyzed, the hardy cells took longer to round up than did the nonhardy cells (Kessler and Ruhland, 1938).

c. No Brownian movement or streaming occurred in hardy Catalpa cells, though both were observable in nonhardy cells (Scarth and Levitt, 1937).

d. Long protoplasmic threads were visible in hardy Sempervivum cells, but absent from, or less frequent in nonhardy cells (Kessler and Ruhland, 1938).

e. Guard cells of open stomata have higher protoplasmic viscosities and are more frost hardy than the guard cells of closed stomata (Weber, 1935).

Analysis of these results, together with further evidence using the same methods, leads to the following conclusions:

a. The results with the centrifuge method depend not only on protoplasmic consistency but on the relative densities of the plastids and the surrounding cytoplasm. In some cases it was necessary to expose cells to darkness in order to rid the plastids of starch in the nonhardy cells (Kessler, 1935). This led to inexplicable results, however, e.g. the more ready displacement of the now lighter plastids instead of the reverse (Kessler, 1935). In Catalpa, displacement was even in opposite directions in hardy and nonhardy cells; and in Sempervivum, a difference in consistency between subepidermal and inner cells was apparently unaccompanied by a difference in frost hardiness (Kessler, 1935). Furthermore, the opposite results—a higher consistency in nonhardy cells— were obtained by Levitt and Siminovitch (1940) for Catalpa, as well as by Hirai et al. (1950) in the case of wheat-leaf sheaths. In the latter, starvation due to reduced light (which reduces hardiness) decreased displacement. Thus, inconsistent results are obtained by this method, and it is definitely unreliable when applied to frost-hardy and frost-sensitive cells due to the marked differences between the two in the densities of plastids, cytoplasm, and cell sap, in the thickness of the cytoplasm layer, etc. A positive correlation is easily explained by the higher cell sap concentration of the hardier varieties (e.g. in the wheats used by Granhall), leading to dehydration and therefore increased viscosity of the protoplasm.

b. The plasmolysis-time method requires the use of more concentrated solutions in the case of hardy cells due to their higher cell sap concentration. Their protoplasm is therefore in equilibrium with more strongly dehydrating solutions when the plasmolysis time is being determined. Furthermore, in order to obtain the same degree of plasmolysis as in the case of nonhardy cells, still higher concentrations may have to be used, due to the larger nonsolvent space in the hardy (Levitt and Scarth, 1936). This may lead to an apparent (but unreal) higher consistency in hardy cells, e.g. in the case of Catalpa (Table 65). Hardy

TABLE 65

Rounding-up time of hardy (uninjured by —20°C) and nonhardy (killed by —5°C) cortical cells of Catalpa (from Levitt and Siminovitch, 1940)

Dextrose conc. (Molar)	Rounding-up time (hr)	Degree of plasmolysis
	(a) Nonhardy	
0.4	1.75	
0.5	2	0.77
0.6	2.3	
0.7	3	
0.8	5	0.63
0.9	6	0.53
1.0	10	0.48
	(b) Hardy	
0.9	3	0.72
1.1	4.5	0.69
1.3	7	0.67

cabbage cells, however, round up more rapidly than the nonhardy even when both are plasmolyzed to the same degree (Scarth and Levitt, 1937). When both are plasmolyzed in solutions of the same concentration, the hardy round up more rapidly even in the case of Catalpa (Table 65). Ideally, both conditions should be kept constant but this is impossible. Furthermore, if both are plasmolyzed very strongly by slowly allowing an isotonic solution to become concentrated by evaporation, the hardy cells show a much better ability to round up (Fig. 18). This was corroborated by Kessler and Ruhland (1938).

c. Brownian and streaming movements are not always more active in nonhardy cells—e.g. in the case of cabbage (Scarth and Levitt, 1937). In Sempervivum, in fact, streaming is more rapid in the hardy cells

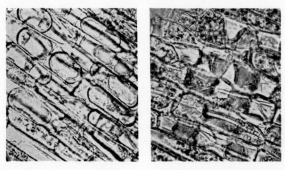

FIG. 18. Plasmolysis shape in hardened (left) and dehardened (right) Catalpa cells in isotonic CaCl$_2$ solutions after evaporation in air for six hours (from Scarth and Levitt, 1937).

(Kessler and Ruhland, 1938). But these are not reliable indications of viscosity, since streaming movement is related to the release of metabolic energy (which may be greater in the nonhardy—DeLong et al., 1939; Andersson, 1944), and Brownian movement to the size of the particles.

d. The presence of long cytoplasmic threads gives no evidence of consistency and usually fails to occur in hardy cells (Levitt and Scarth, 1936).

e. The viscosity of the protoplasm in the guard cells is not the only difference between open and closed stomata. As pointed out by Lepeschkin (1937), the frost hardiness of the open stomata is at least partly due to the much higher cell sap concentration, which has already been shown to be correlated with frost hardiness. This again results in dehydration of the protoplasm and a consequent rise in viscosity.

The above evidence, therefore, fails to show a direct relation between consistency and hardiness. From the plasmolysis-time method, it can only be concluded that the consistency of the protoplasm of hardy cells is lower than that of nonhardy cells, *when they are both in equilibrium with the same solution* (*i.e. the same dehydrating force*). Such differences seem more pronounced at higher dehydrations. The methods of micromanipulation are not open to the objections raised against the above

methods, but they are qualitative and somewhat subjective. In any case, no difference in consistency between hardy and nonhardy cells in the fully hydrated state could be detected by use of these methods (Levitt and Siminovitch, 1940).

(2) The following evidence indicates a higher consistency in the protoplasm of nonhardy than of hardy cells when both are in the partially dehydrated state.

a. Plasmolysis shape and resistance in concentrated solutions. In very concentrated solutions, the hardy cells round up but the nonhardy do not (Fig. 18). These hardy cells can be deplasmolyzed without injury but the nonhardy cannot (Scarth and Levitt, 1937; Siminovitch and Levitt, 1941).

b. The shape assumed by cytoplasm when expressed through a punctured pit in the cell wall. Hardy protoplasm rounds up on emergence; nonhardy remains elongated and irregular (Fig. 19, also Levitt and

FIG. 19. Comparison of the forms assumed by cytoplasm when expressed through a punctured pit in a hardened (left) and an unhardened (right) cell of Catalpa in a balanced solution of NaCl and CaCl$_2$ (9:1) with an osmotic potential of 50 atmospheres (from Scarth, 1941).

Siminovitch, 1940). In higher concentrations of plasmolyte, the hardy protoplasm could still be squeezed out, the nonhardy could not.

c. The shape assumed by oil drops injected into cytoplasm. The drop remains rounded in hardy cells, becomes flattened in nonhardy cells on deplasmolysis (Fig. 20, also Levitt and Siminovitch, 1940).

d. The ductility of cytoplasmic strands. On severe plasmolysis, the strands rupture readily in nonhardy cells and remain wavy. In hardy cells they do not rupture (Fig. 21, also Siminovitch and Levitt, 1941).

The above four lines of evidence all apply primarily to the protoplasmic surface, and show conclusively that it becomes stiffer in nonhardy cells on dehydration. Whether it is the surface or the internal protoplasm that is being compared, the hardy and nonhardy cells should be in equilibrium with the same dehydrating forces if the comparison is to mean anything. Hardy and nonhardy cells in the unplasmolyzed state are seldom, if ever, in equilibrium with the same dehydrating force,

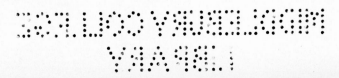

since the cell sap is, as a rule, more concentrated in the hardy cells. From measurements on such cells, no generalization can be made, and no interpretation of the results is possible.

This greater protoplasmic stiffening in nonhardy cells is so pronounced and so closely related to frost-hardiness that plasmolysis and deplasmolysis injury can actually be used as a measurement of frost hardiness

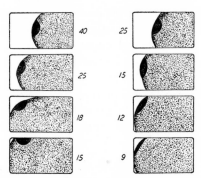

FIG. 20. Shape assumed by oil drops injected into cytoplasm of hardy (left) and nonhardy (right) cortical cells of Cornus, during progressive hydration on deplasmolysis. Tension in the more rigid, nonhardy protoplasm flattens the drop (from Scarth, 1941).

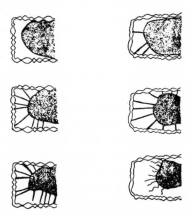

FIG. 21. Visibility of cytoplasm strands in nonhardy cortical cells of Hydrangea at lower degrees of dehydration (i.e. in plasmolyte of lower concentration). Highest concentration of plasmolyte produces rupture of strands in nonhardy but not in hardy cells. Molar concentrations of dextrose from top to bottom:

Left (hardy): 1.0, 2.0, 6.0
Right (nonhardy): 0.6, 1.5, 3.0

(from Scarth, 1941).

(Tables 66 and 67). Siminovitch and Briggs (1953) have recently fully confirmed this fact, showing that one can dispense with freezing tests and determine frost hardiness by deplasmolysis hardiness. An interesting observation, in agreement with this relationship, is the complete,

TABLE 66

Frost killing temperature (50% killing in 10 hours) and osmotic hardiness (normality of glucose in sea water causing 50% killing after one day) of algae
(from Kylin, 1917)

Species	Frost killing temperature	Osmotic hardiness
Trailliella intricata	> —2.9°C	%N
Delesseria sanguinea	—4.0	1
Laurencia pinnatifida	—4.0	1
Laminaria saccharina (1 yr.)	—4.8	1.5
Ceramium rubrum	—5.7	2
Chondrus crispus	—16.8	>2
Porphyra hiemalis	< —20	>2
Pylaiella litoralis	—20	>2
Fucus vesiculosus	< —20	>2

TABLE 67

Frost hardiness and deplasmolysis injury in alfalfa. All were hardened for 11–15 days before testing. Deplasmolysis after plasmolysis for 4–5 hr in 3–4M dextrose. Frost killing determined by survival two weeks after freezing at —11°C for 7 hr (from Siminovitch and Levitt, 1941)

Variety	Frost killing	Deplasmolysis injury (average %)
Kansas	4 of 6 plants dead	80
Arizona	all dead	90
Grimm	all alive	35
Hardistan	all alive	30

reversible solidification of the protoplasm of the frost-tender *Griffithsia setacea* on exposure to 2°C for 15 hr (Biebl, 1939).

PROTOPLASMIC HYDRATION

Due to the large specific surface of protoplasm and its high water permeability, it must be essentially in aqueous equilibrium with the cell sap. Consequently, hardy cells that have higher cell sap concentrations would be expected to have less hydrated cytoplasm. But the question is whether other changes occur in the protoplasm itself that may affect its hydration.

The following is the evidence for an increased protoplasmic hydration on hardening:

(1) Increased protoplasmic viscosity (Kessler, 1935; Kessler and Ruhland, 1938). Since it has already been shown that the evidence for such a change is invalid (see above), this cannot be accepted as any indication of protoplasmic hydration. Furthermore, the relation between the viscosity and the hydration of a colloid is complex. If a fixed quantity of the colloidal dispersion exists, any factor (e.g. the addition of an electrolyte) which increases the hydration of the particles reduces the amount of free solvent and therefore increases the viscosity of the dispersion. If, on the other hand, the dispersion is in vapor pressure equilibrium with another aqueous system that is also changeable, an increase in hydration of the particles will lead to a movement of water from the second system to the dispersion, and viscosity may even be lowered. Protoplasm is an example of the second situation since it is in contact with a vacuole. But there is still another complication. Protoplasm possesses "structural" viscosity as well as the true viscosity of a liquid. Consequently, an increased hydration may lead to disruption of the structure and conversion from the gel to the sol state, as happens, for instance, when a gelatin gel is made alkaline. In this case, there is reason to expect, not an increase, but a decrease in protoplasmic viscosity if hydration increases.

(2) Direction of displacement of plastids and protoplasm. According to Lepeschkin (1937), Kessler's own results indicate decreased rather than increased hydration. In Kessler and Ruhland's (1938) later results, however, displacement of the plastids was centrifugal in the hardy, centripetal in the nonhardy. Similarly, displacement of the protoplasm was centripetal relative to the vacuole in the hardy, centrifugal in the nonhardy (Levitt and Siminovitch, 1940). Both of these results could be due to an increased protoplasmic hydration on hardening, leading to a decreased specific gravity. But such evidence is inconclusive, since it could just as easily be explained by an increased specific gravity of the plastids or the vacuole, respectively, on hardening, and it would be complicated by viscosity changes.

(3) Increased permeability of protoplasm to polar substances. This can be explained by an increased hydration of the plasma membrane, though it reveals nothing about the state of the internal protoplasm.

(4) Thickness of protoplasmic layer. Measurements of the protoplasmic caps of onion epidermal cells revealed a slight decrease on ex-

posure to hardening temperatures (Scarth and Levitt, 1937). This indicated a decrease in hydrophily; but the onion does not develop frost hardiness. Cortical cells of apple twigs, however, showed no change in thickness of the protoplasm layer during partial loss of frost hardiness. Since this was accompanied by a decreased vacuole concentration, it indicated that dehardening failed to increase protoplasmic hydration though now in equilibrium with a less strongly dehydrating vacuole.

(5) Nuclear size. Kessler and Ruhland (1938) found the nuclei to be larger in frost-hardy than in nonhardy Sempervivum. Unfortunately, the measurements were made on fixed and therefore dehydrated material, though both swelling and shrinking fixatives gave the same results. This could be explained by an increase in dry matter in the nucleus, since the nuclei were in the dehydrated state when measured.

(6) Refractive index. The cytoplasmic strands of hardy cells are not visible until in equilibrium with much more concentrated dehydrating solutions than in the case of nonhardy cells (Fig. 21). This can only be explained by greater hydration in hardy cells. As a result, the refractive index of the strands remains practically as low as that of the surrounding solution and they are therefore invisible.

(7) Lower protoplasmic consistency in hardy than in nonhardy cells when partially dehydrated by plasmolysis (see above). This seems to indicate that dehydrating forces are capable of removing more water from nonhardy than from hardy protoplasm. The latter, therefore, remains more ductile and less rigid.

(8) Resistance to pressure. Hardy wheat leaves are less injured in a hydraulic press than are nonhardy leaves (Dexter, 1932). Even individual cells when frost hardy can survive pressures under the microscope far greater than those that kill them when they are not hardy (Levitt and Siminovitch, 1940). This can be explained by the greater hydration protecting the proteins from pressure denaturation.

(9) Bound water content. Measurement of the nonsolvent space indicates that the protoplasm of cortical tree cells has a higher bound water content when hardy than when not hardy (Chapter 10). More direct measurements on Aspergillus niger revealed the same thing (Chapter 10).

The following three protoplasmic changes may therefore be stated to occur during an increase in hardiness:

1. An increase in cell permeability to polar substances.
2. An increase in ability to remain fluid when dehydrated.
3. An increase in hydration.

Chapter 14.

The Mechanism of Frost Injury and Hardiness

The conditions that result in frost injury have been described. But the reasons for the injury or for the plant's hardiness have hardly been touched on. The caloric and rupture theories of frost injury (Chapters 1, 3) are solely of historical interest. So also is the "air-expulsion theory" (Morren, 1838; Lindley, 1842; Hoffman, 1857), since it was based on the misconception that the plant contains certain organs or cells filled with air, others with water; and that either a displacement of one by the other or a mixture of the two must lead to death. It has been solidly established, however, that unfrozen plants are able to withstand far lower temperatures than when they are allowed to freeze (Chapter 1). The ice crystals themselves must therefore exert some harmful influence due to either intracellular or extracellular freezing, or to both.

INTRACELLULAR FREEZING

In this case, injury apparently is due to the formation of crystals within the protoplasm (Chapter 5). Chemical effects are excluded, since water in the solid state can obviously have no chemically injurious influence that it does not exert in the liquid state, and since the same concentration of the protoplasm may be harmless when ice forms outside it. The only possible explanation, therefore, seems to be a mechanical injury, though its precise nature has not been determined. Molisch (1897) and Ullrich (1941) describe the mechanical injury resulting from ice formation in colloidal gels, which may be similar to that in living protoplasm. Presumably, the structure is destroyed, resulting in denaturation of the proteins and death of the protoplasm. Iljin (1933) suggests that the injury is due to a compression of the protoplasm between an ice hull outside the wall and the subsequently frozen cell sap. If this were true, hardy cells should survive intracellular freezing better than nonhardy cells, since they are better able to withstand pressure (Chapter 13). But there is no evidence of this (Siminovitch and Scarth, 1938). Scarth and Levitt (1937) suggest a laceration of the membranes and other structures by the ice crystals.

Frost hardiness toward intracellular freezing injury has been explained by (1) small crystal size, (2) prevention of intracellular freezing, (3) prevention of syneresis.

1. SMALL CRYSTAL SIZE.

If injury is due to a mechanical disruption of the protoplasmic structure. it should be preventable by reducing the crystal size (Gortner, 1929; Stiles, 1930). But since the structure is submicroscopic, the crystals would also have to be of this size or smaller. As already mentioned (Chapter 1), if freezing is rapid enough to produce ice crystals too small to be seen under the microscope (the "vitrified" state according to Luyet 1937), no injury occurs. But this requires fantastically rapid freezing, and cannot be duplicated in nature. Luyet (1937) implied that once tissues are undercooled below —20°C, crystallization cannot occur at all, since the water is in the amorphous or "vitrified" state. If this were true, no further temperature drop could cause injury. Recently (1954), however, he pointed out that this "vitrified" state is not qualitatively but only quantitatively different from the normal frozen state. It simply means that the crystals are no larger than some thousands of Ångstrom units in diameter, if indetectable by the ordinary microscope. He also mentions Meryman's demonstration of crystal growth at as low as —130°C. At —80°C they grew from 200 to 10,000 Å in 8 minutes, becoming microscopically visible. It seems obvious, then, that the prevention of injury by maintenance of crystal size below microscopic visibility is excluded, at least at temperatures that the plant is normally exposed to. This is in agreement with the fact that all observed cases of ice formation in the protoplasm have been fatal (Chapter 5).

2. PREVENTION OF INTRACELLULAR FREEZING.

Müller-Thurgau (1886) observed that if the rate of water movement to the ice loci is too slow, new centers of crystallization will suddenly appear. In the same way, whether or not ice forms inside the cell depends on the rate of exosmosis of the water to the extracellular ice loci (Scarth and Levitt, 1937). Since the permeability of hardy cells to water is high, and the cells frequently are small, exosmosis will be more rapid than from nonhardy cells. Furthermore, due to the higher osmotic potential of the hardy cells, less water has to leave them at any one temperature. Thus, hardiness may involve the prevention of the fatal intracellular freezing. Direct observation has confirmed this, for unhardened cells do freeze intracellularly more readily than hardened cells (Table 68).

3. PREVENTION OF SYNERESIS.

Apparently unaware of earlier observations (see Chapter 5), Becquerel (1949, 1951, 1953, 1954) has recently described his "discovery" of the reduction in diameter of the nucleus as a result of killing in liquid nitrogen. From this simple observation, he concludes that frost killing is due to irreversible syneresis. He ignores the fact that proteins are less hydrophilic when denatured than in the native state, and that, therefore, death by any method results *in* rather than *from* a reduction in protoplasmic volume. From another simple experiment, he arrives at a theory of frost hardiness. Normally hydrated mosses proved dead on thawing

TABLE 68

Intracellular freezing in hardy and nonhardy cortical tree cells, frozen rapidly by inoculation at subfreezing temperatures (from Siminovitch and Scarth, 1938)

Temp. at	Average percent of cells frozen intracellularly			
inoculation	Catalpa		Cornus	
(°C)	Nonhardy	Hardy	Nonhardy	Hardy
—2 to —3	75	15	25	0
—3 to —4	90	30	15	0
—4 to —5	100	55	35	0
—5 to —6			90	10

after being plunged into liquid nitrogen. Yet they remained alive if the freezing was gradual and thawing was rapid at 30°C. Though two factors were altered, he concludes that the rapid warming "gave the protoplasmic particles the energy to recapture the water lost." However, as he himself admitted, the mosses lost 20 to 30% water during the slow freezing, and as he showed earlier, they are uninjured if frozen in this dehydrated state. This is a much more reasonable explanation of the protection than the assumption that the plant can "recapture" water at the expense of heat energy available at 30°C but not at lower temperatures. Since he froze rapidly at temperatures no higher than —25°C, all his experiments dealt with rapid, intracellular freezing, and have no bearing on extracellular freezing injury.

EXTRACELLULAR FREEZING

Under natural conditions, ice formation has been observed only outside the cells (Chapter 3). It is, therefore, the injury due to extracellular ice formation that is most in need of explaining. Müller-Thurgau (1880) first showed that ice forms in potato tubers in large druses widely separated from each other. On thawing, injury was found to be greatest at these loci, and a transition occurred from them to uninjured regions farther removed from the ice formation. Quantitative measurements have shown that at least 10 to 20% (Maximov, 1914) or as much as 35% (Luyet and Condon, 1938) of the tuber's water must be frozen before injury sets in. Ice formation and injury both increase progessively with the drop in temperature (Table 69). It is thus apparent not only that frost injury is absent from undercooled tissues, but that it is quantitatively related to the amount of ice formed. Any theory of frost injury must therefore assume that ice formation is either directly or indirectly responsible for the injury.

TABLE 69

Relation of frost injury to amount of ice formed in tissues of potato tuber
(from Luyet and Condon, 1938)

Freezing time (min)	Temp. of tissue °C	Percent of water frozen	Percent of cells still living
12	—1.5	34.8	100
15	—1.9	43.6	93.3
18	—2.2	52.1	78.9
20	—2.8	57.5	61.5
22	—3.2	62.7	23.1
25	—4.6	70.4	2.7
26	—4.7	72.7	0.0
31	—8.0	83.3	0.0

1. DIRECT EFFECT OF ICE.

In this case, reducing the quantity of ice formed without changing the amount of water removed, would reduce the frost injury. As first shown by Maximov and later corroborated by others, cells normally killed at —5°C can withstand freezing in solutions at —20°C (Chapter 1, Table 7). The solutions reduce the amount of ice formed, though the water removal at the lower temperature is much more severe. But such evidence is more apparent than real. Only if plasmolysis occurs are the cells protected. Furthermore, the strongly plasmolyzed cells, though alive after severe freezing, may either rupture before reaching the cell wall (Iljin, 1927; Stuckey and Curtis, 1938) or may die shortly after deplasmolysis (see Chapter 1). But the final proof that the effect of the protective solutions is in no way related to a reduction in the amount of ice formed has been produced by Iljin (1927). He showed that these solutions give the same protection against drought injury (Chapter 17), though in this case no ice formation is involved.

In order to prove a direct relation between the quantity of ice formed and frost injury, it is therefore necessary to avoid plasmolysis. This can be done by wilting the plant before freezing. At any one freezing temperature, the total amount of water removed will be the same, though less ice is formed in the plant when wilted than when turgid. If injury is related to the quantity of ice, the frost killing point should be lowered by wilting. This has actually been reported by some investigators (Chapter 10). But the effect is small and due to the prevention of freezing (e.g. Phajus labellum, Müller-Thurgau, 1880); or if the plants are capable of hardening on exposure to drought (see Chapter 10), it is due to secondary changes that occur during the relatively long time needed to wilt the plant. Any real effect is too small to be explained by the marked reduction in quantity of ice formed; and in some cases wilting has completely failed to affect the frost killing temperature (Ulmer, 1937).

From the available evidence, it can therefore be concluded that frost injury is not directly related to the amount of ice formed in the tissues. Nevertheless, a theory based on this concept attributes the injury to pressure exerted by the ice crystals. In a sense, this is a modification of the discredited rupture theory, which was also based on ice pressure (Chapter 3) and is open to the same objections. Lidforss (1907) points to the large intercellular spaces of overwintering leaves and considers them useful in providing room for ice formation. Maximov (1914) suggests that ice in the intercellular spaces or between the protoplasm and cell wall might enhance frost injury by exerting pressure on the plasma membrane. Lepeschkin (1924) supports Maximov's theory but feels that it could account for injury only at the instant of ice formation, and that further cooling could have little effect.

As in the case of the rupture theory, there is no direct experimental evidence in favor of the ice pressure theory. The only indirect evidence in its favor is the fact that frost-hardy cells are resistant to injury by pressure (see Chapter 13). But this, of course, in no way proves that ice pressure causes injury. In fact, frozen tissues are under tension rather than pressure, since they contract instead of expanding (Chapter 3). Many other less valid objections have been raised against the pressure theory (Schander and Schaffnit, 1919). Åkerman (1927) suggested that the greater protection against frost injury by strong solutions than by weak ones may be due to less ice formation between the cell wall and the plasmolyzed protoplast. But there is no need for such an assumption, since he himself observed stronger plasmolysis during freezing in the more concentrated solutions, due presumably to an insufficient amount of unfrozen liquid in the weaker solutions. Obviously not only is there a lack of evidence in support of the ice pressure theory, but the absence of a positive pressure during freezing renders such a hypothetical source of injury impossible. This is in agreement with the above conclusion that injury is not directly related to the quantity of ice formed.

2. INDIRECT EFFECT OF ICE DUE TO WATER REMOVAL.

In the absence of a direct relation between frost injury and ice formation, the only alternative is an indirect one due to dehydration injury
(Vogel, 1820; Sachs, 1873; Frank, 1879; Müller-Thurgau, 1880; Molisch,
1897; Matruchot and Molliard, 1900, 1901, 1902; Wiegand, 1906; Buhlert, 1906). The best supporting evidence for this theory is that frost
hardiness and drought hardiness are correlated as has been shown by
many independent investigators (Chapter 23). Such positive evidence,
together with the above negative evidence, leaves only one possible conclusion: that frost injury during extracellular freezing is caused not by
the amount of ice formed but by the amount of water removed. Two
explanations of this dehydration injury have been proposed: (a) salt
precipitation of the proteins, and (b) mechanical injury to the protoplasm. The evidence for each is as follows.

(a) Salt precipitation.

Many of the early workers suggested that frost injury is due to toxicity
of the concentrated cell sap (Sachs, 1873; Kunisch, 1880; Molish, 1897).
The first direct attempt to prove this was made by Gorke (1906) at the
suggestion of Buhlert (1906). Freezing of expressed sap was found to
cause precipitation in Pelargonium (—4°C), summer barley (—7°C),
winter rye (—12°C), pine needles (—40°C); the hardier the plant,
the lower was the precipitation temperature. Similarly, salting out
of the proteins required the addition of more salt to the sap of the
hardier plants; and there was less protein in their sap expressed
from frozen than from unfrozen plants. These results were confirmed
by others (Lidforss, 1907; Schaffnit, 1910; Harvey, 1918; Newton, 1924;
Mudra, 1932; Wilhelm, 1935; Fuchs, 1935b; Ivanov, 1939), though many
found it necessary to modify the concept (Schaffnit, 1910; Schander and
Schaffnit, 1919; Harvey, 1918; Clements, 1938). Voigtländer (1909)
raised some objections to Gorke's conclusions—e.g. the fact that enzymes
(which are, of course, proteins) maintain their original activity in spite
of freezing. Kessler (1935) claims that proteins are already denatured
in the unfrozen solution, though present as small particles. If these are
filtered off before freezing, no frost precipitation occurs. In agreement
with this statement is the fact that unlike salt precipitation, frost precipitation is irreversible (Schander and Schaffnit, 1919; Fuchs, 1935b); but
this objection is not conclusive, since acid precipitation may also be involved (Harvey, 1918).

Though many have confirmed the greater frost precipitation in the
juice of nonhardy than in that of hardy grains, tests with other plants

have consistently failed to reveal any difference (fruit trees, Chandler, 1913; alfalfa, Mark, 1936; cabbage, Levitt and Scarth, 1936). Consequently, the evidence in favor of the theory is, at best, confined to one group of plants. Yet, attempts have been made to explain the frost hardiness of all plants as a protection against frost precipitation of the proteins. Four factors have been suggested.

(1) *Sugars.* The addition of sugars to protein solutions was found to prevent or at least reduce frost precipitation (Lidforss, 1907; Schaffnit, 1910; Newton, 1924). That this is not merely due to an osmotic reduction in ice formation (and therefore in salt concentration), as suggested by Åkerman (1927), was indicated by the sugar-induced delay in the slower precipitation at room temperature (Newton, 1924). But in the case of unhardened sap, more sugar must be added than is present in sap of hardy plants (Fuchs, 1935b). Furthermore, the sugar formed during hardening accumulates in the vacuole and therefore cannot exert any direct protective effect on the protoplasmic proteins.

(2) *Protein splitting.* Lidforss (1907) suggested that if the proteins split to smaller molecules, as some work seemed to indicate, they may then be more stable toward salt precipitation. This concept was favored by Schaffnit (1910), Harvey (1918), Newton and Brown (1931). As already seen, such protein splitting is not characteristic of the hardening process (Chapter 12). It has even been suggested (Newton, Brown, and Anderson, 1931), that protein splitting is a harmful result of frost and that sugars protect against it. But even this explanation was opposed by Mudra's (1932) results, since the increase in soluble nitrogen due to freezing was greatest in the uninjured hardiest variety.

(3) *Bound water.* When this factor has been associated with frost hardiness, one common explanation has been that it prevents dehydration injury (Gortner, 1929). But the concentration of the salts on freezing would not be reduced, since they are presumably insoluble in the bound water (Gortner, 1938). On the other hand, if the water is bound by the proteins, it would confer an increased stability on them, and in this way tend to prevent their salting out (Gortner, 1937, personal communication).

(4) *Salt content.* It has already been shown that there is no correlation between salt content and frost hardiness (Chapter 12). Therefore this factor provides no evidence in favor of the frost precipitation theory. Harvey (1918) has, in fact, suggested that acid precipitation is involved, though here again there are too many exceptions to the correlation (Chapter 12).

None of the above evidence proves that protein precipitation is the cause of frost injury or that its prevention is the cause of frost hardiness. But neither can it be said that the theory can be discarded on the basis of the above results. The strongest evidence against the theory, however, is provided by the experiments with protective solutions. Bartetzko (1909) showed that high concentrations of salt in the medium actually protect Aspergillus against frost injury, and Chandler (1913) found the same for higher plants. But Maximov (1912) suggests that this may be due to the accumulation of protective substances inside the cells. When he eliminated this possibility by rapid tests with sections, salts still proved capable of reducing frost injury. It would seem impossible for salts to cause protein precipitation in the cell when they occur in the vacuole but to prevent it when they are outside the cell. Furthermore, even salts present inside the cells were able to become much more concentrated (i.e. the cells could be frozen at much lower temperatures) without injury, when the cells were frozen in solutions. As pointed out by Stiles (1930), the mere fact that frost-tender cells are killed by such small amounts of ice (e.g. 10 to 35% of its water in potato tubers), shows that salt precipitation cannot occur, since at least a $2M$ salt solution is usually required for this process. From all these facts, one can only conclude that frost precipitation is not the cause of injury.

(b) Mechanical injury.

In opposition to the salt precipitation theory, several investigators suggested that frost injury is mechanical (Buhlert, 1906; Hedlund, 1917; Fukuda, 1932; Pfeiffer, 1933). But Iljin (1933) was the first to describe observations that directly confirmed this concept. He observed that the opposite walls of red cabbage cells are drawn together during freezing. On thawing, they pull apart and also separate from the protoplast, causing pseudoplasmolysis. The protoplast then begins to round up and deplasmolyze. Some cells burst during the deplasmolysis, others deplasmolyze completely, though some subsequently die. If frozen at very low temperatures, the cells show no pseudoplasmolysis on thawing, indicating that death occurred during freezing. According to Scarth (personal communication), this killing previous to thawing may also be mechanical in nature, for the collapse of the contracted cell causes a tension on the protoplasm, due to the liquid cohesion and adhesion to the cell wall. The shrinking cell undergoes deformation of shape, tangential stretching of the protoplast, and shearing actions. The result may be disruption of the organized structure of the protoplasm.

Frost hardiness may prevent such mechanical injury in several ways. The higher water permeability of hardy cells, their smaller cell size, higher osmotic potential, and higher colloidally bound water, would all help the protoplast to expand as rapidly or nearly as rapidly as the cell wall. This would prevent pseudodeplasmolysis injury (Scarth and Levitt, 1937); for the first two properties would increase the rate of water uptake by the cell, the last two would reduce the amount that has to be taken up after freezing at any one temperature. Catalpa is a good example of the latter kind of protection. In the fully hardened state, the maximum contraction possible (even at the lowest temperatures) is less than their contraction in the unhardened state when frozen at —6°C (Levitt and Scarth, 1936). When frozen, the hardy cell is, therefore, never subjected to the extreme stresses that the nonhardy cell receives at the same temperature. But there is evidence of another factor. Protoplasm in the hardy state is more tolerant of plasmolysis and deplasmolysis as well as of the injurious effects of pressure (Chapter 13). It is not surprising then, that the hardy cells can survive a greater contraction in the frozen state as well as a greater expansion on thawing than can the nonhardy cells (Table 70). Yet it seems difficult to understand

TABLE 70

Relation between lethal degree of cell contraction in cabbage during freezing and during plasmolysis respectively (Levitt, 1939; Siminovitch and Levitt, 1941)

	Unhardened		Hardened	
	Contraction (to % of original volume)	Injury %	Contraction (to % of original volume)	Injury %
Freezing	45	85	33	50
Plasmolysis	65	50	28	35

how tender plants that are killed by freezing of only 10 to 30% of their water can be injured mechanically. The amount of contraction is small and pseudodeplasmolysis injury seems inconceivable. However, it must be emphasized that at low temperatures plasmolysis and deplasmolysis injury is more severe than at room temperatures (Scarth and Levitt, 1937), due, presumably to an increased stiffening of the protoplasm (Weber and Hohenegger, 1923; Biebl, 1939). In this state even small contractions may conceivably be injurious to sensitive protoplasm. And even at room temperatures some plants are injured by moderate plasmolysis (Chapter 23).

As already mentioned, the vacuolar factors associated with frost hardiness would reduce deplasmolysis injury by reducing the frost contraction of the cells. But they also contribute to frost hardiness when thawing injury is apparently not a factor. Early suggestions that sugars protect by favoring undercooling (Lidforss, 1896) or by warming the plant on crystallization at the eutectic point (Mez, 1905) cannot be seriously considered, since their correlation is with true frost hardiness—i.e. the ability of the plant to survive freezing at lower temperatures. According to current concepts (see above), (1) they act as protective substances, preventing the frost precipitation of proteins, or (2) they protect by reducing the quantity of ice formed in the plant, or (3) their effect is negative due to the injurious influence of starch.

(1) *Protection of proteins.* This factor has already been considered in connection with the salting out theory. But though the evidence is against this theory, it does not eliminate the possibility of a protective effect of sugars against other factors that tend to induce protein denaturation. An attempt has recently been made to test this concept. Sugar determinations, on whole tissue or on sap, measure primarily the vacuole content, since this makes up the major part of living cells. The fact that sugar content, so determined, is correlated with frost hardiness in some plants but not in others, might conceivably mean that it is the sugars in the protoplasm that are important. The proteins in hardy protoplasm might be combined with larger quantities of sugars than those in nonhardy protoplasm. That protoplasmic potato proteins are combined with carbohydrates was previously shown (Levitt, 1954). The same methods revealed a similar combination in cabbage leaves. But the quantity of carbohydrate per unit of protein was at least as high

TABLE 71

Carbohydrate contents (%) of protein fractions (from Levitt, 1954b)

Fraction	Cabbage		Potato	
	Unhardened	Hardened	10 days at 26°C	at 3°C
Microsomes	17.5	17.1	6.8	9.8
Acid-insoluble proteins	5.7	6.1	5.0	6.0
Globulins	10.8	6.4	4.5	3.9
Albumins	28.8	22.3	6.7	6.0

in the nonhardy as in the hardy cabbage (Table 71). Consequently, no evidence was obtained in favor of the concept.

(2) *Reduction in quantity of ice formed.* It has been repeatedly suggested that the sugars protect the plant from frost injury by their osmotic effect, e.g. by lowering the freezing point sufficiently to prevent freezing (Goeppert, 1830; Senebier, 1800; D'Arsonval, 1901; Lidforss,

1907). As pointed out by Magistad and Truog (1925), this mechanism is important only in tender plants, since hardy plants do survive freezing. It seemed obvious, therefore, to many workers that the small increase in concentration is unable to account for the large increase in frost hardiness that accompanies it (Bartetzko, 1909; Apelt, 1908; Maximov, 1912; Lidforss, 1907; Harvey, 1918; Newton, 1924a). Some (Hafekost, 1930; Mudra, 1930; Walter, 1931) have suggested that the very dehydration of protoplasm, due to the increased cell sap concentration, protects it from injury. But the many cases of a lack of correlation between concentration and frost hardiness speak against this view. Simple calculations show, however, that the amount of water frozen in the tissues at any one temperature is markedly affected by the concentration of the cell sap (Table 72).

TABLE 72

Relation between amount of ice formed at any one freezing temperature and original concentration of solution (from Chandler, 1913; Åkerman, 1927)

Temperature (°C)	Concentration of solution in equilibrium with ice (M)	Percent of water frozen in solution with the original concentration of:			
		0.25	0.5	1.0	2.0 molar
— 0.46	0.25	trace			
— 0.93	0.5	50	trace		
— 1.86	1.0	75	50	trace	
— 3.72	2.0	87.5	75	50	trace
— 7.44	4.0	93.8	87.5	75	50
—14.88	8.0	96.9	93.8	87.5	75

(3) *Prevention of injurious effect of starch.* The possibility must be considered that it is the starch that injures the frozen cell, rather than the sugar that protects it (Levitt, 1941; Siminovitch and Briggs, 1954). The frost-contracted cell may conceivably be injured by compression of the protoplasm between the contracting cell wall and the rigid starch grains. Thus, according to Haberlandt (1877), chloroplasts are more easily injured by frost when they contain starch. But this concept certainly cannot be generally applied, since the best correlation between frost hardiness and sugars is in those plants that accumulate sugars photosynthetically without any change in starch content. It must be concluded that, of the three suggested modes of action of the sugars, only the second is in accord with the known facts.

COMPREHENSIVE MECHANICAL THEORY OF FROST INJURY AND HARDINESS

On the basis of the above analysis, the following are the main features of the mechanical theory:

1. When freezing occurs inside the protoplasm, it always kills the cell. This is a mechanical injury produced by the ice crystals. Only when these are submicroscopically small do they fail to disrupt the protoplasm, and the cell survives uninjured. But this cannot happen under natural conditions.

2. When freezing occurs outside the cell, injury may or may not result, depending on whether or not the protoplasm suffers mechanical injury of another sort. Two factors are involved: (a) Frost dehydration leads to a progressive increase in protoplasmic consistency, until with extreme dehydration it actually becomes brittle. (b) Due to water removal from the cell as a whole, contraction subjects the protoplasm to tensions. When the protoplasmic consistency has increased enough and the cell contraction is sufficiently severe, the tension results in mechanical damage to the brittle protoplasm. Due to its greater ductility, hardy protoplasm can withstand more severe frost contraction. The damage may occur either while the cell is still frozen and contracted, or when, on thawing, it expands due to water uptake. If the injury is insufficient to kill the cells, it may either progress after thawing until the cell dies, or it may heal and the cell will survive. The result depends on the extent of the injury and on the post-thawing conditions that the cell is exposed to. Repeated freezing and thawing may increase an injury from which the cell could have recovered after a single freezing, and may therefore lead to death. Similarly, the longer the cell remains contracted (i.e. in the frozen state), the more chance there is for the protoplasmic rigidity to become "set," leading to damage during either freezing or thawing.

On the basis of this theory, the frost-hardy cell has two main lines of defense, which may be called primary and secondary. The primary defense is the development of protoplasm that is capable of resisting the mechanical stresses during freezing. This results from an increase in the hydrophily ("bound water") of its proteins. The protoplasm, therefore, remains ductile when subjected to frost dehydration (and temperatures) that would otherwise render it brittle.

The secondary defense is a reduction in the stresses that the cell is subjected to when frozen. For any one decrease in cell volume, the stresses would be reduced: (1) By a reduction in cell size; since stress is a force per unit area, the increase in specific surface would reduce the value of this ratio. (2) By less rigid cell walls; this would reduce the springlike pull on the protoplasm of the contracted cell. (3) By higher cell permeability; this would reduce the stress during pseudoplasmolysis and deplasmolysis on thawing.

For any one freezing temperature, the cell contraction may be reduced: (1) By increasing the ratio of protoplasm to vacuole. Due to the usually high colloidal content of protoplasm, less water is removed from it by a strongly dehydrating force than from the vacuole. (2) By increasing the percent of solids, and therefore reducing the possible cell contraction due to water removal. If the solids are soluble, they will be doubly effective, because of the osmotic reduction in water frozen at any one temperature. (3) By increasing the amount of water bound by colloids and therefore reducing the amount removed at any one freezing temperature.

The two lines of defense are not completely distinct from each other, for they may both be affected by the same factors, and the development of the one may affect the development of the other. Nevertheless, without the development of the primary line of defense, the secondary line is useless, and the cell will be killed by "the first touch of frost." Not all these factors are developed in all hardy plants, nor do they develop to the same degree in different plants. It is, therefore, easy to understand that all degrees of hardiness occur and that no one factor is capable of differentiating between plants in all cases.

3. The usefulness of any hypothesis depends on whether it fits the known facts, and can predict events accurately. The following is a point by point examination of the facts discussed in earlier chapters.

(1) Dehydrated protoplasm is uninjured by the lowest temperatures. In this state no freezing occurs; therefore, there are no ice crystals either to lacerate the protoplasm or to dehydrate it.

(2) Undercooling prevents frost injury. The same explanation holds as for (1). If the undercooling cannot be maintained, however, this may lead to sudden, intracellular freezing and death.

(3) Plasmolysis prevents frost injury. Though plasmolysis dehydrates the protoplasm just as effectively as does freezing, it permits the protoplast to separate from the wall and therefore prevents the tensions that arise when the cell as a whole contracts. It also prevents the rapid expansion during thawing that might otherwise lead to rupture of the protoplasm. But this protection is to some extent superficial rather than real, for these plasmolyzed cells may be doomed to death during or after deplasmolysis. In fact, the degree of this subsequent mechanical injury can even be used as a measure of frost hardiness, in complete

agreement with the assumption that frost injury is itself mechanical in nature.

(4) Rapid freezing increases injury. This is apparently true only when it causes intracellular freezing, which is fatal in all cases (at least if it occurs in the protoplasm).

(5) Rapid thawing increases injury. This gives more opportunity for pseudoplasmolysis and therefore is more likely to lead to deplasmolysis injury.

(6) Small cell size is correlated with hardiness. Due to the greater specific surface of small cells, (a) extracellular is favored over intracellular freezing; (b) the protoplasm is subjected to less tension at any one degree of frost dehydration; (c) the amount of frost dehydration is reduced due to the smaller proportion of the cell occupied by the vacuole, (d) protoplast expansion can keep up better with cell wall expansion on thawing, thus preventing pseudodeplasmolysis injury.

(7) Growing plants are not frost hardy. In actively growing cells, the protoplasm becomes highly viscous and inelastic on dehydration (Strugger, 1934), while in dormant cells it remains more mobile or plastic. The developmental stage may also affect cell permeability (Weber, 1931).

(8) The various factors that are frequently correlated with frost hardiness have been shown above to fit this theory.

If this theory is correct, the protoplasm of all frost-tender plants (plants killed by the "first touch of frost") must either already be relatively rigid in the normal cell, or must become so on slight dehydration at low temperatures. In such a case, no cell sap concentration could protect in any other way than by preventing freezing (e.g. sugar cane).

THE SERIES OF CHANGES DURING HARDENING

On the basis of all the above, it is possible to formulate a logical series of events in the hardening of the plant. One fundamental assumption must be made, viz. that a reduction in the water content of protoplasm leads to a gradual increase in the binding of water by its proteins. This assumption actually follows from Le Chatelier's principle, for the proteins would be expected to change in such a direction as to oppose the reduction in water content. It is also in agreement with the available experimental evidence (Chapter 13) for: (1) Increases in cell sap concentration always or nearly always occur during the development of hardiness, yet they may also precede it. (2) Artificial increases in cell sap concentration have little effect by themselves on frost hardiness. (3) Growth of Aspergillus niger in media of high concentration increases the bound water in the cells. The effect may, of course, be much more pronounced in some plants than in others.

The following series of changes may then be visualized. Before any appreciable frost hardiness develops, growth stops and carbohydrates accumulate. An activation or accumulation of certain enzymes occurs during late summer or early fall, perhaps as a result of the progressively shorter photoperiod. Due to these enzymes, the insoluble carbohydrates are converted to soluble sugars which accumulate in the vacuole and increase its osmotic potential. Water, therefore, moves into it from the protoplasm. In plants capable of becoming frost hardy, the dehydration of the protoplasm leads to a slow change in the proteins, resulting in an increased binding of water. The process may continue for days or weeks until the maximum binding of water is achieved. In the case of perennials, therefore, maximum hardiness may occur some weeks after the maximum sugar accumulation. In herbaceous winter annuals, however, the two processes occur almost simultaneously, for the sugars accumulate slowly due to photosynthesis and the progressive dehydration of the protoplasm is therefore more gradual than in the case of some perennials. Some plants cannot become frost hardy because they are unable to develop high cell sap concentrations, others because in spite of high cell sap concentrations their proteins cannot undergo the increased water binding. Even hardy species may, at times, not be able to undergo these proteins changes—e.g. in summer. On the other hand, in some plants the protein changes may occur with a very small increase in cell sap concentration (e.g. conifers).

In late winter or early spring, a reverse change in enzyme activity or content occurs and sugars are reconverted to starch, the vacuole concentration drops, and the protoplasm undergoes an increase in water content. As a result, there is a gradual release of bound water from the proteins, and a few days or weeks after the starch accumulation, the plant loses its frost hardiness.

The inability of growing plants to harden is easily understood on this basis. The carbohydrates are used up so rapidly that the cell sap concentration remains very low and the protoplasm has a high water content. Consequently, the proteins do not bind much water. The same is true of aquatic plants with their low cell sap concentrations. The proteins may also be unable to respond to dehydration. The actual changes in the proteins that lead to the changes in their hydrophily are completely unknown.

Chapter 15.

The Relative Importance of Protoplasmal and Nonprotoplasmal Factors in Frost Hardiness

As mentioned earlier (Chapter 6), the standardized tests determine the frost killing temperature when injury is due to extracellular freezing. According to the mechanical theory, this frost injury is due to the stresses that the cell contraction produces in the partially dehydrated protoplasm. Frost hardiness is, therefore dependent on (1) protoplasmal properties that permit survival of severe stresses and (2) nonprotoplasmal properties that reduce the severity of the stresses in the frozen plant. The relative importance of these two kinds of properties can be determined only if methods of measuring them are available.

DEGREE OF CELL CONTRACTION (G)

The severity of the stresses is proportional to the degree of cell contraction in the frozen plant, which can be calculated from the ratio of the original cell volume to that in the frozen plant:

$$G = \frac{V_o}{V_f} \tag{1}$$

where G = degree of cell concentration, V_o = original cell volume, V_f = cell volume in the frozen plant.

The original cell volume can be calculated from the separate volume of its water and solids. Since the average density of the cell solids is about 1.6, and since about half of them are in solution and occupy only about 50% of their volume when dry, the weight of the cell solids must be divided by 2 to obtain the approximate volume occupied by them in the cell. Therefore,

$$V_o = W_o + \frac{100 - W_o}{2} \tag{2}$$

where W_o = the original water content of the cell as percent of the fresh weight and

$$\frac{V_o}{V_f} = \frac{W_o + \dfrac{100 - W_o}{2}}{W_f + \dfrac{100 - W_o}{2}} \tag{3}$$

120

where W_f = the water content of the cell in the frozen plant. Therefore

$$G = \frac{W_o + \dfrac{100 - W_o}{2}}{W_f + \dfrac{100 - W_o}{2}} \tag{4}$$

In order to determine the degree of cell contraction, it is therefore necessary to know the value of W_f. This can be calculated if the concentration of the cell sap is known in both the frozen and the unfrozen cell. By definition:

$$\frac{W_f}{W_o} = \frac{C_o}{C_f} \tag{5}$$

where C_o = cell sap concentration (g/100g water) in the cell of the unfrozen plant, C_f = cell sap concentration in the cell of the frozen plant. Substituting for W_f in (4):

$$G = \frac{W_o + \dfrac{100 - W_o}{2}}{\dfrac{C}{C_f} \times W_o + \dfrac{100 - W_o}{2}} \tag{6}$$

If the frost killing point (T_k) of the plant is known, the cell sap concentration at the temperature (C_k) is used. From (6), the tolerance of cell contraction (G_k) can then be calculated.

In order to calculate the degree of cell contraction in the frozen plant, the three following values must therefore be known: W_o, C_o, C_f (or C_k). W_o is taken as the water content of the whole plant tissue or organ (though this may not be quite correct; see below). If the cell sap were a pure sugar solution, C_o and C_f could be easily obtained from standard tables, knowing the freezing point lowering of the juice and the temperature frozen at. For if the plant is at equilibrium, its temperature in the frozen state represents the freezing-point lowering of the cell sap in the contracted cell. But the cell sap consists of a mixture of sugars and electrolytes. Among these, the hexoses bind very little water, sucrose binds much more and the electrolytes the most. Consequently, the values for sucrose should yield a good approximate average for all three. This is especially true in frost-hardened plants, since sucrose may account for such a large fraction of their cell solutes (Chapter 11). Conversion values for sucrose are given in Table 73. The highest ones were obtained by extrapolation (Weismann, 1938).

It is fortunately possible to test the validity of this conclusion by comparison with direct measurements of the amount of ice formed in frozen plants. These measurements have been made by both the dilatometric and calorimetric methods.

1. DILATOMETRIC MEASUREMENTS.

Lebedincev (1930) compared direct measurements of ice formation in wheat plants with calculated values. The two failed to agree and she ascribed the difference between them to colloidally bound water.

TABLE 73

Equivalent values for sucrose solutions. Columns 3 and 4 for 20° C
(from Walter, 1924; Weismann, 1938)

Conc. (g/100g H_2O)	Δ (°C)	Osmotic potential (atm)	Relative humidity (%)
0.0	0.0	0	100
9.5	0.52	7	99.5
18.2	1.05	14	99
26.8	1.55	20.5	98.5
34.7	2.10	27	98
42.6	2.65	34	97.5
49.2	3.10	40	97
55.0	3.55	46	96.5
61.5	4.05	52	96
68.0	4.55	58.5	95.5
74.5	5.05	65	95
81.0	5.60	72	94.5
87.0	6.15	79.5	94
94.0	6.75	87	93.5
100.5	7.35	95	93
107.0	7.95	102.5	92.5
114.0	8.55	110	92
120.5	9.15	118	91.5
126.5	9.75	126	91
133	10.40	134	90.5
140	11.0	142	90
146	11.6	150	89.5
153	12.3	158	89
158	12.8	165.5	88.5
164	13.4	173	88
169	14.0	181	87.5
176	14.7	189	87
181	15.3	197	86.5
186	15.9	205	86
192	16.5	212.5	85.5
196	17.1	220	85
269	22.9	295	80

But, as already pointed out (Chapter 10), she erroneously assumed that the calculations could be made directly from the freezing-point lowerings instead of using the concentrations of the cell sap corresponding to these. Weismann (1938) showed that when her results are recalculated using the actual sucrose concentrations that would produce these freezing point lowerings, the calculated and measured values agree almost perfectly (see Table 46).

Rosa's (1921) measurements of unfrozen water in cabbage leaves fluctuate above and below the values calculated from $\dfrac{C_o}{C_f}$. But his measurements for sweet potatoes and cauliflower are 50 to 90% above the calculated values. Weismann (1938), however, points out that air bubbles can never be completely removed when the dilatometer method is used, and this may lead to large errors. Another possible source of error is undercooling. The cell contents undercool due to their separation from the ice masses by their lipid membranes (Chapter 3). In the same way, infiltrating the tissues with petroleum ether in the dilatometric method might prevent both the spread of ice crystals and the diffusion of water vapor from the unfrozen parts, leaving islands of undercooled cells in the tissues. Both sources of error would lead to underestimates of the amount of ice formed, particularly at the moderate temperatures used by Rosa. Evidence of the undependability of the dilatometric method is the lack of agreement between Lebedincev's values for the same variety and the same date in different tables.

2. CALORIMETRIC MEASUREMENTS.

This method is not open to the above objections since it is based on the heat of fusion of ice and the tissues are frozen in their normal state. Table 74 shows that the calculated values for cabbage agree nearly per-

TABLE 74

The fraction of water unfrozen in cabbage leaves at their frost killing temperature (T_k). Average of three to five results (from Levitt, 1939)

Hardiness	Δ (°C)	T_k (°C)	Original wt of water (g)	Wt of ice at T_k (g)	Measured	Calculated $\left(\dfrac{C_o}{C_f} \right)$
Unhardened	0.81	—2.1	14.10	8.46	0.40	0.41
Hardened	1.257	—5.6	12.54	9.46	0.25	0.27

fectly with the experimentally determined ones, at least down to about —6°C. Values are available for lower temperatures using wheat crowns (Dexter, 1934). Two sets of data are given for consecutive freezes of two hours. Larger quantities of ice were formed during the second freeze in the early fall. According to Dexter, this is due to injury during the first freeze, since the difference between the two becomes progressively smaller from early to late fall. If his explanation were correct, the late fall values (when no injury occurs) should approach the larger values of the first freeze in the early fall. But his results show just the opposite trend. The two freezes during late fall agree with each other and are closer to those of the second freeze during early fall. It seems more likely that the discrepancy is due to lack of equilibrium in the first, early fall freeze. The late fall plants had previously been frozen in the field and the nuclei for ice formation were already present in them. Consequently, undercooling was less likely to occur (Luyet and Hodapp, 1938). At any rate, the values for the second freeze are so consistent (Table 75) that their choice is logical. The results for —7°C do not all agree with the calculated values as well as in the case of cabbage at slightly higher temperatures. But those at —13°C are in excellent agreement. In view of the lack of exact data for the freezing point lowerings, the few discrepancies at —7°C are not significant.

TABLE 75

The fraction of water unfrozen in wheat crowns at two freezing temperatures (from Dexter, 1934) $\Delta = 1.00$ to $1.25°C$

	Fraction of water unfrozen			
	Measured values			Calculated Values $\dfrac{C_o}{C_f}$
Variety	Oct. 19–20	Nov. 1–2	Nov. 22–23	
	At —7°C			
Minturki-Marquis	0.29	0.28	0.29	
Minturki	0.24	0.33	0.28	
				0.18 to 0.23
Kanred	0.22	0.26	0.25	
Blackhull	0.19	0.27	0.29	
	At —13°C			
Minturki-Marquis	0.12	0.15	0.15	
Minturki	0.12	0.14	0.14	
				0.11 to 0.14
Kanred	0.09	0.09	0.13	
Blackhull	0.09	0.10	0.12	

Greathouse's (1935) results for clover roots are somewhat larger than the calculated values (Table 76); but his results for potato tubers are in excellent agreement (Table 77). This may, perhaps, be due to the presence of large amounts of woody and other material in the clover roots. In conformity with this suggestion, results for pine needles (Meyer, 1932) and apple twigs (Stark, 1936) also fail to agree with the calculated values.

TABLE 76

The fraction of water unfrozen in clover roots at —15°C
(from Greathouse and Stuart, 1934)

| | | | Fraction of water unfrozen | |
Date	Variety	Δ (°C)	From calorimetric measurements	From $\dfrac{C_o}{C_f}$
Greenhouse	Ohio	0.335	0.042	0.035
	French	0.340	0.044	0.035
Jan. 24/34	Ohio	0.935	0.17	0.09
	French	0.730	0.13	0.07
Feb. 21/34	Ohio	0.970	0.16	0.10
	Maryland	0.700	0.12	0.07
	French	0.630	0.10	0.07
	Italian	0.610	0.09	0.06
March 21/34	Ohio	0.500	0.10	0.05
	Maryland	0.465	0.09	0.05
	French	0.430	0.09	0.05

TABLE 77

The fraction of water unfrozen in potato tubers. Δ not given; assumed to be that commonly found in potato tubers (0.75°C) (from Greathouse, 1935)

| | Fraction of water unfrozen | |
Freezing temperature (°C)	From calorimetric measurements	From $\dfrac{C_o}{C_f}$
—10	0.11	0.10
—15	0.09	0.07
—20	0.08	0.06
—23	0.06	0.05

What are we to conclude from these discrepancies? Which values are preferable, the experimentally determined or the calculated? Before choosing between the two, it must first be made clear what the values are to be used for. The aim of the calculations is to estimate the degree of dehydration of the *living protoplasts.* Unfortunately, no experimental determinations can be made without including the cell walls of these living protoplasts, as well as the many nonliving cells that also occur in the organ investigated. Both of these factors will exaggerate the difference between the calculated and the determined values, since in the organ as a whole a much larger fraction of the water will be colloidally held than in the protoplast. But what of the several cases where the two sets of values agree so well? Does this mean that no appreciable amount of colloidally bound water occurs in these tissues? In answering this question, it must first be realized that the freezing point determination is made on a solution that contains not only molecularly dissolved but also colloidally dispersed material. It is, therefore, only the colloidal gels which remain behind in the squeezed tissues that are not taken into account in the calculated value. That the error due to this omission is negligible in many tissues, at least near the freezing point, is shown by the fact that the freezing-point lowering of whole dead tissue is usually practically identical with that of the expressed juice (see Chapter 2). It seems safe, therefore, to conclude that the several cases of excellent agreement between measured and calculated values of frost dehydration prove the correctness of the method of calculation. The exceptional cases of disagreement simply show either that freezing equilibrium was not attained or that the experimentally determined values on whole tissues or organs do not apply as accurately to individual living cells. The use of sucrose conversion tables therefore seems justified in calculating the amount of unfrozen cell water and the degree of cell contraction in the frozen plant. It should be realized, of course, that all these calculated values are approximations, though accurate enough to reveal the relatively large differences that do exist. The following questions may be answered by means of these calculated values:

(a) What degree of cell contraction must a plant tolerate before it can be considered frost hardy? Freezing-point lowerings in nonhalophytes are seldom as low as —2.5°C. In order to possess a frost hardiness of 2.5°C (i.e. a killing temperature of —5°C in a plant with this large a freezing-point lowering—see Chapter 6), such plants would have to survive the freezing of about 45% of their water and a maximum degree of cell contraction of 1.8 if their water content is 90% or 1.5 if it is as low as 50%. This, then, can be accepted as the minimum tolerance of cell contraction in order for a plant to be hardy. The validity of this choice is borne out by results with potato tubers. Their tissues are unable to become frost hardy, and are killed when 10 to 40% of their water is frozen (Chapter 14). Since the water content of potatoes is about 80%, this means that they cannot survive a degree of cell contraction of more than 1.3.

(b) To what extent are varietal differences in frost hardiness dependent on hardiness to cell contraction? If there is a close correlation between hardiness and cell sap concentration or sugar content, it might be expected that all the varieties would be killed at about the same degree of cell contraction. When no such correlation can be found, the varieties might be expected to differ in hardiness to cell contraction. Thus, when eight wheat varieties are arranged in order of decreasing hardiness, they also fall—with one exception—in the order of decreasing cell sap concentration and increasing water content (Table 78).

TABLE 78

Relation of cell contraction to frost hardiness in wheat varieties (from Tumanow and Borodin, 1930). Exceptional values marked with an asterisk.

Variety	T_k(°C)	Δ(°C)	W_o(%)	$\dfrac{C_f}{C_o}$	G_k
Minhardi	—15	1.424	86.2	7.2	4.9
Lutescens	—15	1.371	87.4	7.5	5.2
Hostianum	—14	1.343	87.7	7.2	5.1
Erythrospermum	—14	1.227	89.1*	8.0	5.7
Durable	—14	1.141	88.0	8.5	5.7
Ukrainka	—13	1.344*	88.8	6.9	5.1*
Zemke	—13	1.106	89.2	8.4	5.9
Schroder	—12	1.021	90.8	8.4	6.2

T_k = frost killing point
Δ = freezing point lowering of cell sap
W_o = water content of tissues
C_f = concentration of cell sap in frozen plant
C_o = concentration of cell sap in unfrozen plant
G_k = degree of cell contraction at frost killing temperature

But the relation to cell contraction is an inverse one—the greater the hardiness, the less the degree of cell contraction at the frost killing point, again with one exception. This does not mean that the protoplasmic factors are less developed the hardier the variety. Even if they were identical in all the varieties, the hardiest would be killed by less of a cell contraction, because at their lower killing temperature their protoplasm would be more dehydrated and therefore more sensitive to stresses. The differences in hardiness among 7 of the 8 varieties are apparently due to nonprotoplasmal factors leading to differences in the degree of cell contraction in the frozen plant at any one temperature. But the eighth variety—Ukrainka—has an exceptionally low tolerance of cell contraction. The logical conclusion is that its protoplasm is well below that of the other seven varieties in hardiness to stresses. In agreement with these conclusions, Granhall (1943) failed to find any difference in protoplasmic permeability between wheat varieties showing a good correlation between sugar content and frost hardiness. Even his differences in protoplasmic viscosities are just what would be expected from these sugar differences (see Chapter 13). If the above conclusions are correct, it should be possible to raise the hardiness of the least hardy varieties (with the exception of Ukrainka) to that of the most hardy, simply by increasing their cell sap concentrations and simultaneously lowering their water contents to that of the most hardy. This might be done by uptake of glycerin.

TABLE 79

Hardiness quantities in *Pinus cembra* (from Pisek, 1950). Symbols as in Table 78. C_k = concentration of cell sap at temperature T_k.

Date	Leaves tested	Treatment	$W_o(\%)$	$\Delta(°C)$	$T_k(°C)$	$\dfrac{C_k}{C_o}$	G_k
23/9/42	current	—	59	1.55	—10	4.8	2.4
	one-yr	—	57	1.68	—12	5.3	2.4
	current	hardened	57	1.77	—15	6.0	2.5
	one-yr	hardened	54	1.74	—16	6.3	2.4
8/10/42	current	—	56	1.64	—15	6.4	2.5
	one-yr	—	54	1.60	—15	6.5	2.5
	current	hardened	56	1.57	—26	9.6	2.8
	one-yr	hardened	55	1.63	—26	9.3	2.7
27/11/42	current	—	57	1.78	—35	10.5	2.9
	one-yr	—	55	1.87	—37	10.4	2.8
	current	dehardened	57	1.49	—27	10.5	2.9
	one-yr	dehardened	56	1.54	—28	10.3	2.9
11/1/43	current	—	57	1.73	—40	11.8	3.0
	one-yr	—	56	1.85	—40	11.1	2.9
	current	dehardened	57	1.58	—26	9.5	2.9
	one-yr	dehardened	56	1.68	—25	9.0 *	2.9
28/3/43	current	—	55	1.69	—30	10.0	2.8
	one-yr	—	55	1.78	—30	9.6	2.7
	current	dehardened	55	1.62	—23	8.7	2.7
	one-yr	dehardened	55	1.74	—23	8.2	2.6
3/5/43	current	—	50	1.96	—13	4.9	2.1
	one-yr	—	49	1.83	—14	5.5	2.2
	current	hardened	52	2.25	—17	5.3	2.2
	one-yr	hardened	51	2.18	—17	5.5	2.2

(c) How does the plant's tolerance of cell contraction change during the hardening period? Conifers are particularly interesting in this respect since (1) they show such marked changes in hardiness and (2) their cell sap concentration parallels these changes only to a minor degree. Pisek (1950) has, in fact, shown that the two properties may actually change in opposite directions during spring. When his data are analyzed (Table 79), one reason for the great hardiness of pine needles is immediately apparent. Due to their low water content, the degree of cell contraction at their frost killing point is not much greater than that in plants with frost killing points 30° higher. Yet there is a small but significant increase in tolerance of cell contraction as hardiness increases.

TOLERANCE OF FROST DEHYDRATION (D_k)

The value that shows the best correlation with frost hardiness in pine is $\dfrac{C_k}{C_o}$. Since this gives the ratio of the total water in the cell to that unfrozen in it at the frost killing point, it may be called the cell's tolerance of frost dehydration. It is interesting to note that artificial hardening during early fall increases this tolerance of frost dehydration but has little effect on cell sap concentration. During spring, on the contrary, artificial hardening has little effect on tolerance of dehydration but markedly increases cell sap concentration. Dehardening treatment during late fall also fails to alter tolerance of frost dehydration appreciably, though it lowers cell sap concentration. In midwinter, dehardening decreases both factors. The hardiness of Rhododendron (Table 80) is even more dependent than that of Pinus on its ability to oppose cell contraction, due to its lower water content and higher cell sap concentration. The hardier Pinus, on the other hand, is able to develop a much higher tolerance of frost dehydration.

As a further test of the importance of the quantity, the tolerance of frost dehydration has been calculated for a large number of plants (Table 81). It can be seen that freezing point lowering is, in general, low in nonhardy plants and high in hardy plants; but there is an overlap and no strict parallel exists between the two (in full agreement with Chandler, 1913). Thus *Saxifraga aizoon* in the nonhardy state has only half the freezing-point lowering of red beet roots but is four times as hardy; in the hardy state, its freezing-point lowering is about the same as that of the beet but it is twenty times as hardy. There are many other similar exceptions. Tolerance of frost dehydration shows a much closer correlation with frost hardiness than does freezing-point lowering. In nonhardy plants, the range of frost hardiness is from 0.9 to 8.5; the range of tolerance is from 1.7 to 5.4. In hardy plants the respective ranges are 11 to 38 and 4.4 to 15.2. But here, too, there are exceptions. Among the nonhardy, *Sempervivum glaucum* has a definitely larger tolerance of frost dehydration than *Pinus cembra,* yet it is less than one third as hardy; among the hardy, it has the highest tolerance of frost dehydration, though eight others are more frost hardy.

TABLE 80

Hardiness quantities in *Rhododendron ferrugineum* (from Pisek, 1950). Symbols as in Table 78.

Date	Leaves tested	Treatment	$W_o(\%)$	$\Delta(°C)$	$T_k(°C)$	$\dfrac{C_k}{C_o}$	G_k
31/8/42	current	—	52	1.50	— 5.5	3.1	1.9
	one-yr	—	51	1.35	— 5.5	3.4	1.9
	current	hardened	51	1.91	—11	4.4	2.1
	one-yr	hardened	50	1.63	—11	5.0	2.1
23/9/42	current	—	50	1.55	— 7	3.6	2.0
	one-yr	—	52	1.56	— 7	3.6	2.0
	current	hardened	50	2.04	—12.5	4.6	2.1
	one-yr	hardened	50	1.91	—12.5	4.9	2.2
16/11/42	current	—	54	1.78	—18	6.8	2.5
	one-yr	—	56	1.70	—10	4.5	2.3
	current	hardened	53	1.98	—24	7.6	2.5
	one-yr	hardened	55	1.64	—12	5.4	2.4
	current	dehardened	53	1.37	—10	5.4	2.3
11/1/43	current	—	53	1.80	—24	8.2	2.5
	one-yr	—	55	1.54	—13	6.0	2.4
	current	dehardened	55	1.59	—10	4.8	2.3
	one-yr	dehardened	55	1.48	— 7	3.7	2.1
22/3/43	current	—	51	1.83	—15	5.8	2.3
	current	dehardened	52	1.58	— 9	4.4	2.1
3/5/43	current	—	50	1.49	—14	6.5	2.3
	one-yr	—	50	1.55	—12	5.6	2.2
	current	hardened	52	1.87	—17	6.3	2.4
	one-yr	hardened	52	1.93	—13	5.0	2.2

The striking correlation with frost hardiness implies that tolerance of frost dehydration is an important quantity. Yet it is equally obvious from all these examples that a high tolerance of frost dehydration may not be due to the same factor in different plants. It may indicate (a) tolerance of a high degree of cell contraction (e.g. in wheat), or (b) tolerance of a high degree of cell dehydration without a very large degree of cell contraction (e.g. in pine), or (c) tolerance of a wide range of hydration and dehydration (e.g. in succulents). If its basis is so broad, what then is the significance of the quantity?

One similarity between the above three cases is the fact that they are all based on protoplasmic properties. In case (a), the protoplasm must be able to survive large stresses when exposed to moderately large dehydrating forces. In case (b), it must be able to survive moderate stresses when exposed to very large dehydrating forces. In case (c), it must be able to survive the largest stresses when exposed to moderately large dehydrating forces and also must be rapidly adaptable to a wide range of states of hydration and dehydration. It therefore follows that $\dfrac{C_k}{C_o}$ is a measure of the sum total of protoplasmic properties that enable cells to survive small or large stresses when in the partially or highly dehydrated state.

The reasons for the above conclusion become clearer if we reexamine the data on which the quantity $\dfrac{C_k}{C_o}$ is based—the freezing-point lowering of the cell sap and the frost killing temperature. The plant juice obtained in the usual way for freezing-point determinations consists essentially of vacuolar sap. Little protoplasmic juice is expressed with it. Consequently $\dfrac{C_k}{C_o}$ actually measures tolerance of vacuolar dehydration. It reveals how much of the vacuolar water is removed by extracellular ice formation at the frost killing point. Why, then, should this vacuolar property be more closely correlated with frost hardiness than the freezing-point lowering itself? Since the vacuole and protoplasm are in aqueous equilibrium, the protoplasm must have the same freezing-point lowering as the vacuole. Consequently, as soon as ice formation begins to dehydrate the vacuole, the protoplasm must also suffer some loss of water. But it has already been shown (Chapter 13) that hardy protoplasm is more hydrophilic and therefore loses less water than nonhardy protoplasm at any one vapor pressure. It has also been stated (Chapter 14) that the frost injury depends on both the severity of the stress and the ability of the protoplasm to resist the stress. The latter property is greater the more hydrophilic the protoplasm (see Fig. 21). Consequently, the greater the cell's tolerance of vacuolar frost dehydration, the greater the protoplasmic resistance to dehydration must be. In other words, tolerance of frost dehydration represents the degree to which the vacuole must be dehydrated in order to reduce the protoplasmic hydration to the critical point for frost injury. This quantity

TABLE 81

Hardiness data for plants arranged in order of increasing frost hardiness. Leaves used unless otherwise specified.   NH = nonhardy (minimum hardiness), H = hardy (maximum hardiness).   Other symbols as in Tables 78, 79.

Species	Δ	T_k	$T_k - \Delta$	$\dfrac{C_k}{C_o}$	Observer
Potato tuber	0.64	1.53	0.89	2.3	Maximov, 1914
Red beet root	1.25	2.15	0.90	1.7	Maximov, 1914
Cabbage (NH)	0.81	2.10	1.3	2.4	Levitt, 1939
Vaccinium vitis idea (NH)	1.09	2.50	1.4	2.1	Ulmer, 1937
Erica carnea (NH)	1.07	3–4	2.4	2.9	Ulmer, 1937
Sempervivum glaucum (NH)	0.50	3.0	2.5	5.3	Kessler, 1935
Rhododendron ferrugineum (NH)	1.17	4	2.8	3.0	Ulmer, 1937
Globularia nudicaulis (NH)	1.00	4	3.0	3.5	Ulmer, 1937
Globularia cordifolia (NH)	0.99	4	3.0	3.5	Ulmer, 1937
Saxifraga caesia (NH)	1.01	4	3.0	3.5	Ulmer, 1937
Homogyne alpina (NH)	0.89	4	3.1	4.0	Ulmer, 1937
Saxifraga aizoon (NH)	0.63	4	3.4	5.4	Ulmer, 1937
Hedera helix (NH)	0.94	4.5	3.6	4.1	Kessler, 1935
Rhododendron hirstum (NH)	1.22	5	3.8	3.5	Ulmer, 1937
Saxifraga cordifolia (NH)	0.95	5	4.1	4.4	Kessler, 1935
Cabbage leaves (H)	1.26	5.6	4.3	3.7	Levitt, 1939
Carex firma (NH)	1.08	5–6	4.4	4.2	Ulmer, 1937
Pinus mugo (NH)	1.36	6	4.6	3.6	Ulmer, 1937
Empetrum nigrum (NH)	1.19	6	4.8	4.1	Ulmer, 1937
Juniperus nana (NH)	1.31	6–8	5.7	4.1	Ulmer, 1937
Pinus cembra (NH)	1.71	9	7.3	4.1	Ulmer, 1937
Pinus cembra (NH)	1.55	10	8.5	4.9	Pisek, 1950
Wheat (H)	1.02–1.42	12–15	11–13.6	6.9–8.6	Tumanov and Borodin, 1930
Homogyne alpina (H)	2.92	18	15.1	4.4	Ulmer, 1937
Erica carnea (H)	2.96	18–19	15.5	4.4	Ulmer, 1937
Globularia cordifolia (H)	2.59	18–19	15.9	5.0	Ulmer, 1937
Globularia nudicaulis (H)	2.61	19	16.4	5.0	Ulmer, 1937
Hedera helix (H)	1.65	18.5	16.9	7.4	Kessler, 1935
Saxifraga aizoon (H)	1.33	18–19	17.2	9.0	Ulmer, 1937
Saxifraga cordifolia (H)	1.50	19	17.5	8.2	Kessler, 1935

TABLE 81 (*continued*)

Species	Δ	T_k	$T_k - \Delta$	$\dfrac{C_k}{C_o}$	Observer
Vaccinium vitis idea (H)	1.86	22	20.1	7.7	Ulmer, 1937
Sempervivum glaucum (H)	0.96	25	24.0	15.2	Kessler, 1935
Rhododendron hirsutum (H)	3.48	28–29	25	5.1	Ulmer, 1937
Rhododendron ferrugineum (H)	1.92	28	26.1	8.6	Ulmer, 1937
Empetrum nigrum (H)	2.22	29	26.8	7.7	Ulmer, 1937
Carex firma (H)	2.28	29–30	27.2	7.5	Ulmer, 1937
Saxifraga caesia (H)	1.61	29–30	27.9	10.3	Ulmer, 1937
Juniperus nana (H)	3.02	36	33	6.6	Ulmer, 1937
Pinus cembra (H)	2.07	38	35.9	9.6	Ulmer, 1937
Pinus mugo (H)	2.21	40–41	38.3	9.4	Ulmer, 1937
Pinus cembra (H)	1.73–1.85	40	38	11.3	Pisek, 1950

would then measure the protoplasmal component of frost hardiness. The vacuolar component is measured by the degree of cell contraction at a standard freezing temperature. From these two calculated values, it should be possible to determine how much of the frost hardiness of a variety or of a hardened plant is due to the protoplasmal component and how much to the vacuolar component. The aim of any breeding program would then be to combine both components in one plant.

Factors also included in the tolerance of frost dehydration are the rigidity of the cell wall and the cell size and shape. As Iljin mentions, the stresses on the protoplasm will also depend on these cell properties. But there is, as yet, no satisfactory method of measuring them separately from the protoplasmic factors, so they must be included with them.

It should be pointed out that tolerance of frost dehydration is not the same as the dehydration intensity ($\log \dfrac{P_o}{P}$) of Siminovitch and Briggs (1953). The latter gives the same value for all cells at the same freezing temperature—i.e. it is dependent on the activity of the water in the tissues and can give no information with respect to the amount of water removed from the cells.

From Table 81 frost-hardy plants can be classified as follows:

(1) Those with a small tolerance of frost dehydration (4–5) but a large freezing-point lowering (2.5°C or more).

(2) Those with a large tolerance (10–15) but a small freezing-point lowering (around 1°C).

(3) Those with relatively large values of both (a tolerance of more than 5 and a freezing-point lowering of more than 1.3°C).

The frost hardiness of these three groups increases in the above order— i.e. tolerance of frost dehydration by itself confers more frost hardiness than freezing-point lowering, but a combination of the two yields the greatest frost hardiness. The different kinds of hardiness can be seen more clearly from the changes that take place in the plants from fall to winter and spring (Figs. 22–25).

(1) *Hedera helix* owes most of its hardiness to its large freezing-point lowering, the seasonal curve closely following the hardiness curve. The tolerance of frost dehydration plays a minor, but nevertheless essential, role.

(2) *Sempervivum glaucum* owes nearly all its hardiness to its extraordinarily high tolerance of frost dehydration. The seasonal curves for the two quantities follow each other closely. The freezing-point lowering also rises slightly with hardiness, but the values are too low at all times to play more than a minor role.

(3) *Pinus cembra* resembles *S. glaucum* in that the seasonal changes in hardiness are followed by similar though smaller changes in tolerance of frost dehydration. Freezing-point lowering shows little seasonal change. Nevertheless, to say that the freezing-point lowering is unimportant would be a gross error; for it can be seen that the frost killing point far exceeds the tolerance of frost dehydration, due to the fact that the freezing-point lowering, though nearly constant, is large at all times of the year. The importance of cell sap concentration in *Pinus cembra* is further emphasized during spring, when the tolerance of frost dehydration has dropped so low that the frost killing temperature of —13°C is attained only because of a spring rise in freezing-point lowering to the year's maximum. Thus, even plants with the largest tolerance of frost dehydration would have their frost killing point raised many degrees if their freezing-point lowering were 0.5°C less. As shown earlier (Table 79), an important vacuolar factor in the hardiness of *Pinus cembra* is its low water content, leading to a relatively small degree of cell contraction even at the lowest freezing temperatures. It is these two vacuolar properties, therefore, that are responsible for the superior hardiness of *Pinus cembra* over *Sempervivum glaucum*.

(4) *Saxifraga cordifolia* is apparently equally dependent on freezing-point lowering and tolerance of frost dehydration, since both follow the hardiness changes rather closely.

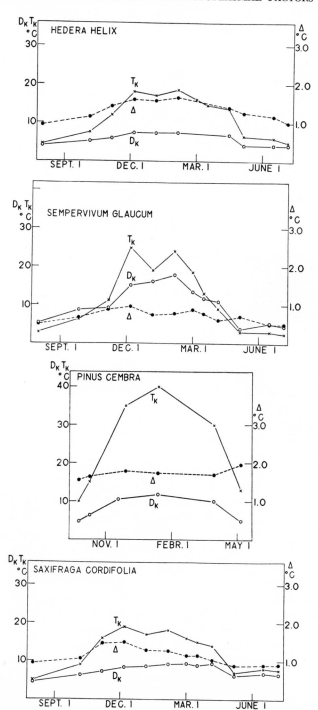

FIGS. 22–25. Seasonal changes in frost hardiness (T_k), freezing point lowering (Δ), and tolerance of frost dehydration (D_k) in four plants (from Kessler, 1935, and Pisek, 1950).

It appears that tolerance of frost dehydration is a more stable quantity than freezing-point lowering; for it remains at its maximum during winter in all cases. Freezing-point lowering, on the other hand, shows marked fluctuations during winter, though care must be taken to insure that this is not due simply to a passive loss of water. It appears, however, that plants depending mainly on freezing-point lowering for hardiness are more likely to lose it too early during winter. But if freezing-point lowering is an important factor in frost hardiness, how can one explain the several relatively futile attempts to increase frost hardiness by artificially increasing cell sap concentration (Chapter 11)? If the solutes are taken up quickly (within 24 hr or less), it must be assumed that tolerance of frost dehydration remains essentially unaltered. Therefore the fractional lowering of the frost killing temperature must be the same as the fractional lowering of the freezing point. Such a change will be readily detected only in plants that already have a low frost killing temperature. If the freezing point is lowered by even 50% in plants killed by — 3 to —4°C, the frost killing point will be lowered by only 1½ to 2°C. Though the actual frost killing points are not given, Chandler's results indicate differences of this order (see Table 50). One experiment of Kessler's (1935) gives quantitatively nearly perfect results (Table 82).

TABLE 82

Measured and calculated increases in frost hardiness due to artificial increase in cell sap concentration (from Kessler, 1935)

	Δ	T_k	Calculated T_k
Original	—1.12°C	—7 (60% injury)	
After glycerin uptake	—1.23	—8 (80% injury)	—7.7 (60% injury)

But such small differences in frost killing temperature are extremely difficult to detect experimentally, and it is not surprising, therefore, that in one case Kessler failed to find any difference. In the case of plants killed by —10°C, on the other hand, a lowering of the freezing point by 50% would lower the frost killing point by an easily detected 5°C. There is, therefore, a crying need for similar experiments with such plants that already have a relatively low frost-killing temperature.

One mystery that has long puzzled and confused investigators now becomes crystal clear. It has been pointed out over and over again (see Chapter 11), that many plants develop high cell sap concentrations before they become frost hardy. This fact has even been cited as evidence that freezing-point lowering is unimportant. But the contrary is the case, for it can now be seen that the plant is in this way able to take full advantage of even a small improvement in tolerance of frost dehydration. Protoplasmic changes producing an increase in tolerance from 2 to 4 at the beginning of the hardening process, would lower the killing point only 1°C in a plant with a freezing point of —0.5°C, a full 3°C in one with a freezing point of —1.5°C. The former plant would succumb to the first light frosts of fall, the latter would not.

All these results conclusively prove that both the protoplasmal and vacuolar properties are important in frost hardiness. This is in complete agreement with the comprehensive theory proposed above (Chapter 14).

PART II.

LOW MOISTURE OR DROUGHT HARDINESS

"Increased drought resistance is to be regarded as one aspect of a general increase of the power of enduring injurious conditions. . . . The center of interest . . . is tending to be transferred to the specific properties of protoplasm. . . . The problem thus falls . . . with other phenomena depending on the stability of the protoplasm, such as the power of resistance to frost, to injury by salts or poisons, and even to attacks by plant or animal parasites."

—Maximov, 1929

Chapter 16.

The Limits of Drought Hardiness

A general characteristic of protoplasm in the resting state is its ability to become air-dry without loss of life—e.g. in seeds, spores, and other reproductive bodies. But even when their rest is broken and growth recommences, they may still retain this ability for some time. Thus, seedlings, sporelings, and mosses may survive drying over concentrated sulfuric acid (Table 83). But not all plants show the same degree of

TABLE 83
Survival of extreme drought by various plants

Plant	Treatment	Observer
Germinated wheat, rye, and barley; radicle half the length of the grain	dried in vacuo over H_2SO_4 for six months	de Saussure, 1827
Funaria, *Grimmia pulvinata*	18–22 wk over H_2SO_4	Schröder, 1886
Bulbils of *Cystopteris bulbifera*	5 months of air drying plus 2 wk over H_2SO_4	Heinricher, 1896
Fungal cultures (14 of 21 species)	dried in air for 2½ years	Wehmer, 1904
Germinated spores of leafy mosses and some thallus cells	dried over H_2SO_4	Rabe, 1905
Myrothamnus flabellifolia	lost 93% of its water	Thoday, 1921
Covillea glutinosa	air dry	Maximov, 1929
Pelvetia (brown alga)	air dry	Isaac, 1933
Notochlaena marantae	powder dry for 2 months at 50% relative humidity	Iljin, 1931
Cololeugenia calcarea *Madotheca platyphylla*	dried over conc. H_2SO_4 for more than a month	Höfler, 1942

tolerance. Among seedlings, the Gramineae are most hardy, those from oily seeds less so, and legumes least; and the germinated spores of liverworts and ferns possess as little ability to survive water loss as do the mature plants they develop into (Rabe, 1905). Most mature plants do not attain as high a tolerance as the resting organs. The hardiest survive air drying for months without injury (Table 83), though killed

141

by drying over concentrated sulfuric acid (Iljin, 1931). But most grow-ing plants are killed by a loss of 40 to 90 % of their normal water content (Tables 84 and 85); or when they come to equilibrium with relative humidities of 92 to 97% (Iljin, 1931). Iljin states that survival of rela-tive humidities as low as 88% is not uncommon, though only the ex-ceptional plant can tolerate values as low as 85%.

There is a survival factor of prime importance under conditions of drought, for which no counterpart exists in the case of low temperature

TABLE 84

The water loss resulting in death of half the leaves in different plants
(from Schröder, 1909)

Species	% of water content lost	% of fresh wt lost
Kalmia latifolia	95	47
Ilex aquifolium	90	53
Helianthus annuus	87	70
Sambucus nigra	85	68
Fagus sylvatica	80	40
Myrica cerifera	77	41
Tropaeolum majus	75	60
Acer pseudoplatanus	71	45
Platanus orientalis	63	40
Polygonum cuspidatum	57	40
Impatiens parviflora	44	40

TABLE 85

The water loss found under natural conditions on July 1 and 2 (column 1), and the critical water loss (column 2), in percent of the water content when saturated (from Höfler *et al.*, 1941).

Species	Natural sat. deficit	Critical sat. deficit	D_k	Degree of droughting (column 1/ column 2)
Hieracium pilosella	73.6	87.2	7.8	84.5
Potentilla arenaria	52.5	81.8	5.5	63.8
Anthyllis vulneraria	77.0	80.4	5.1	95.8
Globularia cordifolia	56.2	75.1	4.0	74.8
Thymus praecox	44.3	70.8	3.4	62.7
Teucrium montanum	57.2	70.2	3.3	81.5
Bupleurum falcatum	28.1	66.2	3.0	42.6
Anemone pulsatilla	33.3	66.0	2.9	50.5
Linum tenuifolium	57.2	65.0	2.9	87.0
Helianthemum canum	53.2	60.5	2.5	88.0
Aster linosyris	45.3	48.2	1.9	93.3

effects. The temperature of a plant relatively rapidly approaches that of its environment. And the same tendency exists to reach aqueous equilibrium. But though the plant may require only minutes, or at most hours, to come to temperature equilibrium with its environment, it may maintain a considerably higher (though slowly dropping) vapor pressure than that of its environment for days, months, or even years (Maximov, 1929). This is due to its possession of protective barriers with a very high resistance to water movement, and an ability to replenish its water supply from the soil. Plants differ very markedly in these two respects (Table 85). In fact, so many investigations have been made of this complex property of maintaining a high vapor pressure in the tissues, that drought hardiness itself has usually been dealt with as a mere adjunct to it (Maximov, 1929).

Even in the case of small, isolated plant parts, it should not be assumed that all the water is removed when they are exposed in vacuo over concentrated sulfuric acid for weeks or even months. De Saussure (1827) found that if seeds are ground up after such treatment, a further loss of weight may then occur under the same conditions. Schröder (1886) suggests that absolute dryness can occur only on death, and that about 5% of the plant's water is needed to keep it alive (e.g. in the case of *Sticta pulmonaria*). In agreement with this, the exceptionally drought hardy fern—*Notochlaena marantae*—survives only as long as 6% of its water remains (Iljin, 1931). There is, therefore, no evidence that protoplasm can tolerate the loss of all its water.

Chapter 17.

Drought Injury

INDIRECT OR METABOLIC INJURY

Though there can be no drought effect completely analogous to chilling injury, it is conceivable that here too, under certain conditions, the injury may be indirect due to upset of the metabolic balance. According to Smith (1915), the effect on respiration rate depends on the extent of the water loss. Up to a 30% loss, respiration increases gradually. This maximum rate is maintained up to a loss of 50 to 60% of the plant's water. Any further loss is accompanied by a progressive decrease in respiration rate. Somewhat similar results have since been found by many others (Iljin, 1923a; Simonis, 1947; Domien, 1949; Montfort and Hahn, 1950), the effect varying with the plant (Table 86). No change in respiration rate could be detected, however, in droughted *Helodea canadensis* (Walter, 1929).

TABLE 86
Maximum respiration increase on dehydration (from Domien, 1949)

Species	% increase in respiration
Hedera helix	34, 67 (different experiments)
Triticum vulgare	63
Arum maculatum	44
Rumex acetosa	10
Phaseolus vulgaris	0

The first effect of water reduction in leaves has been stated to be stomatal closure (Iljin, 1923). This markedly slows up the movement of carbon dioxide into assimilating leaves, reducing the photosynthetic rate 2 to 10 times according to the amount of water removal and the sensitivity of the plant. But others (see Walter, 1929) have shown a marked reduction in assimilation rate even in the absence of stomatal control. In very sensitive plants, such as *Helodea canadensis,* the rate is reduced at relatively slight degrees of dehydration, and in sucrose solutions above 0.5M, CO_2 is actually evolved in full sunlight (Walter, 1929). These immediate effects of water loss on assimilation and respiration rates must not be confused with the gradual effects of long-continued growth under conditions of drought. Simonis (1952) showed

144

that this results in a marked increase in rate of photosynthesis, though respiration rate sometimes increased, sometimes decreased.

The possibility exists, that injury may sometimes result from a drought-induced reduction in rate of photosynthesis, coupled wth an increase in respiration rate. In support of this concept, Iljin and Demidenko (see Tumanov, 1930) report a significant decrease in the dry matter of wheat and corn exposed to drought. But Tumanov was unable to detect any loss during a 10-day wilting period, though he suggests that a more gradual and longer lasting wilting might have produced a different result. According to Schafer (1928, see Tumanov) and Mothes (1928), however, the increased respiration occurs only at water losses of not more than 20%, at which point the assimilation rate is quite adequate to compensate for the higher respiration rates. Recent results uphold this contention. In apple leaves, a marked reduction in photosynthesis and an increase in respiration may occur even before wilting has set in (Schneider and Childers, 1941). When the plant was definitely wilted, photosynthesis was reduced 87%. Maize leaves showed less than 10% the normal rate of photosynthesis only when the leaves were badly wilted (Verduin and Loomis, 1944). Both of these are measurements of *net* photosynthesis; consequently, no loss in dry weight could occur. At the degrees of wilting necessary to produce injury, the rates of both respiration and photosynthesis are inhibited (Tumanov, 1930). Since drought injury may occur while the plant still contains large quantities of reserves, it seems reasonable to conclude that any starvation of wilted plants is due not to the desiccation but to the prevailing high temperature (see Part III), and would not occur at any degree of wilting provided the temperature is moderate.

Metabolic drought injury of another kind is suggested by Mothes (1928). He allowed sunflower and tobacco plants to lose water until the lower (but not the upper) leaves wilted. If these lower leaves were allowed to regain their turgor, the recovery was only apparent, for they died sooner than on control, unwilted plants. Soluble substances, as well as water, moved from these lower leaves to the upper ones during the onset of wilting. Protein was converted to asparagine or glutamine which were translocated to the younger, upper leaves and re-synthesized there to proteins. The injury, according to Mothes, is therefore due not only to the water removal but also to the protein loss. He suggests that wilting may speed up the aging of leaves by decreasing the protein synthesizing power of the chloroplasts.

Much more evidence is needed before such concepts of metabolic drought injury can be accepted as proved. Even Mothes points out that if the young leaves wilt due to a sudden water loss, the protein hydrolysis in the older leaves is less intense, and the wilting injury must be due to some other cause. Most of the experimental work, in fact, has been with drought injury that occurs far too rapdily to be accounted for on a metabolic basis.

DIRECT INJURY

Since the water is taken completely out of the tissues by drought, there is no analogy with intracellular freezing. Similarly, when water is made available again, it is not in immediate contact with the cells as in the case of thawing, but has to penetrate through a surface layer that may be relatively impermeable, thence from cell to cell. In this way the water reaches the cells more gradually than on thawing. The reduction in water content due to drought is also much more gradual than that due to freezing. Consequently, the rates of water loss and uptake are not likely to play so important a role in drought injury as in frost injury, at least in the case of the whole large plant. On the other hand, in small plants or plant parts, and in tissue sections used for artificial tests, speed of water movement may be expected to play a more important role. Schröder (1886) points out that slow water removal allows the plant to go over into a resistant, resting state; but if the plant is already in this state, he believes that rate of drying is of no importance. Thus, a shoot of *Grimmia pulvinata* was quickly made powder-dry by moving air previously dried over $CaCl_2$ and H_2SO_4 at 35 to 40°C. This drying was continued for 18 hours; yet, on remoistening, the shoot was completely alive. Similarly, he concluded that there is usually no difference in survival whether the water is added slowly or rapidly. If the plants were alive in the dried state, they remained alive whether moistened rapidly or slowly; if they were injured, slow remoistening failed to help. Under natural conditions, he points out, plants are rapidly remoistened by rain.

On the other hand, the rapid addition of water to dried seedlings has frequently been reported to be more harmful than gradual moistening, though different workers have obtained different results. Rabe (1905) explains the discrepancy by the harmful effect of fungus growth during the slow moistening. In the case of mosses (Irmscher, 1912), more rapid drying by placing immediately in a desiccator was more injurious than drying first in air, then in a desiccator; but the same amount of injury resulted, whether the addition of water was slow or rapid. Höfler (1942) confirmed the protective effect on liverworts of slow drying and in some cases of slow remoistening (1942). Allowing them to take up water slowly from saturated air enabled them to survive a relative humidity of 72 to 77%, though they were killed by relative humidities of 86 to 88% if remoistened directly in water. But this was true of only two species; others showed little difference. Both slow and rapid drying gave rise to the same differential response between species.

In sections, Iljin (1933) found that the dried cells were killed if plunged directly into water, but they survived if allowed to take up water slowly from a saturated atmosphere. Rapid drying (within a period of minutes or even seconds) immediately killed 6 out of 10 species tested (Table 87). The remaining species died after longer

TABLE 87
Percent of living cells after different methods of drying (from Iljin, 1935a)

Species	No. days kept dry	Dried in air		Dried in sugar solutions	
		Rapid	Gradual	Rapid	Gradual
Syringa vulgaris	3	0	45	85	100
	7	0	25	80	100
Centaurea scabiosa	3	0	0	20	100
	7	0	0	0	100
Ligustrum vulgare	3	0	0	100	100
	6	0	0	25	25
Buxus sempervirens	3	0	0	0	100
	7	0	0	0	5
Berteroa incana	2	50	100	100	100
	6	0	20	5	20
Bupleurum falcatum	3	65	100	100	100
	7	5	85	5	20

periods of time in the dried state (1 hr to a few days). Gradual drying resulted in better survival but in some cases, best results were obtained when they were dried at intermediate rates (during 14 hr). The injury increased with the time in the dry state (Table 87) even after equilibrium had been attained. These results are far more significant than earlier reports (Rabe, 1905) which gave no evidence that equilibrium had been reached. Irmscher (1912) showed that mosses suffer greater injury from repeated drying and wetting than from a single continuous desiccation.

All these results, though far less numerous, agree admirably with those for frost injury—even to the extent of the discrepancies. Thus, not only are the same time factors operative in drought as in frost injury; but the same qualifications must be added—e.g. some plants are so hardy that they are uninjured by any kind of drought treatment and therefore the time factor does not apply to them. The moment of injury in both frost and drought may occur, therefore, during either drying or remoistening. Injury during remoistening was observed directly by Iljin in those cases in which pseudoplasmolysis occurred followed by pseudodeplasmolysis leading to cell rupture (Fig. 26). The possibility that, as in the case of post-thawing, injury may occur after turgor is regained, has not, as yet, been adequately studied.

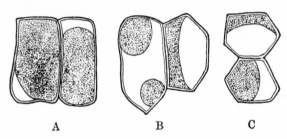

A   B   C

Fig. 26. Pseudoplasmolysis of dried cells on transfer to water. (A) *Cirsium canum*, (B) *Rhoeo discolor*, (C) *Tradescantia Fluminensis*. Protoplast torn into two fragments in *B* (from Iljin, 1933).

As in frost injury, drought injury can be prevented by protective solutions. Rabe (1905) showed that though the sporelings of certain fungi do not normally withstand drying, they survive month-long dehydration in concentrated sucrose and dextrose solutions (except when these contained considerable amounts of inorganic salt). The most thorough investigation of this phenomenon was made by Iljin (1927, 1930, 1933, 1935a). He found that the degree of drying tolerated by the tissues is proportional to the concentration of the protective solution used (Table 88). Similar results were obtained with several different plants, and salt solutions were just as effective, though (in agreement with Rabe) injurious after a long time. Otherwise, the length of time the cells were kept in the solutions had no effect on the results. The solutions plas-

TABLE 88

Survival of mesophyll cells of Iris in protective solutions of different concentrations. Sections left in solutions for 24 hr, then kept for 2 days in chambers of different relative humidities (from Iljin, 1927)

Solution (M glucose)	Minimum relative humidity survived
0.0	>99
0.1	97
0.2	93
0.5	90

molyzed the cells, and, according to Iljin, the protective effect was proportional to the degree of plasmolysis. When epidermal sections were gradually transferred from weak sucrose solutions to stronger ones and then blotted, they could be exposed to lower and lower humidities and even finally dried in a desiccator over concentrated H_2SO_4 without injury. They survived for weeks or even four months in this condition— the plasmolyzed protoplasts had a regular shape, and the sap retained its color. Iljin concluded that plant protoplasm can withstand complete drying in all except those cells having a high vacuolar content.

There is no question of the validity of Rabe's (1905) results, since he actually grew the germinated spores after their drought treatment. Iljin, however, accepted plasmolysis (usually in 2.7M sucrose) and dye retention as proof positive of survival. By this method, he even produced evidence (1933, 1935) that the protection could be obtained by adding the solutions to the already dried sections. It was shown earlier (Chapter 1) that his similar results in frost injury could not be repeated by others and was interpreted by them as due to tonoplast survival. He, himself, states (1933) that the outer protoplasm is more easily destroyed by desiccation than is the tonoplast. And even when the cells deplasmolyze completely, he observed that death may occur after deplasmolysis is complete. He clearly demonstrated that the plasmolyzed cells are often abnormal, for sometimes pseudoplasmolysis persisted for 1 to 2 hr before deplasmolysis could occur. Obviously the protoplast was prevented from expanding by a rigid surface layer. As further evidence against this method, even those cells of *Helodea canadensis* that appear normal some time after deplasmolysis may still be injured, according to Walter (1929), and may die after a few days.

It can be seen from these facts that Iljin estimated survival on the basis of incompletely killed cells; and when he speaks of 100% survival he may really mean that 100% of the cells were incompletely killed. This may not detract from the validity of many of his conclusions, assuming that the degree of injury to the protoplasm parallels the degree of injury to the plant. In favor of this assumption are the following results. After very severe drying, the cells died immediately on transfer to water; after less severe drying they showed pseudodeplasmolysis and died shortly after swelling was complete; after intermediate severities of drying they died during pseudodeplasmolysis. This parallels the response of the plant as a whole to different degrees of drying, but more severe drying is required to kill the cell completely than to kill the plant completely. His results, therefore, apparently give an exaggerated picture of the drought hardiness of the plant and even of the protoplasm. His statement that the protoplasm of growing plants can withstand complete drying cannot be accepted in the sense that the protoplasm remains fully alive and functional and can resume normal growth. Thus Kaltwasser (1938) was unable to obtain any protection against drought injury by Iljin's method of applying protective solutions to the dried tissues. He judged injury not by plasmolysis, but by the effect on assimilation rate which was followed for eight days after the reabsorption of water. Iljin (1935) himself showed that his method does not work with some species, so Kaltwasser's negative results may not detract from Iljin's positive results. More experiments such as Kaltwasser's are needed, however, using categoric tests of survival.

Drought plasmolysis is no more to be expected during the dehydration process than is frost plasmolysis (Chapter 5), since there is no solution to enter between the wall and protoplast. The appearance of the dried cell has been described by many. According to Schröder (1886), it loses its transparency on drying and air enters. Dried Grimmia leaves, when mounted in oil, showed many folds in the cell wall. In places where the wall was no longer able to follow the collapsing protoplast, air penetrated the cell. Immediately after remoistening, an air bubble could be seen in each cell. It rapidly rounded up, became smaller, and in a short time disappeared. The protoplasm refilled the cell and full turgor was quickly regained. In other plants the process took longer. Steinbrinck (1900, 1903, 1906) also showed that instead of the protoplasm separating from the wall during desiccation, the cell wall is pulled in with the cell contents. As a result, folds and concavities arise, and finally the opposite walls meet (Fig. 27). If folds are absent, it is

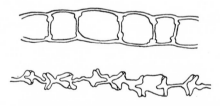

Fig. 27.   Folded and collapsed cells in desiccated leaf of *Mnium punctatum* (below) compared with turgid state (above) (from Steinbrinck, 1903).

due to the rigidity of the wall or, as in many pith tissues, to the surrounding rigid cover that opposes a volume decrease. The addition of water returns the cells to their original volume. As shown by Schröder and others (Thoday, 1922), this may occur without injury. Folds do not occur in the case of thick-walled cells, such as in some mosses (Steinbrinck, Laué, 1938). It is in such cells that the protoplasm apparently contracts from the wall in places, forming the air pockets earlier observed in Grimmia by Schröder (1886) and later by Holle (1915). Iljin (1927) also noticed a partial separation of plasma from cell wall, but nothing that he could call plasmolysis. Holle (1915) showed that plasmolysis may occur at the locus of a cut due to the concentration of sap exuded from the cut cells, which can then plasmolyze the uninjured cells. This may be the basis of the assumption that drought plasmolysis occurs (Livingston, 1911; Caldwell 1913). If the sections are first rinsed with water, plasmolysis is avoided (Holle, 1915).

The actual degree of contraction normally suffered by the leaves of plants exposed to drought is clearly evident from Schratz's (1931) measurements on a small-leaved xerophyte (Table 89). On progressive drying, the leaves turn yellow brown, shrivel up, and become brittle. They are then in their rest period. Schratz compared these with the leaves of control bushes which had been continuously supplied with sufficient water so that the leaves had their maximum possible water content. The reduction in size of the individual cells on drying varies with the tissue and the kind of plant (Table 90). Moss cells and cells of storage tissue (e.g. in seeds) undergo only a 1.5-fold reduction in diameter. At

TABLE 89

Comparative leaf measurements on normal (i.e. droughted) and control (watered) plants of *Covillea tridentata* (from Schratz, 1931)

Quantity measured	Control leaves	Normal leaves	Ratio, normal: control
Water content (% fresh wt)	58	32	0.55
Water content (% of dry wt)	139	47	0.34
Leaf thickness (mm)	0.206	0.120	0.58
Leaf surface (cm²)	0.540	0.240	0.44
Leaf volume (cm³)	0.0111	0.0029	0.26

TABLE 90

Reductions in cell dimensions on drying (from Iljin, 1930)

Species	Ratio of original dimension to dimension after drying		
	Diameter	Surface	Volume
Pelargonium stem	8.9 – 9.3		7.3 – 9.0
Red beet root	5.4 – 7.5	4.8 – 5.3	5.0 – 6.6
Pea seeds	1.4	1.5	
Bean seeds	1.5	1.7	
Moss leaves (5 species)	1.3 – 1.5	1.7 – 2.3	1.8 – 3.1

the other extreme are the pith cells of Pelargonium. On drying, they undergo a 9-fold reduction in diameter.

The tensions that the desiccated cells are subjected to are evident from Chu's (1936) "suction force" measurements on conifer leaves. The threshold for death occurred at values of 50 to 75 atm in summer, 300 atm in winter. Since the "suction force of the cell contents" (i.e. their osmotic potentials) never exceeded 50 atm, negative wall pressures must have been responsible for the high values. The largest of Blum's (1937) values (17.9 to 73.4 atm) in dry regions must also have been due to negative wall pressures. Holle (1915) had previously recorded a value of 20 atm for leaves of *Catharinea undulata;* in the epidermis of *Rochea falcata,* the tensions during pronounced wilting split and lifted the cuticle.

Chapter 18.

The Measurement and Meaning of Drought Hardiness

METHODS OF MEASUREMENT

Under Maximov's direction, Tumanov (1927) measured drought hardiness by leaving plants unwatered for two weeks in the greenhouse, then watering them and determining survival. More recently, this method has been largely replaced by use of droughting chambers (Bayles *et al.*, 1937; Shirley and Meuli, 1939; Kenway and Peto, 1939; Dexter, 1942; Platt and Darroch, 1942; Mueller and Weaver, 1942; Carroll, 1943; McAlister, 1944). But no standardization of procedure has been adopted. As an example, Carroll exposed his plants to a relative humidity of 20% at 35 to 37°C for 12 to 24 hr in a draft oven. Others have used different combinations of humidity, temperature, and time. Consequently, only relative hardiness can be evaluated in this way, and the results of one investigator cannot be directly compared with those of another.

Since the whole plant is used in the above two methods, there can be no assurance that vapor pressure equilibrium with its environment is attained. This is unlikely even in the case of thin leaves, due to morphologic protection against water loss and the transfer of water from other parts of the plant or from the soil. For more accurate determinations, which can be put on a quantitative basis, it is necessary to use tissue sections that come to equilibrium relatively rapidly with the surrounding air, due to their small size, large specific surface, and lack of a protective layer to impede the movement of water. Earlier tests estimated the effects on survival of large differences in relative humidity. Mosses, for instance, remained alive at relative humidities of 50 to 60% but failed to survive drying over sulfuric acid (Schröder, 1886; Irmscher, 1912). More recently, a graded series of solutions has been adopted and the sections are placed in small chambers and allowed to come to equilibrium with the atmosphere directly above these solutions (Iljin, 1927, 1930, 1933, 1935). In order to maintain a constant relative humidity, the chambers are opened only when the sections are put in and after 24 to 48 hr, when they are removed. The sections are immediately transferred to hypertonic sugar solutions containing neutral red, and after some time examined for living cells. In this way the relative humidity that is just sufficient to cause drought killing is more accurately determined (Table 88), and the range of drought hardiness among the different species of an order is readily shown (Table 91).

Another method, developed by Walter (1931), is to determine the "maximum osmotic value"—i.e. to dry the tissues until the killing point is reached and then to calculate the osmotic potential of the cell sap from the freezing point lowering. The greater the drought hardiness, the

TABLE 91

Drought hardiness of different species of liverworts determined by survival in chambers of different relative humidities (from Höfler, 1942, 1942a)

Species	Minimum desiccation causing complete killing	
	H_2SO_4 (%)	Relative humidity (%)
Lophozia incisa	10	95.0
Aplozia riparia	15	91.3
Calypogeia neesiana	20	87.0
Chiloscyphus rivularis	25	81.9
Chiloscyphus palescens	30	75.0
	35	66.2
Aplozia caespiticia	40	56.5
Metzgeria pubescens, Lophozia quinquedentata, Scapania nemerosa	50	36.4
Plasiochila asplenioides-maior, Ptilidium pulcherrimum	60	15.4
	80	1.0
Frullania dilatata	100	0.0
Modotheca platyphylla Cololeugenia calcarea	not killed even at 0% relative humidity	

larger is this "maximum osmotic value." It should be possible to compare this value directly with that obtained by the relative humidity test, since the one is readily converted into the other.

The above two methods measure the intensity of dehydration—i.e. the activity of the water remaining in the tissues at the drought killing point. Many workers have preferred to measure the quantity of dehydration—i.e. the percent of the plant's water that must be removed in order to kill it (Table 84). Tumanov (1930) adopted this method to investigate the effect of various factors on drought hardiness. Kisselew (1935) dried leafy twigs to different degrees then transferred them to water. After 24 hr he observed them for survival. An interesting method that he also used to identify the death point was to measure the "suction force" of the tissues. This value rose gradually with water loss until the death point was reached, when it gave a sudden jump upward. Höfler *et al.* (1941) elaborated on this water loss method by determining the water deficit (see Stocker, 1929) at the drought killing point. In order to obtain this value—which they call the critical saturation deficit—they determine the dry weight at the end of the experiment, and the saturation weight on duplicate branches. From these, they calculate the percent critical saturation deficit as follows:

$$\text{c.s.d.} = \frac{\text{saturation wt} - \text{fresh wt at critical pt}}{\text{saturation wt} - \text{dry wt}} \times 100$$

No one method has succeeded in giving generally uniform results. Tumanov (1927) found that the order of injury as a result of artificial wilting agreed in most cases with field experiences (Table 92). More

TABLE 92

Drought resistance of summer wheats according to field survival and survival of permanent wilting (from Tumanov, 1927)

Variety	Line	Field survival (Pisarew)		Survival of permanent wilting (Tumanov)
		1919	1920	
Ferrugineum rossicum	Tulun 81/4	72.6	67	90
Ferrugineum rossicum	Tulun 120/32	77.4	75	94
Ferrugineum rossicum	Tulun 916/4	50.0	67	50
Pseudohostianum	Prélude	8.1	43	49
Lutescens	Marquis	3.1	43	77
Anglicum	Pusa 4	5.5	20	23
Ferrugineum rossicum	Tulun 324	2.9	—	42

recent results with the drought chambers have also sometimes given good agreement with field survival (Shirley and Meuli, 1939). But Maximov (1929) admits that such methods cannot entirely replace field tests, and many workers have amply borne him out. Field performance of fruit trees parallels water loss (Table 93) and is therefore no indication of drought hardiness. Xerophytic varieties of oats, wheat, and barley develop better in the field than hygrophytic varieties and show less difference between growth under favorable and unfavorable moisture conditions (Binz, 1939). Yet when sections are tested in drying chambers, no difference in the degree or time of injury can be distinguished between them. Drought chambers have also failed to yield results in agreement with field behavior (Kenway, Peto, and Neatby, 1942); Platt and Darroch, 1942; Cook, 1943; Milthorpe, 1950). It has, of course, long been known that many xerophytes have developed methods of reducing water loss and increasing water absorption, and may therefore possess little or no drought hardiness (Maximov, 1929, 1929a).

TABLE 93

Wilting resistance and water retaining power of Crimean almond leaves
(from Eremejev, 1938)

Variety	Original water content (% of d.w.)	Final water content (% of d.w.)	% recovery	Field estimate
53	195	116	100	most resistant
50	200	80	75	resistant
174	168	62	61	fairly resistant
175	158	65	42	fairly resistant
44	154	47	5	nonresistant
180	137	28	9	nonresistant

The effect of environment on drought hardiness has not received as much attention as its effect on frost hardiness. But the evidence that is available all points to the same relationship. Tumanov (1927) showed that repeated wilting increases the yield of grains grown under conditions of drought. It also increases the hardiness of lower plants such as mosses (Irmscher, 1912) and liverworts (Höfler, 1942). Iljin (1933) found that cabbages grown under cool and dry conditions were not killed until the relative humidity of their tissues dropped to 90%; those grown in a warm greenhouse were killed at 95 to 96%. Kisselew (1935) showed that Scorzoneras survive a greater loss of water during the drier month of July than in June. Whiteside (1941) obtained similar results with wheats. Pisek and Larcher (1954) have recently shown the same fall increase in drought hardiness of evergreens to a winter maximum as in the case of frost hardiness. Tumanov (1930) was unable to find any effect of mineral nutrition on drought hardiness, but shading reduced it. All these results emphasize the essentiality of a prehardening treatment before comparing the drought hardiness of varieties or species. This fact has not received sufficient attention in such tests, though some have attempted to take it into account.

TERMINOLOGY

Due to this frequent discrepancy between field survival and drought hardiness, there is much more confusion in terminology than in the case of frost hardiness. The term drought resistance has been most commonly used in a generic, all-inclusive sense to describe all plants suitable for cultivation in dry conditions, no matter what the mechanism (Maximov, 1929; Raheja, 1951). Yet there is some tendency (sometimes by the same people) to use it in a more restricted sense. Tumanov (1927) states that drought-resistant forms can tolerate permanent wilting without injury for longer times than nonresistant forms. Maximov (1929) repeatedly points out that "the capacity to endure without injury an intense loss of water is one of the most important properties of true drought resistant plants." In agreement with the general meaning, Stocker (1947) defines drought resistance quantitatively as the ratio of the yield under dry conditions to the yield under optimal conditions of water supply. This differs from Maximov's interpretation by placing the emphasis on ability to grow and develop rather than ability to survive. He then subdivides drought resistance into two classes: (a) protoplasmic—the ability to remain alive at a low water potential, and (b) constitutional—the ability to maintain its protoplasm at a higher water potential than that of the atmosphere. The former would be similar to Maximov's "true" drought resistance, and to our drought hardiness.

Iljin (1931) introduced the term "desiccation resistance" (*Austrocknungsfähigkeit*) and defined it as the lowest relative humidity with which the plant can come to equilibrium without suffering injury. One obvious disadvantage of this is the inverse relation between the numerical value and the resistance. Migsch (see Höfler *et al.*, 1941) adopted the same term but defined it as the water loss that a plant can withstand without injury, and expressed it as a percentage of the saturation content. Later, Höfler *et al.* (1941) call this the critical saturation deficit (see above). Thus the term desiccation resistance is used in two fundamentally different senses: the one based on the water potential, the other on the quantity of water in the plant at the killing point.

By analogy with the terminology used for frost hardiness, the following system seems logical. The term drought resistance has been used by so many investigators in so many ways, that the original use in a generic, all-inclusive sense seems the only logical one. The term drought hardiness will be used for the specific property that is analogous to frost hardiness. Just as, in practice, frost hardiness is measured by determining the frost killing temperature, drought hardiness may be measured by determining the drought killing relative humidity—i.e. the relative humidity that causes killing of about 50% of the cells. Good agreement can be obtained between the frost killing and drought killing values if the drought killing relative humidity is expressed as a saturation deficit; since a freezing point lowering of 1°C is equivalent to an osmotic value of 12 atm, and a saturation deficit of 1% to a value of about 13 atm.

For a more exact definition of frost hardiness, the freezing point of the cell sap in the turgid plant had to be subtracted from the frost killing temperature. In the same way, the relative humidity of the cell sap in the turgid plant must be subtracted from the drought killing relative humidity to give a more accurate value for drought hardiness. The similarity between the two quantities can be seen from the definitions:

The frost hardiness of a plant is the number of degrees that the frost killing temperature is below the freezing point of the cell sap of the turgid plant.

The drought hardiness of a plant is the number of percent that the drought killing relative humidity is below the relative humidity in equilibrium with the cell sap of the turgid plant.

The following are some advantages of these definitions:

(a) Each quantity is easily obtained from two simple measurements.

(b) The value for plants killed by the first touch of frost or drought is zero and it increases progressively for those that survive increasing freezing or droughting of their tissues.

(c) The two sets of values are closely comparable and are inversely related to the activity of the water remaining in the tissues at the killing point.

Since relative humidity is a quantity that is markedly affected by temperature, the drought hardiness values should be determined at a constant temperature, e.g. at 25 or 30°C.

From the same two experimentally determined values as are used for measuring hardiness, tolerance of dehydration can also be calculated. Thus for hardiness:

$$H_f = \Delta_o - \Delta_k \tag{7}$$

$$H_d = R_o - R_k \tag{8}$$

and for tolerance of dehydration:

$$D_f = \frac{C_{fk}}{C_o} \tag{9}$$

$$D_d = \frac{C_{dk}}{C_o} \tag{10}$$

where H_f = frost hardiness, H_d = drought hardiness, D_f = tolerance of frost dehydration, D_d = tolerance of drought dehydration, Δ_k = frost killing temperature, Δ_o = freezing point of cell sap in the turgid plant, R_k = drought killing relative humidity, R_o = relative humidity of cell sap in the turgid plant, C_o = cell sap concentration in the turgid plant, C_{fk} = cell sap concentration at the frost killing point, C_{dk} = cell sap concentration at the drought killing point.

Drought hardiness, as defined above, is a quantitative measure of Maximov's "true or physiological drought resistance" and Stocker's "protoplasmic drought resistance," properties that were not put on any quantitative basis by the authors. It also measures the same property as Iljin's desiccation resistance, in contrast to Iljin's numerical values which are inversely related to the property. Tolerance of drought dehydration is equal to the saturation water content divided by the water content at the critical point, and can therefore be obtained from Höfler, Migsch, and Rottenberg's (1941) direct measurements, as well as from the defining ratio.

Chapter 19.

The Relation of Drought Hardiness to Growth and Development

De Saussure (1827) clearly showed that the drought hardiness of seedlings decreases with the progress of development (Table 94). Similar results (Table 95) were obtained by Rabe (1905) and Milthorpe (1950), though a xerophyte (Sedum) was able to survive drying for two months in all three stages of development (Rabe, 1905). Another drop occurs in later stages, from a maximum osmotic potential of 63 and 76 atm for oats and wheat in the early stages of growth to 32 and 40 atm

TABLE 94
Survival of drought by seedlings at different stages of development
(from de Saussure, 1827)

Plant	Germination stage	Drying treatment	Survival
Wheat	I. (radicle half the length of the grain)	35°C for several days then free air for several weeks. Total time 2½ months.	Normal growth
	II. (radicle equal to or longer than the grain, plumule 3 mm long)	Same as above	Normal growth of plumules; radicles dead
	III. (whole plumule emerging)	Same as above	Slow growth if only base of plant in contact with water
Oats (glumes removed)	I.	3-wk drying	Recovered
	II. III.	3-wk drying	All failed to recover

TABLE 95
Resistance of Avena seedlings to drying in air for three weeks (from Rabe, 1905)

Stage	% survival
I. 1 root 5–10 mm. long	84
II. 1–3 roots 15–20 mm long	65
III. 1–3 roots 30–40 mm long	20

160

at heading time (Binz, 1939). Brounov (see Maximov, 1929) applied the term "critical period" to the stage of development at which the plant is particularly susceptible to injury. This period occurred during the rapid internode growth that preceded heading in cereals. Moliboga (1927, see Maximov, 1929) showed that the critical degree of wilting for this period, did little harm in earlier or later stages.

Within a single plant, the younger tissues are more hardy than the older—e.g. in the plumules of seedlings (Rabe, 1905), the dormant buds of mosses (Irmscher, 1912), and the younger parts of liverworts (Höfler, 1942, 1942a). But it may not always be drought hardiness that is involved, for Pringsheim (1906) found a movement of water from older to younger parts on wilting. This protected the younger parts longer and permitted them to develop further. In many cases, the water in the stems moved directly to the growing points and the fully developed leaves were sacrified, sometimes even before drying up (e.g. Sedum, Erica, Bryophyllum, Euphorbia, etc.). Christ (1911) observed the same phenomenon in beech, oak, and ash trees which retained small rosettes on the ends of twigs; Tumanov (1930) and Clements (1937) describe it in crop plants. Thus, the better survival of drought by younger tissues cannot be accepted as evidence of greater drought hardiness so long as they are still attached to the older tissues. Recent direct determinations have shown that well-ripened, 1- to 2-year leaves of evergreens are more drought hardy than both underdeveloped and overage leaves (Pisek and Larcher, 1954).

The effect of artificial changes in development on drought hardiness has received little attention. According to Parija and Pillay (1945), pre-sowing treatment increases the survival of rice plants subjected to severe wilting, but they indicate that this may be simply due to the alternate wetting and drying. It has already been shown (Chapter 8) that frost hardiness is similarly increased due to the low temperature treatment. The developmental change itself may have the opposite effect both in the case of frost and drought injury. Attempts to improve drought hardiness by preventing growth with naphthalene acetic acid have not been successful (Maki et al., 1946). That the rest period may play a part is indicated by the fact that some "labile" evergreens (Rhododendron ferrugineum and Arctostaphylos uva-ursi) show much more pronounced changes in drought hardiness in response to temperature changes than do the more "stable" conifers during winter (Pisek and Larcher, 1954).

Besides the stage of development, the rate of growth may also be a factor. The inverse correlation between drought hardiness and cell size (Chapter 20) is an indication of this; and so is the greater hardiness of plants grown with low moisture supply (see above).

Chapter 20.

Factors Associated with Drought Hardiness

Those factors that have received the most attention in connection with frost hardiness have also been investigated for possible roles in drought hardiness, though the investigations have been fewer in number. Unfortunately, many of the results are difficult to interpret, since drought hardiness was not measured. Sometimes field performance is recorded, but, as already emphasized, such differences may be completely unaccompanied by differences in drought hardiness.

Morphological factors have been intensively investigated in relation to xerophily (Maximov, 1929) but have received relatively little attention in connection with drought hardiness. Maximov (1929), however, has drawn attention to the extensive work of Kolkunov (1905–1915) which showed a pronounced converse relation between drought resistance and cell size when different varieties of crop plants were compared (wheat, beets, corn—Table 96). Before attempting to interpret these results, Maximov cautions that the early maturation of small-celled plants enables them to escape the drought of late summer, and therefore the relation

TABLE 96

Relation between cell size and yield of beetroots under dry and moist conditions
(from Kolkunov, see Maximov, 1929)

Cell diameter	Average wt of root (g)	
(μ)	Dry year	Humid year
8–11	271.7	—
11–14	172.7	64.3
14–17	67.0	139.2
> 17	33.3	207.6

may be coincidental. Kolkunov explains the small cell size as a means of conserving and improving the water supply of the plant. Maximov discusses the errors on which this explanation is based, and points out that a general ability to endure injurious conditions usually accompanies reduction in cell size. Many others have shown that plants have smaller cells when grown with a reduced water supply (Maximov, 1929). But Iljin (1930) was the first to determine the drought hardiness of the plants whose cells were measured. He concludes (1931) that, in general, drought-hardy plants, such as xerophilic mosses and resting organs of higher plants, have cell volumes of 100-1000 μ^3 compared with an average of 100,000 (and as high as 1-2 million) μ^3 in higher plants. The ratio of volume/surface is an expression of this factor. The smaller the ratio the greater the hardiness. In xerophilic mosses it is 1 to 2 or even lower. In sensitive cells (with a desiccation resistance of 99 to 97%) it is near 20. Cells of intermediate hardiness have ratios of 5 to 10. He points out that small elongated cells with a long vacuole and a visible protoplasm layer are also hardy. When his data (Table 97) are examined, however, an inverse relation between cell size and osmotic value is evident. Since

TABLE 97

Relation between average cell dimensions and drought hardiness
(from Iljin, 1930)

Species	Organ	Drought killing relative humidity (%)	Osmotic value (moles sucrose)	Volume (μ^3)	Volume Surface
Begonia maculata	stem	99	< 0.2	1,690,000	21.4
Clerodendron fragrans	stem	97	0.3	720,000	16.2
Pelargonium zonatum	stem	93	0.4–0.5	885,000	17.2
Nerium oleander	leaf	90	< 0.5	3,600	2.3
Dianthus sp.	leaf	87.5	0.7–0.8	21,660	4.4
Hedera helix	leaf	85	0.85	18,100	4.2
Buxus sempervirens	leaf	85	1.0	6,350	3.1
Mnium hornum	thallus	0	0.7	3,350	2.7

the relation between osmotic value and drought hardiness has been thoroughly established (see below) and may occur independently of any difference in cell size, the inverse relation between cell size and drought hardiness may be coincidental. In agreement with Iljin, Whiteside (1941) has shown that when wheat plants are grown with low moisture, their cells are smaller and they are more drought hardy. Kisselew (1935) found that small leaved forms of Scorzonera survive a greater loss of water than do the broad-leaved forms.

Iljin also considers cell structure important. Thus, elimination of the vacuole by contraction or thickening of the protoplasm (e.g. in Fuligo) or by filling with nondrying substances (seeds and spores) accompanies the development of extreme drought hardiness. Many other drought-hardy cells—e.g. those of leafy mosses and of the meristems of higher plants—have very small vacuoles. Maximov (1929) believes, however, that the physicochemical factors are more important than the morphological and anatomical factors.

There are many reports of an increased osmotic value on exposure to drought (Table 98), though the degree of response varies with both the species and organ (Table 99). All the tissues do not even behave in the same way (Table 100). There is a marked and rapid response to drought

TABLE 98

Observations of a direct relation between osmotic value of cell sap and dryness of habitat (see Maximov, 1929)

Plant	Observer
Cucurbita pepo	Pringsheim, 1906
Plants of Sahara desert	Zalenski, 1909
Desert plants	Fitting, 1911
	Hannig, 1912
	Keller, 1913-14, 1918, 1920
Helianthus annuus, Zea mays, etc.	Iljin *et al.,* 1916
	Maximov and Lominadze, 1916
	Maximov *et al.,* 1917
Various mountain plants	Blagowestchenski, 1926
Various plants	Iljin, 1929
Vicia faba, Trifolium incarnatum, etc.	Simonis, 1952

TABLE 99

Relation of cell sap concentration to soil moisture in different plants and plant parts (from Iljin, 1929)

Soil moisture (%)	Osmotic value (moles sucrose)				
	Roots			Leaves	
	Maize	Wheat	Barley	Wheat	Barley
32	0.240	0.192	0.240	0.200	0.440
27	0.264	0.264	0.272	0.390	0.490
22	0.264	0.304	0.304	0.630	0.588
19	0.272	0.450	0.400	0.784	0.644

TABLE 100

Osmotic values of tissues in leaves of *Hedera helix* before and after drying. Expressed as molarity of sucrose used as plasmolyte (from Beck, 1929)

Tissues	Initial value	Final value	Increase	No. days alive
Upper epidermis	0.675	0.65	—0.025	8+
Lower epidermis	0.75	0.625	—0.125	8+
Palisade cells	1.0	1.6	0.6	4
Spongy parenchyma	0.775	1.3	0.525	5
Conducting parenchyma	1.05	1.35	0.25	3
Guard cells	0.775	0.925	0.15	7

in the palisade cells, the conducting and the spongy parenchyma; a less regular one in the guard cells. The epidermal cells respond very irregularly, and the response may be completely masked by the effects of other factors such as temperature; low temperature increases, high temperature (38°C) decreases the osmotic value under conditions of drought (Beck, 1929). Besides the effect of drought on the osmotic value, there is also an inherent difference between plants that are adapted and those that are not adapted to drought even when growing under the same conditions (Tables 97, 101).

TABLE 101

Osmotic values in leaves of mesophytes and xerophytes. Expressed as molarity of KNO$_3$ used as plasmolyte (from Maximov, 1929)

	Mesophytes	
Erodium ciconium		0.3
Papaver strigosum		0.3
Hirschfeldia adpressa		0.3
Senecio vernalis		0.4
	Succulents	
Sedum maximum		0.15
Sedum oppositifolium		0.15
	Xerophytes	
Artemisia maritima		0.5
Gypsophila acutifolia		0.5
Kochia prostrata		0.6
Centaurea ovina		0.7
Parietaria judaica		0.8
Zygophyllum fabago		0.8
Dianthus fimbriatus		0.9

Since these results were obtained plasmolytically, they cannot be due to a passive loss of water, but must indicate an increase in solute content. Some of the differences may, however, be exaggerated, since KNO$_3$ was used as the plasmolyte. It is now known that cells are somewhat permeable to KNO$_3$, and too high values are therefore obtained (Tadros, 1936). Since hardy cells are more permeable than nonhardy cells, the differences might be spurious. That differences nevertheless do exist is proved by those investigators who used nonpenetrating solutes (such as sucrose) for the plasmolyte (Beck, 1929; Iljin, 1929, 1930; Schmidt, 1939; Whiteside, 1941; Bartel, 1947). Bartel even found the osmotic increase during the droughting of four wheat varieties to parallel their accepted differences in drought resistance, in agreement with Schmidt et al. (1940). In sugar beets, however, the osmotic value was lower in the more resistant variety (Schmidt et al., 1940). Höfler et al., (1941) also found that drought-resistant species, in general, have high osmotic values, though there are exceptions.

Many of the above results must be accepted with caution, however, since most of the investigators failed to measure drought hardiness as distinct from field drought resistance. That osmotic value definitely is a factor, however, is evident from the astonishingly close correlation with Iljin's desiccation resistance (Tables 97, 107). On the other hand. Höfler (1942) later showed that younger parts of liverworts are more drought hardy than older parts, though they frequently have lower osmotic values. It seems obvious, therefore, that in drought hardiness, just as in frost hardiness, cell sap concentration is a factor though not always the deciding one.

The reason for the correlation was already suggested by Rabe's (1905) observation that the drought hardiness of seedlings and sporelings decreases with the progress of germination and exhaustion of reserves. He also found that the storage regions were the most hardy parts of the seedlings. Wilting was soon shown to result in the disappearance of starch (Lundegårdh, 1914; Neger, 1915; Molisch, 1921; Horn, 1923; Ahrns, 1924; Iljin, 1927); Henrici, 1945), accompanied by a sugar increase (Table 102). Even after a 2-hr wilting there was a significant

TABLE 102

Starch → sugar conversion in detached leaves allowed to wilt for 24 hr in the dark compared with similar leaves kept moist for the same time (from Ahrns, 1924)

Species	Treatment	Water content	Starch (parts per thousand)	Total sugar (parts per thousand)
Tropaeolum majus	control	85.92	62.87[*]	101.1
	moist	87.2	40.74	117.4
	dry	79.8	3.28	149.3
Vitis vinifera	control	71.03	47.76	70.33
	moist	72.06	17.80	99.38
	dry	69.75	7.54	110.7
Phaseolus vulgaris	control	79.51	128.1	38.49
	moist	81.7	30.24	130.6
	dry	70.4	12.82	115.9
Helianthus annuus	control	84.8	41.27	52.49
	moist	86.0	16.20	54.85
	dry	77.3		85.45
Pisum sativum	control	82.6	40.65	124.9
	moist	84.2	30.65	127.4
	dry	77.7	13.09	170.4

increase in sugars; and the greater the water loss, the greater the sugar increase (Ahrns). By 24 hr the starch had completely disappeared and sugars reached their maximum. A reabsorption of water by the wilted leaves resulted in a sugar decrease, though no starch formation could be detected. In mesophyll cells, high temperature may produce starch hydrolysis, but water loss is more effective (Kisselew, 1928). Lundegårdh (1914) made the interesting observation that osmotic dehydration has the same effect (Table 103). Leaves floated on 40% sugar solutions showed a starch → sugar conversion which was reversed when they were transferred to 10% sugar. By this same method, Iljin (1930a) showed that the degree of dehydration needed to produce the starch → sugar conversion differs with the plant (Table 104).

TABLE 103

Effect of osmotic dehydration on starch content of leaves of *Homalia trichomanoides*
(from Lundegårdh, 1914)

Conc. of glucose in external solution (%)	Starch content after 24 hr	Plasmolysis
15	much	none
20	some	insignificant
25	traces	slight
30	none	considerable
35	none	strong
40	none	strong

TABLE 104

Concentration of sucrose just sufficient to prevent starch formation in leaf pieces floated on solutions (containing 0.06M dextrose) for 36 hr in diffuse light (from Iljin, 1930a)

Aquatic plants	0.46–0.96M
Meadow plants	0.76–0.96
Forest plants	0.66–1.06
Sand plants	1.06–1.46
Rock plants	1.06–1.26

Many others reported an increase in sugar content on exposure to drought (Rosa, 1921; Iljin, 1927, 1929a; Vassiliev and Vassiliev, 1936; Clements, 1937a; Miller, 1939; Julander, 1945). Iljin (1929a) also showed that when plants are grouped ecologically, their sugar content increases with the dryness of the habitat. Though these differences were unaccompanied by measurements of drought hardiness, the conditions were the same as had previously been shown to increase drought hardiness (Chapter 18). The sugar increase is easily understood, since the reduced moisture stops or at least decreases growth, without having as much effect on photosynthesis (see Chapter 16). Consequently, carbohydrates must accumulate. Insoluble as well as soluble carbohydrates may increase (Willard, 1922; Clements 1937, 1937a; Grandfield, 1943; Eaton and Ergle, 1948). But in most cases, there is a clear increase in sugars without any increase in other carbohydrates, or else the sugar increase exceeds the increase in other carbohydrates (Table 105).

TABLE 105

Effect of 18 days' drought on total carbohydrate and sugar content of wheat plants
(from Vassiliev and Vassiliev, 1936)

Variety	Condition	Water content (relative)	Total carbo- hydrates (mg)	Total sugars (mg)
Kitchener	check	100	118.8	29.9
	droughted	69	98.5	34.7
Gemtchoujina	check	100	97.8	22.6
	droughted	63	98.7	24.9
Caesium —0111	check	100	97.5	17.8
	droughted	62	108.0	29.0
Sarroubra	check	100	90.3	18.3
	droughted	65	107.9	51.4
Erithrospermum —341	check	100	85.1	14.8
	droughted	67	105.2	32.8

Some have failed to find any effect of drought on carbohydrates (Magness et al., 1932; Schneider and Childers, 1941), and wilting has even been reported to produce a decrease in sugars (Barinova, 1937). This decrease, however, has been shown to occur only when wilting is severe enough to produce injury (Vassiliev and Vassiliev, 1936; Henrici, 1946) or when respiration is increased sufficiently to counterbalance the reduced rate of photosynthesis (Chapter 16). Tadros (1936) found that though the freezing point lowerings of Egyptian desert plants are large, this is mainly due to electrolytes. But these plants grow under special conditions. The annual rainfall is less than two inches, and as a result most of the plant body is subterranean. Consequently, the relatively small amount of photosynthate formed per plant must be quickly used up by the large root system, and no accumulation of sugars can occur. Furthermore, in many cases the plants were growing on somewhat saline soils.

Fitting gives two explanations of the role of high cell sap concentration in drought resistance: (1) an increased water absorbing power, and (2) a reduced water loss. The erroneous bases of these explanations are fully discussed by Maximov (1929), though he does not completely reject them. But such roles would, of course, have no bearing on drought hardiness, with which osmotic value seems definitely correlated. Maximov (1929) suggests two other explanations: (1) the accumulation of substances might protect the protoplasm from coagulation and desiccation, (2) the high concentration might prevent visible wilting for a long time, in spite of an increasing water deficit. Thus, xerophytes wilt only after loss of 30 to 40% of their water content, delicate shade plants (e.g. some of the Balsaminaceae) after loss of 1 to 2%. But the latter difference is more likely due to differences in physical properties of the cell wall.

Increased bound water has been correlated with drought hardiness (Rosa, 1921; Tumanov, 1927; Newton and Martin, 1930; Calvert, 1935; Barinova, 1937; Migahid, 1938; Grandfield, 1943); but Whitman (1941) failed to obtain any consistent difference. The same objections may be raised as against the correlations between bound water and frost hardiness (Chapter 10). A good example is given by Migahid (1938). He compared the bound water in two mesophytes (*Vinca rosea* and *Withania somnifera*) with that in four xerophytes (*Zygophyllum coccinium, Peganum harmala, Pulicaria crispa,* and *Stachys aegyptiaca*). His method was to measure the water lost from the air-dry shoots (intact or ground) on oven drying. According to his data, the water remaining may be four times as much in the xerophytes as in the mesophytes. Unfortunately, aside from his neglect to measure drought hardiness, his results are due to the same error in calculation as was made in frost hardiness investigations (Chapter 10): the bound water is expressed as a percent of the original water. When, however, the bound water per gram dry matter is calculated from his figures, it is found to be 0.15–0.17 g for the mesophytes, 0.12–0.27 g for the four xerophytes. His large differences are obviously due to the much lower original water contents of the xerophytes—as low as 51.9% compared with 87–87.5% in the mesophytes.

Rao *et al.* (1949, 1949a) show a relation between drought resistance and the amount of water taken up by the dried leaf tissue from an atmosphere of 0.5 relative humidity. But no attempt was made to measure drought hardiness, and the relation with rate of growth was just as good. As in the case of frost hardiness, the only evidence that appears to apply to the protoplasm rather than the nonprotoplasmic contents is the previously described increase in the water-holding power of the dry matter of Aspergillus mycelium with the concentration of the medium in which the organism is grown (Chapter 10). Northen (1943) arrived at the same conclusion from indirect evidence. When species of Mnium and Bryum were dried for periods up to 50 min over an-hydrous $CaSO_4$, thus producing "incipient drought," there was a decrease in structural viscosity which he ascribed to protein dissociation. He con-cluded that this assumed protein dissociation induced an increased proto-plasmic swelling pressure.

The relation of metabolism to drought hardiness has received little attention. According to Raheja (1951), sugarcane varieties with lower respiratory activity are more drought resistant in the field.

Investigators have recently turned to protoplasmic factors (see Chap-ter 13) as possible causes of drought hardiness. Levitt and Scarth (1936) found an increase in permeability to urea of more than 100 percent in cells of Spartium plants unwatered for 14 days. Whiteside (1941) ob-served an increase to three times in two wheat varieties droughted for 12 days. During this time he showed that the desiccation resistance of the cells increased from a threshold humidity corresponding to an os-motic potential of 45 to 60 atm to one of about 100 atm.

The Darmstadt workers have obtained results that are not in agree-ment with the above. The permeability of droughted and moist grown *Lamium maculatum* plants was determined by Schmidt (1939) using both the deplasmolysis and plasmometric methods. The droughted plants proved to be of the "glycerin type" (more permeable to glycerin than to urea), the moist grown plants of the "urea type" (more permeable to urea than to glycerin). But this difference was not constant, since the droughted plants were converted to the "urea type" in the fall. The droughted plants were less permeable to urea, thiourea, methylurea, malonamid, and lactamid than were the moist-grown plants, but more permeable to ethylene glycol, glycerine, and erythrite.

Schmidt explains the reduction in amide permeability on the basis of the ultrafilter theory of permeability, i.e., as due to a decrease in size of the pores of the plasma membrane. The increase in alcohol permeability he explains by an increase in lipid permeability. On the basis of con-clusions of other workers he suggests that the surface lipids are more basic in the droughted plants, more acid in the moist-grown plants.

The permeability results of Schmidt et al. (1940) are confined to oats, since wheat failed to give significant differences and the beet cells were too small for experimentation. The resistant variety had a higher perme-ability to water, urea, and glycerin than the tender variety. Yet droughted plants showed a decrease in water and urea permeability and an increase in glycerin permeability. But not all the results agreed with this general-ization. Thus potassium-deficient and nitrogen-deficient plants when droughted had a higher water permeability than when grown with adequate moisture. Unfortunately, these results with oats are meaningless as far as drought hardiness is concerned, since Stocker *et al.* (1943) showed that the drought-resistant variety owed its resistance to a larger root system, a higher osmotic potential, and other similar factors. They gave no direct evidence of any superiority in drought hardiness. Stocker concludes that drought hardening decreases permeability to water and urea, but that "genetic" drought resistance is associated with higher permeability to these substances. Since genetically controlled differences in protoplasmic drought resistance may be evident only following a period of drought hardening, it is inconceivable that the two should be associated with opposite permeability differences. To add to the confusion, the Darmstadt workers conclude that the "genotypic" and "phenotypic" drought resistance are both associated with the same viscosity increase (see below), yet the former involves high permeability to water and urea, the latter low permeability. Their own results do not uphold such conclusions, since potassium-deficient and nitrogen-deficient plants showed an increase in permeability when droughted. This is in agreement with the results obtained by Levitt and Scarth (1936), and by Whiteside (1941). Furthermore, Whiteside showed that the cells he used simultaneously increased in drought hardiness. In view of the fact that the Darmstadt workers in no case determined drought hardiness, the likeliest explanation of their series of opposite permeability relationships is that in some cases they were dealing with drought hardiness, in other cases they were not.

Schmidt (1939) determined the protoplasmic viscosity of *Lamium maculatum* and oat plants (Schmidt *et al.*, 1940) in the droughted and moist-grown condition. Using the plasmolysis-time method he found that the droughted plants had two to three times the protoplasmic viscosity of those grown with adequate moisture. The centrifugal method gave similar results (2 to 2.3 times). As he points out, the higher viscosity may be purely physical, as a result of the increase in osmotic potential of the cell sap, causing a dehydration of the protoplasm. Increases in both protoplasmic viscosity and osmotic value were also obtained by Simonis (1952) in the case of droughted plants. It is interesting to note that Levitt and Siminovitch (1940) obtained similar results when comparing frost-hardy and nonhardy cells, i.e. the lower consistency of the nonhardy cells was obtainable only when these were in equilibrium with a much lower dehydrating force than the hardy cells. However, in the case of sugar beets this complication did not enter, i.e. resistant beets yielded higher viscosity values than tender beets, though the latter had the higher osmotic potential. Five varieties of summer wheat showed the same relation between hardiness and protoplasmic viscosity save that the most tender variety had the highest viscosity. But these varieties were not drought-hardened previous to testing, and their hardiness was not determined. They were simply graded according to the field experience of the grower.

It should be pointed out that the important comparison of viscosities between hardy and sensitive cells is not when these are in the hydrated state but when they are in the dehydrated state. It is only when compared at the same degrees of dehydration that consistent differences between frost-hardy and nonhardy protoplasm can be obtained (Levitt and Siminovitch, 1940), and these are in the opposite direction from those claimed by Stocker for normally hydrated protoplasm. When the cells are highly hydrated, the hardy protoplasm may conceivably have the same, lower, or higher viscosity than nonhardy protoplasm, depending on the degree of hydration and on the balance between structural and true viscosity. In dehydrated protoplasm, only structural viscosity remains.

Much work must be done on the protoplasmic factors before it is safe to make any generalizations. The few reliable determinations indicate that, as in the case of frost hardening, drought hardening increases protoplasmic permeability to polar substances. The effects on protoplasmic viscosity have not been reliably determined.

Chapter 21.

The Mechanism of Drought Injury and Hardiness

Since drought injury occurs at much higher temperatures than frost injury, it is more likely to be metabolic in nature; though, as already pointed out (Chapter 17) it cannot be due to simple starvation. Mothes (1928) concludes that young leaves are more drought resistant than older ones not only because of their higher osmotic values, etc., but also because of their higher protein content, which is well above the minimum necessary for life. He suggests that proteolysis on wilting may be at least partly due to the increased enzyme concentration. As evidence, he points to the less rapid protein breakdown in leaves floated on weaker than in those on stronger sugar solutions. He proposes the following series of changes. Wilting causes proteolysis; the resulting amino acids activate diastase; this produces an increase in soluble carbohydrates which leads to increased respiration. But this series is directly opposed by his own later admission that the proteolysis occurs much more slowly than the starch hydrolysis.

It has already been shown (Chapter 4) that one characteristic of metabolic chilling injury is its greater severity at moderate than at extreme low temperatures. For similar reasons, one would expect a metabolic drought injury to be more severe at moderate than at extreme desiccation. In agreement with this, Mothes states that intermediate aged leaves stand strong wilting better than moderate wilting, due, presumably, to the less intense respiration and proteolysis. But this type of metabolic injury, according to Mothes, occurs only with moderate wilting. It is, therefore, impossible for metabolic changes to occur more rapidly in cells dried over H_2SO_4 than in those dried at relative humidities of 50–60%; yet the former may suffer drought injury though the latter do not (de Saussure, 1827; Schröder, 1886; Iljin, 1931). In general, there is a quantitative relation between the degree of dehydration and the amount of injury. Drought hardiness, for instance, parallels hardiness to osmotic dehydration (Table 106). This relation cannot be explained on a metabolic basis. In most cases, therefore, drought injury cannot be metabolic in nature, either because it occurs too rapidly, or because it occurs at too severe a degree of dehydration to permit the metabolic changes. Even Mothes admits that Iljin's (1927) results cannot be explained on a metabolic basis.

Early implications of mechanical injury can be found in Schröder's statement that resistance must depend on specific properties of the protoplasm. He considered the presence of oil and other reserve substances useful because they prevented too strong cell collapse. Iljin (1927, 1930, 1931, 1935) adopts a completely mechanical explanation of drought injury. He states (1931) that it is not the water loss itself that kills, but the mechanical injuries that accompany drying and remoistening. When

TABLE 106

Drought hardiness and hardiness to osmotic dehydration in sea algae
(from Biebl, 1938)

Region of origin	Maximum concentration of sea water survived for 24 hr (molar)	Minimum relative humidity survived for 13 hr (%)
Deep sea (8–16 m)	1.5–1.6	98.4–96.8
Ebb line (mostly submerged)	1.7–2.2	94.6
Tidal zone (mostly free of the sea)	2.1–> 3.0	88–< 83

a plant part dries, the cells collapse. The protoplasm is pulled inward by the shrinking vacuole, outward by the resisting wall to which it adheres. If the cell wall is sufficiently rigid it opposes the collapse and thereby subjects the protoplasm to a strong tension that may lead to destruction. If the wall is thin and soft, it is pulled together with the vacuole and forms folds and wrinkles. Before regaining their normal size and shape, cells that survive drying are subjected to new mechanical stresses on remoistening, which may lead to death. Iljin's mechanical theory of drought injury is supported by the following facts:

(1) Cell contraction does occur on desiccation (Fig. 23) and the wall is pulled in with the collapsing protoplast (Chapter 17). The cell diameter may be reduced to 1/5 or 1/10 of normal (Iljin, 1931).

(2) Tensions have been measured and are known to reach high values (Chapter 17).

(3) Pieces of torn protoplasm may actually be seen attached to the cell wall during the pseudoplasmolysis following remoistening (Fig. 28).

(4) Plasmolyzing solutions release the walls and prevent tensions. They also prevent drought injury in cells that are normally killed instantaneously by the same drought (see Chapter 17).

(5) Factors that are associated with drought hardiness can be readily explained by this theory. According to Iljin (1930), the amount of tension depends on:

(a) The quantity of water lost. The higher the cell sap concentration, the less the degree of cell collapse. But according to him (1931), this factor operates only at relative humidities above 85%, since the vacuole reaches its minimum volume at this point.

(b) The extent of interface between protoplasm and wall, which is controlled by cell size and structure. Iljin (1931) concludes that the small cell size or large specific surface of hardy plants is one of the most important methods of avoiding the tear during desiccation and re-moistening. For the same reason, the smaller the vacuole, the less the contraction and the greater the drought hardiness. Small cell size is the prevailing factor in cases of extreme hardiness (e.g. mosses), and cell sap concentration plays no significant part since all the water is given up.

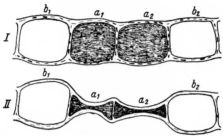

FIG. 28. Approach of opposite walls in desiccated cells of *Mnium undulatum* (II) compared with turgid state (I) (from Iljin, 1930).

(c) Accumulation of carbohydrates and other substances. If these are soluble, the explanation is already given in (a). Insoluble carbohydrates or other substances would also occupy space and reduce cell shrinkage. Iljin (1931) describes an exceptional example of this. The vegetative cells of the fern *Notochlaena marantae* can lose 94% of their water content without injury. Though powder dry, they can regain their normal state within 24 hr of remoistening. He ascribes their extreme hardiness to the fact that the cells retain nearly the same volume when dry as when fully swollen. (Fig. 29). The protoplasm is therefore not subject to severe stresses.

Iljin's theory thus seems capable of explaining all the known facts about drought injury and hardiness. Consequently, most investigators have accepted it as a working hypothesis. Stocker (1947, 1947a) offers Kahl's experiments performed under his direction as support for Iljin's theory, though he interprets the theory in his own way. Kahl found that keeping the plant in a mechanical shaker for a half hour lowered protoplasmic viscosity and increased permeability to water, urea, and glycerin. Hydration capacity, transpiration, and respiration were increased, carbon dioxide assimilation and pH were lowered. Stocker maintains that drought produces the same effects (see Chapter 20).

It has already been shown (Chapter 20) that Stocker and his co-workers produced no evidence of changes in drought hardiness accompanying the protoplasmic changes that he states are characteristic of drought resistance, and that other results with plants whose drought hardiness was measured are diametrically opposed to his. Now it must

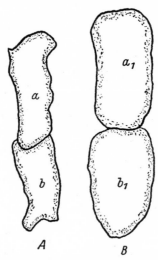

FIG. 29. Relatively small change in cell volume of *Notochlaena marantae* when severely desiccated (*A*) as compared with the turgid state (*B*). Compare with Figs. 27, 28 (from Iljin, 1931).

be emphasized that his mechanical shaking cannot possibly have the same effect on protoplasm as the mechanical drought injury postulated by Iljin. The former involves a rapidly changing multidirectional force acting primarily on the internal protoplasm; the latter is a unidirectional tension acting primarily on the surface layer of the protoplasm. Stocker logically explains the mechanical shaking as producing a thixotropic gel → sol transformation, which can result only from rapid agitation, and not from a slow, steady tension on a dehydrated gel, such as occurs during drought. The kind of mechanical injury that he postulates is therefore basically different from Iljin's. His concept is as follows: desiccation causes mechanical tensions in the protoplasm, due to an unequal hydration capacity of different parts of the protein framework. Sooner or later this causes a loosening and tearing of the network. These protoplasmic changes lead to the following drought reactions:

(a) due to enlargement of the mesh, structural viscosity is lowered, pore permeability is increased, and with it transpiration; (b) by freeing previously joined fibrils, formerly blocked polar and ionizable groups become effective and cause an increased hydration capacity and negative charge of the protoplasm; (c) freeing of enzymes causes an increased respiration and a hydrolytic cleavage; (d) due to a structural injury to the chloroplasts, assimilation is inhibited leading to a lowering of the pH; and (e) the lowering of the pH reduces the potential difference within the protoplasm, the fibrils reapproach each other, and are then able to reform the broken bonds, thus reconstituting the original condition of the protoplasm. This is what he calls the restitution phase.

Rapid water removal, Stocker argues, must produce the first of the above changes. But the drought stimulus is effective only during slow water removal. After reaching a new, lower water equilibrium, the "restitution phase" is attained. Restitution leads to overcompensation of the drought reaction and the plant then enters the hardened condition. This occurs in "dry cultures" that are exposed to continuous strong atmospheric drought. The experimental results obtained by his coworkers applied to this restitution and therefore the results were quite different from those obtained by the shake apparatus, i.e., increased viscosity, lower permeability to water and urea, increased permeability to glycerin. Due to freeing of the blocked polar and ionizable groups, the imbibition capacity of the protoplasm is increased but cannot be satisfied because of the simultaneous water removal. Consequently, there is an increased uptake of bivalent cations (calcium and magnesium) as shown by the reduced ratios of potassium:calcium and potassium:magnesium. Since the bivalent salts of proteins do not dissociate as much as the monovalent, a further decrease in the negative charge of the protoplasmic framework occurs, leading to the restitution phase. In the hardened state, transpiration is decreased due to reduced water permeability. There is also an improved metabolic balance due to inactivation of catabolic enzymes.

Stocker's hypothesis of the fundamental importance of the calcium:potassium ratio as a cause of changes of protoplasmic viscosity and cell permeability is based solely on gross analyses of leaves, which reveal nothing about the ratio of the ions in the protoplasm. Furthermore, his results cannot apply to frost hardiness (and therefore they are almost certain to be inapplicable to drought hardiness), since twigs can be removed from trees and dehardened completely in the laboratory without permitting any total loss or gain of elements (by simply keeping the twigs in a moist atmosphere). It seems certain that drought hardiness can be lost in the same way. Pisek (1950) actually found very little seasonal change in ion content of conifers, though both frost and drought hardiness (Pisek and Larcher, 1954) changed from one extreme to the other. Hardening and dehardening had no influence on the content of individual ions, and both conifers tested had very low quantities of calcium and magnesium. Simonis (1952) also failed to detect any lowering of the potassium:calcium ratio in *Vicia faba* and Roroppa exposed to drought. Werk (1954) has recently found that dry culture actually increases the ratio of potassium:calcium, in opposition to Stocker's results.

Since the protoplasmic and mineral changes on which his theory is based are completely at variance with those found by others and are not even supported by all his own evidence (Chapter 20), it seems unnecessary to consider the theory in more detail until better evidence is produced.

Later results (Table 87), forced Iljin to admit that drought hardiness may involve more than a reduction in the drought-induced tension due to small cell size, high cell sap concentration, etc. He concluded that some protoplasm has a greater ability to withstand desiccation than others, even when the stresses are the same. Earlier (1930), he pointed out that plasmolyzed moss protoplasts show free, ameboid movement inside the cell wall. He suggests that this may explain their ability to tolerate extreme desiccation. Higher plant protoplasts are joined on all sides by plasmodesmata which hold them fast to the cell wall and lead to a tear on plasmolysis.

In contrast to Iljin's concept of protoplasmic differences that would enable survival of more severe stresses, Höfler (1942) attempts to determine whether there can be drought injury without stresses and therefore protoplasmic drought hardiness as distinct from cell drought hardiness. In order to avoid the mechanical injuries described by Iljin, he chose the leafy Jungermanniales. The cell walls of these liverworts are elastically extensible; and instead of being collapsed in folds when the tissues wilt, they closely follow the contracting protoplasts (Laué, 1938). Höfler, therefore, believed that in these cells there is no danger of the protoplasm tearing loose. The wide differences that he found between different species (Table 91) led him to conclude that differences in protoplasmic drought hardiness do exist.

There is little reason to doubt that the absence of plasmodesmata and of folds in the dried cells of liverworts reduces the stresses below those in desiccated cells of higher plants. But it is highly doubtful that stresses can be completely absent. Höfler, himself (1942), was forced to admit that at least some of these liverworts must be injured by mechanical stresses, since speed of drying and remoistening had such a pronounced effect on their survival. In a later paper (1950) he is careful to point out that since 1943 he has been remoistening the cells gradually by allowing them to take up water from moist air, in order to avoid danger of mechanical injury. In those cases where the speed of drying and remoistening had little effect, he concluded that the constancy of the critical relative humidities for each species indicated that protoplasmic hardiness was involved. Other experiments (1945) showed, however, that these values are not so constant but vary with the hardening conditions. But his "hardening" consisted of artificial predrying at relative humidities of 87%. This is equivalent to attempting to frost harden at about —15°C. Since nearly all the water is removed at this relative humidity, it seems obvious that no hardening process can take place. It is more plausible to suggest reduced injury due to less sudden and intense mechanical stresses, as he himself explains in the case of his other experiments on speed of drying and remoistening. It would, in fact, seem impossible to remove completely this kind of injury unless naked protoplasm such as the plasmodia of Myxomycetes, is used.

Thus, in spite of these newer modifications suggested by Stocker and Höfler, Iljin's original mechanical theory is still the only one that fits the known facts.

Chapter 22.

Tolerance of Drought Dehydration

The variations in tolerance of drought dehydration among plants could be easily calculated from the measurements made by Höfler *et al.* (1941) for their critical saturation deficit. Unfortunately, these original measurements are not given, but the value can be derived directly from their critical saturation deficit, for

$$\text{c.s.d.} = \frac{\text{saturation wt} - \text{fresh wt at critical pt}}{\text{saturation wt} - \text{dry wt}} \times 100$$

$$= \frac{W_o - W_k}{W_o} \times 100 \tag{11}$$

Tolerance of drought dehydration, from equation (5) is

$$D_k = \frac{W_o}{W_k} \tag{12}$$

By multiplying both the numerator and denominator of the equation by $\dfrac{1}{W_k}$ and solving it for $\dfrac{W_o}{W_k}$, it can be shown that:

$$D_k = \frac{100}{100 - \text{c.s.d.}} \tag{13}$$

Recalculation of the results of Höfler *et al.* show that the plants listed vary in tolerance of drought dehydration from a minimum of 1.9 to a maximum of 7.8 (Table 85). These results show very clearly that it is not always the plant with the greatest tolerance of drought dehydration that has the greatest drought resistance; for due to differences in water absorption and loss, a plant with a poorer tolerance (e.g. *Bupleurum falcatum*) may be much farther from the danger point under conditions of drought than one with a much higher tolerance (e.g. *Hieracium pilosella*). But this ability of a plant to retain its water potential above that of the air, though a major factor in drought resistance, is in no way related to drought hardiness. It would be analogous to a kind of frost resistance (if it existed) due to the ability of the plant to maintain its temperature above that of the surrounding air.

Iljin's (1930) data can be easily used to calculate tolerance of drought dehydration. He compared the drought hardiness of different plants and was able to show a good correlation with both osmotic value and cell size (Table 107). As might be expected from this correlation with osmotic value, large differences in drought hardiness (a range of more than 13X) are accompanied by much smaller variations in tolerance of drought dehydration (a range of 3X). The range of tolerance (3–10)

TABLE 107

Tolerance of drought dehydration, osmotic values, and drought hardiness in different plants (from Iljin, 1930)

| | Species | Osmotic value (moles) | Osmotic potential (atm) | Drought killing | | Drought hardi-ness | Tolerance of drought dehy-dration |
				rel. hum. (%)	osm. pot. (atm)		
I.	*Coleus hybridus*	< 0.2	< 4.7	99	14	> 0.7	>3.0
II.	*Malachium*						
	aquaticum	0.26	6.2	97	40	2.6	6.5
	Rumex acetosa	0.28	6.7	97	40	2.6	6.0
	Bidens tripartitus	0.35	8.2	96	52	3.4	6.3
III.	*Scrofularia nodosa*	0.40	10.0	94	79.5	5.3	8.0
	Plantago media	0.45	11.4	92	110	7.2	9.7
	Dorycnium						
	germanicum	0.50	12.8	92	110	7.1	8.6
	Iris pseudacorus	0.55	14.2	92	110	7.0	7.7
IV.	*Ranunculus repens*	0.60	15.8	92	110	7.0	7.0
	Clematis vitalba	0.60	15.8	94	79.5	4.9	5.0
	Centaurea rhenana	0.60	15.8	90	142	9.0	8.9
V.	*Aster trifolium*	0.65	17.2	90	142	8.9	8.3
	Tetragonolobus						
	siliquosus	0.75	20.7	90	142	8.7	6.9
	Linaria genistifolia	0.80	22.4	90–88	142–173	8.6–10.5	6.3–7.7
	Plantago maritima	1.00	30.0	90	142	8.1	4.7
	Red beet	0.8	22.4	87.5	181	11.0	8.1
	Hedera helix	0.85	24.3	85	220	13.4	9.1
	Buxus sempervirens	1.0	30.0	85	220	13.1	7.3

is, in fact, less than in the case of frost dehydration (2–15). But many more data are available for calculating the latter, including those for plants in both the hardened and unhardened state, so this is not surprising.

In one case (*Hedera helix*), values are available from which the tolerance of both frost and drought dehydration can be calculated (Table 108). Though the determinations were made by different investigators

under different conditions, the value for drought dehydration fits in perfectly with those for frost dehydration.

Judging from Iljin's results, drought hardiness shows very little correlation with tolerance of drought dehydration. Some of the most hardy
have the lowest tolerance (e.g. *Plantago maritima*) and some of the
least hardy have the highest tolerance (e.g. *Plantago media*). The latter, however, is hardier than *Clematis vitalba*, though its cell sap con-

TABLE 108

Hardiness and tolerance of dehydration in *Hedera helix*
(from Iljin, 1930; Kessler, 1935)

Condition of plant	Osmotic-value of cell	Critical point	Hardiness	Tolerance of dehydration
		(a) *frost hardiness*		
Unhardened	0.48	—4.5°C	3.6°C	4.1
Hardened	0.82	—18.5	16.9	7.4
		(b) *drought hardiness*		
	0.85	85% r.h.	13.3%	6.4

centration is lower. The hardiness differences between these plants is
therefore primarily due to vacuole factors leading to differences in degree of cell contraction at any one relative humidity. This is apparently
due to two facts. (1) Iljin did not investigate any very hardy plants.
The hardiest are equivalent to the frost hardiness of the less hardy
varieties of wheat. (2) All the plants investigated had as high a tolerance as is ever obtained in plants that have not been exposed to hardening conditions (see Table 81). Thus, the plants investigated by Iljin
are analogous to a series of wheat varieties differing in hardiness. None
of them would possess any hardiness at all if it were not for their high
tolerance of dehydration, but the differences in hardiness are primarily
due to differences in vacuole factors. It also appears that tolerance of
dehydration tends to be a subordinate factor in both frost and drought
hardiness, when unhardened plants are investigated.

Chapter 23.

Dehydration Hardiness

THE RELATION BETWEEN FROST AND DROUGHT HARDINESS

Comparisons between frost and drought hardiness have been made throughout Chapters 16-22. The main basis for these comparisons has been the assumption that frost and drought injury are both mechanical in nature owing to the dehydration of the cell. It is, in fact, the correlation between frost and drought hardiness that affords the strongest argument for this assumption (see Chapter 14). The evidence for this correlation can be summarized as follows (see Table 109).

1. When plants become drought hardy due to a reduced water supply, they also become frost hardy.

2. When plants become frost hardy due to a low temperature exposure, they also become drought hardy.

3. Species and even varietal hardiness to drought and frost may run parallel.

4. Changes in hardiness with development are similar (Chapters 8 and 19).

5. At least many of the same physiological changes occur during frost and drought hardening (Chapters 10–13 and 20).

6. Small cell size is correlated with both frost and drought hardiness (Chapters 9 and 20).

In several cases no such correlation has been obtained (Table 110). But this is to be expected, since it is commonly not drought hardiness that is measured but field survival. This may be due to drought evasion (e.g. in succulents such as pineapple—Clements, 1938). Other complications have also been suggested—e.g. the greater speed of the frost dehydration (Müller-Thurgau, 1886; Fischer, 1911), the possibility of intracellular freezing injury which is not due to dehydration, etc. In some cases, instead of drought hardiness, only one component of it is measured. Thus Pisek and Larcher (1954) determined the critical quantity of water in the plants instead of the intensity of dehydration (Table 111). That the two do not necessarily run parallel has already been shown (Chapter 22). The same lack of correlation may be found at times between frost hardiness and tolerance of frost dehydration (Chapter 15). The positive evidence is therefore much more significant than

TABLE 109

Reports of a correlation between frost hardiness and drought hardiness

Plant	Observation	Observer
Aspergillus	Older hyphae were more hardy than younger to both frost and drought.	Rabe, 1905; Bartetzko, 1909
Mosses	Several species showed parallel frost and drought hardiness; frost hardiness was increased by drought.	Irmscher, 1912
Wintergreen plants	Possessed a xerophyllous structure.	Lidforss, 1907
Wheat	Frost-hardy varieties were more xeromorphic and wilted less rapidly.	Sinz, 1914
Horsebeans	A close relation existed between the two.	Kreutz, 1930
Wheat	Bound water varied directly with both frost and drought hardiness (this was probably due to sugars).	Lebedincev, 1930; Newton and Martin, 1930.
Wheat	Relative transpiration paralleled frost hardiness.	Arland, 1931
Wheat varieties	Good agreement was found between the two.	Waldron, 1932
Grains	Good agreement was found between the two.	Fuchs, 1935b; Wilhelm, 1935
Helianthus annuus	Good agreement was found between the two.	Gicklhorn, 1936; Sergeev and Lebedev, 1936
Soaked seeds	Good agreement was found between the two.	Henkel and Kolotova, 1938
Tree cells (cortical)	Frost-hardy cells were more resistant to desiccation injury than frost-tender cells.	Siminovitch, 1941
Wheat	Low temperature hardening hardened against drought and drought hardening hardened against frost.	Whiteside, 1941
Orange peel cells	The three kinds of cells showed the same order of hardiness to frost and drought.	Levitt and Nelson, 1942
Grasses	High N plants showed more frost and drought injury.	Carroll, 1943a
Locust tree (cortical cells)	Frost hardiness paralleled hardiness to desiccation and plasmolysis	Siminovitch and Briggs, 1953
Evergreens	(1) A perfect parallel was found between seasonal changes in frost and drought hardiness. (2) The order of hardiness of broad-leaved evergreen species was the same for both.	Pisek and Larcher, 1954

TABLE 110

Evidence against a correlation between frost hardiness and drought hardiness

Plant	Observation	Observer
Mosses	Some with least drought hardiness were most frost hardy.	Irmscher, 1912
Persian wheat	Suffered little from drought but were frost tender.	Barulina, 1923
Grasses, etc.	Many are frost hardy but adapted only to humid areas.	Salmon, 1917
Wheats (winter)	No direct correlation could be found.	Saxe, 1938
Pineapple	Grow in dry soil but are frost tender.	Clements, 1938
Grains	An inverse relation occurred between the two.	Nizenjkov, 1939
Evergreens	Conifers are more frost hardy but less drought hardy than broad-leaved evergreens.	Pisek and Larcher, 1954

TABLE 111

The greater drought hardiness of evergreens during winter than during summer
(from Pisek and Larcher, 1954)

Species	Critical water content during winter as percent of critical water content in summer
Loiseleuria procumbens	80
Picea excelsa	80
Pinus cembra	73
Arctostaphylos uva-ursi	71.5
Hedera helix	67
Rhododendron ferrugineum	63

the negative evidence, and it is so perfect in many cases as to defy all denials (Figs. 30, 31, 32).

OSMOTIC HARDINESS

In order to complete the evidence, it should be possible to show a correlation between frost and drought hardiness on the one hand and osmotic hardiness on the other hand. But it must be recognized at the outset that there are two distinct kinds of osmotic hardiness—hardiness to osmotic dehydration and hardiness to osmotic pressure. In order to distinguish between the two, it might be desirable to call the latter turgor hardiness.

1. TURGOR HARDINESS

Iljin (1934) showed that plants vary greatly in their ability to survive high turgor pressures (Table 112). The least hardy (succulents) are killed by pressures of 8 to 9.6 atm. The hardiest can withstand as high as 132 atm. In general, turgor hardiness varies directly with the cell sap concentration (i.e. with the turgor pressures that the cells are normally capable of developing). It also varies with the habitat.

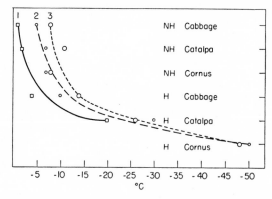

FIG. 30. Parallelism between dehydration hardiness to (1) osmotic water removal (expressed as freezing point of plasmolyte), (2) frost, (3) drought (expressed as freezing point of desiccating solution) (from Scarth, 1941).

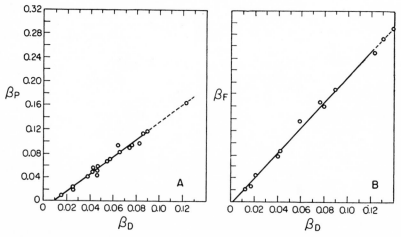

FIG. 31. Straight line relations between critical dehydration intensities produced A by plasmolysis (β_P) and desiccation (β_D), B by frost (β_F) and desiccation (β_D) (from Siminovitch and Briggs, 1953).

In order to measure turgor hardiness, Iljin permitted the cells to undergo an increase in cell sap concentration by placing sections in hypotonic glycerin solutions for periods of 24 to 48 hr. After each 6-

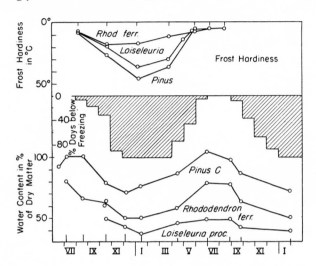

FIG. 32. Parallelism between seasonal changes in frost hardiness (upper curves) and in critical water removal (lower curves) in three evergreens (from Pisek and Larcher, 1954).

TABLE 112

Hardiness of parenchyma cells in different plants to osmotic pressure (turgor hardiness) (from Iljin, 1934)

Species	Habitat	Osmotic value (moles sucrose)	Critical concentration difference (moles)	Turgor hardiness (atm)
Sempervivum soboliferum	rock	0.22	0.35–0.40	8–9.6
Sedum purpureum	rock	0.20	0.35–0.40	8–9.6
Bidens tripartitis	swamp	0.28	0.6 –0.7	14–17
Diplotaxis tenuifolia	field	0.44	0.9 –1.0	21–24
Cirsium canum	meadow	0.36–0.43	0.9 –1.1	21–26
Ranunculus repens	meadow	0.45	1.8 –2.0	43–48
Anthericum ramosum	steppe	0.5–0.6	1.5 –2.3	36–55
Centaurea scabiosa	steppe	0.55	1.5 –2.1	36–50
Lycium barbarum	steppe	—	2.1 –2.2	50–53
Poa badensis	steppe	0.49–0.62	2.7 –3.3	65–79
Festuca glauca	rock	0.6	3.0 –3.2	72–77
Bupleurum falcatum	rock	0.85	3.2	77
Buxus sempervirens	garden	0.8	4.5 –5.5	108–132

hour period in a solution, he transferred the sections to a stronger concentration. The penetration of the glycerin was usually rapid enough for equilibrium to be reached in this way, though there were exceptions. He then transferred the sections from the glycerin solutions to water or to hypotonic sugar solutions in order to determine the turgor pressure tolerated. Killing occurred under the same osmotic gradient for any one plant, regardless of the actual cell sap concentration attained.

It should be pointed out that the osmotic differences assumed by Iljin are not strictly correct. If diffusion equilibrium is reached after 6 hours in the glycerin solution, the glycerin concentrations should be equal inside and outside the cells. Therefore, the total osmotic potential of the cell is approximately equal to that of the glycerin solution plus the original one of the cell. On transfer to a hypotonic glucose solution, the turgor pressure would increase quickly until it reached a maximum approximately equal to the difference between the total osmotic potential of the cell and that of the surrounding glucose solution. But it may take several minutes for enough water to diffuse into the cell in order to achieve this maximum turgor. And during this time, some of the glycerin will be diffusing out of the cell. This error due to loss of glycerin will at least partly counteract the error due to Iljin's failure to take into account the original osmotic potential of the cell. Consequently, his calculated values are probably more nearly correct than if a correction were made for the cell's original osmotic potential. But they are approximations, and the error will vary from plant to plant, depending on: (1) how much water must diffuse into the cells, and (2) how permeable the cells are to water and glycerin. It is a fortunate coincidence that these two antagonistic sources of error parallel each other astonishingly well, for those plants with the highest turgor hardiness also have the highest permeabilities for glycerin (and presumably water). They may be expected, therefore, to cancel each other out. On the other hand, the time during which the cells are exposed to the turgor may be important, and this will be least in the cells most permeable to glycerin. Since these cells are also the most hardy, it is difficult to be sure that he is really measuring turgor hardiness.

2. HARDINESS TO OSMOTIC DEHYDRATION

This has received much more attention than turgor hardiness, and is of more direct interest in relation to frost and drought hardiness. Irmscher (1912) showed that drought-hardy leafy mosses possess osmotic hardiness, for they can be placed in sucrose solutions which may then be evaporated down without injury to the mosses. This is similar to

Iljin's later results with protective solutions. Biebl (1939) found a striking exception. The shoot tips of *Griffithsia setacea* showed great osmotic hardiness, in agreement with the high osmotic values of its cells,
though its frost hardiness was slight. But this plant has cytoplasm that
solidifies reversibly at 2°C, and its osmotic hardiness was low at low
temperatures.

The striking correlation between hardiness to frost and hardiness to
osmotic dehydration has already been discussed (Chapter 13). The
parallelism between the three kinds of hardiness is very clearly shown
in Figs. 30 and 31.

PART III.

HIGH TEMPERATURE HARDINESS

"The different phenomena which supraoptimal temperatures produce in the plant depend on the effect of these temperatures on the protoplasm. In order to explain the observed phenomena, one must therefore first know those processes which take place in the protoplasm under the influence of the high temperature."

LEPESCHKIN (1912)

Chapter 24.

The Limits of High Temperature Hardiness

Although there are records of growth by blue-green algae at temperatures as high as 93 to 98°C in hot springs, these have not been confirmed by others, and the somewhat lower temperature range of 80 to 85°C, which has been recorded by different observers, is usually accepted as the upper limit for growth (Vouk 1923, Robertson 1927). In the case of higher plants, this may be taken as about 58°C, at which temperature succulents have been observed to grow (Huber, 1935).

By analogy with frost and drought, the temperature above which life cannot exist may be called the heat killing temperature. As might be expected, this varies markedly from plant to plant (Table 113). But there is another reason, besides the normal biological variability, for some of the differences recorded. In contrast to the relatively minor role of exposure time in the case of frost and drought, the time subjected to high temperatures is of fundamental importance (Table 118). For not only does the heat killing temperature vary inversely with the exposure time; the relation to time is actually exponential. Logarithmic values of killing time give a practically straight line relation when plotted against temperature (Fig. 36). According to Lepeschkin (1912):

$$T = a - b \log Z$$

where T = heat killing temperature, Z = heating time, a and b are constants.

The agreement between the values calculated from this equation and the measured values is very good (Table 115). Other empirical equations have also been used successfully (Porodko, 1926a; Belehradek, 1935). S-shaped curves relating heating time to injury may be obtained (Porodko, 1926a). According to Belehradek (1935), these are probability curves and simply mean that the organisms of a single kind possess unlike heat killing temperatures, in accord with the laws of variability.

As in low temperature and drought, resting tissues in the dehydrated state have long been known to tolerate much more severe treatment than when active and fully hydrated (Just, 1877). Dry seeds are able to survive as high as 120°C, in contrast to highly hydrated plant tissues that are killed by temperatures below 50°C (Table 113). Seeds can be boiled without losing their ability to germinate, but only if they do not

TABLE 113

Heat killing temperature for different plants and plant parts (see also Table 114)

Plant	Heat killing temperature (°C)	Exposure time	Observer
(a) Lower plants			
Cryptogams	42–47.5	15–30 min	de Vries, 1870
Ulothrix	24		Klebs, 1896 (see Belehradek, 1935)
Mastigocladus	52		Loewenstein, 1903
Blue-green algae	70–75	few hr	Bünning and Herdtle, 1946
Thermoidium sulfureum	53		Miehe, 1907
Thermophilic fungi	55–62		Noack, 1920
Hydrurus foetidus	16–20	few hr	Molisch, 1926
Sea algae	27–42	12 hr	Biebl, 1939
Ceramium tenuissimum	38	8.5 min	Ayres, 1916
(b) Higher plants			
(1) Herbaceous plants			
Nicotiana rustica			
Cucurbita pepo			
Zea mays	49–51	10 min	Sachs, 1864
Mimosa pudica			
Tropaeolum majus			
Brassica napus			
Aquatics	45–46	10 min	Sachs, 1864
19 species	47–47.5	15–30 min	de Vries, 1870
Citrus aurantium	50.5	15–30 min	de Vries, 1870
Opuntia	> 65		Huber, 1932
Shoots of Iris	55		Rouschal, 1938
Sempervivum arachnoideum	57–61		Huber, 1935
Succulents	> 55	1–2 hr	Huber, 1935
Succulents	53–54	10 hr	Huber, 1935
Potato leaves	42.5	1 hr	Lundegårdh, 1949
(2) Trees			
Pine and spruce seedlings	54–55	5 min	Münch, 1914
Cortical cells of trees	57–59	30 min	Lorenz, 1939

TABLE 113 (*continued*)

Plant	Heat killing temperature (°C)	Exposure time	Observer
(3) Seeds			
Barley grains (soaked 1 hr)	65	6–8 min	Goodspeed, 1911
Medicago seeds	120	30 min	Schneider-Orelli, 1910
Wheat grains (9% H_2O)	90.8	8 min	Groves, 1917
Wheat (soaked for 24 hr)	60	45–75 sec	Porodko, 1926a
Trifolium pratense seeds	70	short time	Büchinger, 1929
(4) Fruit			
Grapes (ripe)	63		Müller-Thurgau (see Huber, 1935)
Tomatoes	45		Huber, 1935
Apples	49–52		Huber, 1935
(5) Pollen			
Red pine pollen	50	4 hr	Watanabe, 1953
Black pine pollen	70	1 hr	Watanabe, 1953

TABLE 114

Relation between heat killing time and temperature (from Collander, 1924)

Temp. (°C)	Heat killing time (min)				
	Tradescantia discolor	*Beta-vulgaris*	*Brassica oleracea*	*Draparnaldia glomerata*	*Pisum sativum*
35				480	300–400
40	1300 (app)	>1500–2500	1100	80	32
45	725	420	577	7	2.2
50	243	90	45	1.2	0.27
55	44	4.3	3.8	0.32	0.095
60	7	0.7	0.8		
65	1.8				

swell in the process (Just, 1877). Dry barley and oat grains can be made to survive high temperatures for even longer times if further dried. In the ordinary, air-dry state they survived 100°C for only 1 hr without injury. But if carefully dried for 9 days at 50°C, 2 days at 60°C, 2 days at 80°C, and finally transferred to 100°C for 3 days, more than 58% were still able to germinate (Just, 1877). Even hard-coated seeds that survive autoclaving at 120°C for half an hour, are killed by boiling for 10 min if their seed coats are first filed (Schneider-Orelli, 1910). Presumably the filing permits the living cells to take up enough water during this 10-min period to lower their high temperature tolerance. The relation between heat killing point of seeds and moisture content

TABLE 115

Heating time and coagulation temperature for *Tradescantia discolor*, for $a = 79.8$ and $b = 12.8$ (from Lepeschkin, 1912)

Heating time (min)	Coagulation temperature (°C)	
	Determined	Calculated
4	72.1	
10	69.6	67
25	63.2	62
60	57.0	57.1
80	55.7	55.5
100	54.1	54.2
150	52.0	

and the analogous relation to low temperature tolerance are clearly shown in Figure 33.

Even in the case of nonresting tissues, the same relation holds. Dallinger (see Loewenstein, 1903), showed that infusoria can survive 70°C if their water content is first reduced. Sea algae that succumb in sea water if kept at 35°C for 12 hr, survive 42°C for the same length of time if they are first dried on microscope slides (Biebl, 1939).

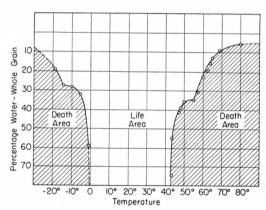

FIG. 33.   Relation of water content to temperature required to kill 75% of Dent corn grains; Reid's yellow Dent exposed for 2 hr to temperatures above zero; Hogue's yellow Dent exposed for 24 hr to temperatures below zero (low temperature data from Kiesselbach and Ratcliff) (from Robbins and Petsch, 1932).

As in frost and drought, many attempts have been made to raise the heat killing temperature by dehydration with plasmolyzing solutions. De Vries (1871) was the first to record this effect. But he used 10% NaCl, and Döring (1932) objects that it may have been a salt effect rather than dehydration, or that de Vries may have been dealing with tonoplasts. Scheibmair (1937), however, counters both of these objections by citing Kaho's evidence against such a salt effect and stating that de Vries used a series of criteria that would not have been fulfilled by tonoplasts. Döring's own experiments with epidermal cells failed to

TABLE 116

Protection by dehydrating solutions against heat killing or shock (inactivation of an enzyme or metabolic process)

Plant	Solution	Killing or shocking temperature (°C)	Time exposed (min)	Observer
(a) Heating killing				
Agave americana	Water	57	10	de Vries, 1871
	10% NaCl	58.2	10	
Hyacinthus orientalis	Water	47.5	10	de Vries, 1871
	10% NaCl	55.4	10	de Vries, 1871
Saxifraga sarmentosa	Water	44.0	10	de Vries, 1871
	10% NaCl	58.2	10	de Vries, 1871
Fucus eggs	Sea water	45	1	Döring, 1932
	Sea water + M sucrose	50	1	
Plagiochila	Water	48	4½	Scheibmair, 1937
asplenioides	2½ M sucrose	> 52	9	
Hookeria luscens	Water	52	3	Scheibmair, 1937
	1 M sucrose	> 52	8	
Rhoeo discolor	Water	60	20	Bogen, 1948
	⅛ M sucrose (hypotonic)	60	17	
	½ M sucrose (hypertonic)	60	36	
(b) Heat shock				
Torula utilis	Water	44	1 hr	Van Halteren, 1950
	1 M – 3 M NaCl, glucose, sucrose	> 44	1 hr	
Torulopsis kefyr	Water	54		Christophersen
	⅓ – ⅔ M maltose	60		and Precht, 1952

reveal any difference between the heat killing point when plasmolyzed (in sucrose or salts) and when unplasmolyzed in water. Scheibmair, however, objects that epidermal strips consist of injured tissues and their killing temperature is thereby lowered. Lepeschkin (1912) showed that such strips must be allowed sufficient time for recovery (some hours) before being tested for heat killing temperature. When Döring used uninjured Fucus eggs, he was able to show a marked rise in the heat killing temperature in protective solutions. Many others have succeeded in obtaining positive results (Table 116). But negative results against which none of the above objections can be raised have also been recorded. In spite of his clear-cut positive results (Table 116), Scheibmair found that plasmolysis actually lowered the heat killing temperature in the case of *Mnium rostratum,* because its cells are actually injured by the plasmolysis, even if not subjected to high temperatures. This is in agreement with Walter (1929), who showed that even a short plasmolysis (30–45 min) in half-molar sucrose produces severe enough injury in *Helodea canadensis* to last for days. This may also explain Illert's (1924) lower heat hardiness in solutions. He used a shade plant (*Oxalis acetosella*) that is among the least heat hardy (Table 125), and perhaps also sensitive to plasmolysis injury. Complications due to plasmolysis injury are also indicated by Bogen's (1948) results. He increased heat hardiness by slightly hypertonic sucrose solutions, but strongly hypertonic solutions had the opposite effect.

Chapter 25.

Heat Injury

OCCURRENCE UNDER NATURAL CONDITIONS

All the above results were obtained with artificially induced high plant temperatures. The question is whether the plant ever reaches high enough temperatures to be injured under natural conditions. It is not enough to know the air temperature exposed to, for it has long been known that the plant's temperature may rise above that of its environment. Dutrochet (1839) showed that this occurs if the plant is kept in saturated air in order to prevent the cooling effect of transpiration. The higher the external temperature, the greater was the elevation of the plant's temperature, though this never exceeded 1/3°C. In the case of fleshy organs, however, the elevations may be much greater (Table 117) —as high as 11°C (Vrolik and de Vriese, 1839), or even 14°R in the spadix of Arum (Goeppert, see Dutrochet, 1840).

TABLE 117

Elevation of temperature above that of the air, in the spadix of *Colocasia odora* (Vrolik and de Vriese, 1839)

Air temperature (°C)	Spadix temperature (°C)
20.0	27.8
16.7	26.1
15.6	26.5
20.7	28.9

But these high plant temperatures are due to metabolic activity and can occur only in fleshy organs that are unable to transfer the excess heat rapidly enough to their environment. Thin leaves, on the other hand, may actually be cooled below the air temperature due to transpiration, though the effect is much less than some have thought (Curtis, 1938). In recent years, more attention has been paid to high plant temperatures well above that of the surrounding air. In midafternoon, succulent leaves of various Sempervivum species had temperatures of 48 to 51°C when the air temperature in the shade was 31°C (Askenasy, 1875). These high temperatures were maintained for three or four hours. Inside ripe tomatoes, temperatures as high as 100 to 106°F were observed at air temperatures of 80 to 83°F (Hopp, 1947). That even thin organs like leaves may show a considerable temperature rise above that of the surrounding air has also often been observed (see Harder, 1930). The highest temperature recorded by Harder was 44.25°C, 7.75°C above that of the air. Fritzsche (1933) detected differences as high as 12.9°C, leading to leaf temperatures up to 37.6°C. The surface soil temperature rose as high as 60°C. Michaelis (1935) reports conifer needle temperatures 9°C above the air temperature 2 cm. away, twig temperatures 11.8°C above it. When compared with the air temperatures in the open, the differences were 3 to 7°C greater. According to Dörr (1941), the leaf temperature increases with its color in the following order: yellow, green, orange, red. The strong absorption by red leaves caused both a rapid uptake and rapid loss of heat. Wilted leaves were always a few degrees warmer than turgid leaves. Herbaceous and especially woody stems reached temperatures as much as 12.2°C above those of the leaves. The temperature of the roots showed the closest agreement with the surrounding temperature. Different parts of the same leaf (or other plant part) may have different temperatures (Fig. 34), and those parts exposed

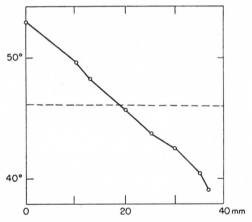

FIG. 34. Temperature gradient with depth (abscissa) in a joint of *Opuntia grandis* (from Huber, 1932).

to the most intense radiation reach the highest temperatures (Konis, 1950; Waggoner and Shaw, 1953). For this reason, position is also important. McGee (1916) found that Opuntia joints in the meridional position heat up more during a day in the sun than those in the equatorial position. But the heating above air temperature is large only in still air (Harder, 1930).

That dangerously high temperatures may occur under natural condi-

tions seems obvious from all these observations. How high they actually do rise is shown in Table 118. In many cases they reach and may even exceed the 45–55°C range that is usually accepted as the normal temperature limit for most plants (Huber, 1935). Heat injury has, in fact, been described by many workers, especially in the case of bulky organs (see Sorauer, 1924; Huber, 1935). A well known type is the sun or bark burn that occurs on the south and southwest side of thin-barked trees.

TABLE 118
High plant temperatures recorded under natural conditions

Plant	Highest temperature (°C)	Observer
Pine tree (south side cambium)	55	Hartig (Sorauer, 1924)
Opuntia	65	Huber, 1932
Sempervivum hirtum	50.2	Dörr, 1941
Globularia	48.7	Dörr, 1941
Tortula (dried out pulvinus)	54.8	Rouschal, 1938
Arum italicum (fruit)	50.3	Rouschal, 1938
Viburnum (leaves)	43.8	Rouschal, 1938
Iris (rhizones)	42.5	Rouschal, 1938
Rhamnus alaternum	52.5	Konis, 1949
Fleshy fruit (various)	35–46	Huber, 1935

This may be followed by drying and stripping of the bark, leading to defoliation and wood injury. The worst affected are the older, stronger stems; pole timber and branches are seldom injured in this way. The injury is thought to be due to overheating of the cambium. Hartig actually records a cambium temperature of 55°C on the southwest side of a spruce tree in the open at an air temperature of 37°C (Sorauer, 1924). But this type of injury is not always due to heat killing, since it may also occur in winter.

Burns have frequently been described in fleshy fruit—more commonly in grapes, cherries, and tomatoes, less commonly in pears and gooseberries (Huber, 1935). As in the case of bark injury, they are usually confined to the most strongly heated southwest side (Huber, 1935). They may later dry up and become separated from the uninjured portion by a cork layer. Less often (e.g. in grapes) the whole fruit is killed. That true heat injury is involved follows from Müller-Thurgau's production of the same kind of injury by raising the fruit temperature artificially above 40°C (Huber, 1935).

Heat injury has been less often reported in leaves and other thin organs (Sorauer, 1924; Huber, 1935). In practice, this has received the most attention when greenhouse-grown or shade plants are placed outdoors directly in the sun. Huber states, however, that it occurs most commonly on inland plains. But it is difficult to be sure that these are true cases of direct heat injury, since there is usually also a water deficiency. Thus, in spite of the many records of high temperatures in plants under natural conditions, Rouschal (1938) concluded that the maximum the leaves can reach in the Mediterranean region during summer cannot produce any heat injury. By enclosing shoots in blackened tubes, he exposed them to temperatures higher than any he was able to observe under natural conditions; 55°C was reached for a short time, and 47°C was maintained for 10 to 15 hr. Even after several days of such treatment, no injury occurred. Konis (1949) used the same method and came to the same conclusion in the case of maquis plants under natural conditions in Israel. The lethal temperature was several degrees higher than the highest temperature recorded in the field.

Perhaps the greatest danger of heat injury occurs when the soil is exposed to insolation, reaching temperatures as high as 55 to 75°C (Lundegårdh, 1949). One of the most serious seedling "diseases," according to Münch (1913, 1914), is the killing of a narrow strip of bark around the stem of young woody plants at soil level (Fig. 35) when

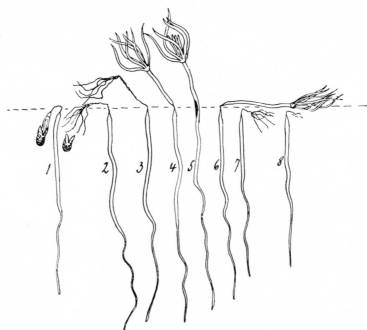

FIG. 35. Heat killing of pine seedlings at soil level due to overheating of soil surface (from Münch, 1913).

soil temperatures exceed 46°C. Since the seedlings usually die, he calls this "strangulation sickness." In laboratory tests, pear seedlings were found to succumb within 3 hours at 45°C or 30 to 60 min at 50°C. Baker (1929) also concluded that fatal temperatures are reached in nature only at the base of the stem of 1- to 3-month-old conifers. He points out that surface soil temperatures of 130 to 160°F have been detected in temperate climates and that injury may occur at as low as 120°F. But though Rouschal (1938) measured maximum soil temperatures as high as 64°C, no injury occurred to the bulky Iris rhizomes he investigated, for their temperature did not rise about 42.5°C. According to Julander's (1945) observations, however, the much thinner stolons of range grasses are in definite danger of injury. He observed a soil temperature of 51.5°C when the air temperature was 36°C. Since he was able to produce definite injury to the stolons at 48°C, and since air temperatures as high as 43°C are not uncommon under severe drought conditions, the possibility of heat injury under natural conditions seems obvious.

In view of the few observations available, no general conclusion can be arrived at. But since the high plant temperatures recorded under natural conditions may reach or exceed the heat killing point for many plants (compare Tables 113 and 118), the possibility of heat injury under certain conditions cannot be denied. By analogy with frost injury, it may be expected only during relatively rare "test summers." Or it may occur only when crop plants are grown in regions not suited to them.

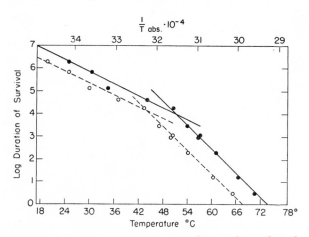

FIG. 36. Break in Q_{10} curve for *Helodea canadensis* relating log of survival time to temperature exposed to (open circles), and in similar curve calculated according to the Van't Hoff-Arrhenius law (closed circles) (from Belehradek and Melichar, 1930).

As in the case of frost and drought, both indirect and direct injury are possible.

INDIRECT INJURY

That moderately high temperatures may induce a different kind of injury from that produced at higher temperatures is indicated by the break in the time vs. temperature curve that is sometimes observed (Fig. 36). The break is at 44°C in the case of *Helodea canadensis,* at other temperatures in other plants (Belehradek, 1935). A logical explanation is that direct heat injury predominates in the higher temperature range, indirect injury in the lower range.

High temperatures are far more likely than low temperatures to cause indirect kinds of injury, since all processes are speeded up instead of being slowed down. One kind of injury is a shock, from which the plant slowly recovers—e.g. the loss of sensitivity in *Mimosa pudica* as a result of 11 hr at 37°C, which is recovered within 2 to 3 days at 20°C (De Candolle, 1806; see Dangeard, 1951b). Injury of two main types must be considered: (1) metabolic and (2) transpirational.

1. METABOLIC HIGH TEMPERATURE INJURY

It has long been known that the growth of plants is stopped at temperatures that are not immediately fatal. Hilbrig (1900) showed that the injury at such temperatures is gradual. The longer the plants are exposed to the high temperatures, the longer it takes them to recommence growth (Table 119). Even fungus spores finally die after 52 days if kept at temperatures too high for growth. Temperatures that are not quite high enough to stop growth completely may also be injurious eventually (Hilbrig, 1900). Results with higher plants (bean, pea, and cucumber)

TABLE 119

Effect of different times of exposure of Penicillium cultures (one day old) to 35°C on subsequent growth (from Hilbrig, 1900)

Exposure time (days)	Time for growth to recommence (days)
2	2
4	3
8	4
12	5
19	6
25	6
30	8
1 month	dead

were similar, though the temperature zone in which growth was stopped without immediate injury was smaller. Growth stoppage (at 45°C) could never be maintained for more than one hour and 45 minutes without killing the seedlings. Dangeard (1951b) states that cessation of cell elongation may be reversed after several days at room temperature.

The gradual injury produced at such high temperatures can be shown by respiration measurements (Table 120). In *Crepis biennis,* respiration decreased with time even at 30° (Kuijper, 1910). The marked decrease in reserves as a result of the high respiration rate affected both the starch and the proteins (Table 121). The production of CO_2 by

TABLE 120

CO_2 evolution by pea seedlings at high temperatures (from Kuijper, 1910). Similar results were obtained with wheat

Temperature (°C)	CO_2 evolution					
	1st hr	2nd	3rd	4th	5th	6th
30	51.7	50.9	52.2	53.6	53.5	53.5
35	68.7	62.8	60.1	61.7	60.9	60.9
40	73.3	55.2	49.0	45.3	43.0	41.2
45	73.5	48.4	41.9	35.9	31.9	28.6
50	74.0	38.8	17.8	12.0	8.0	5.9
55	35.7	12.8	9.7	5.4		

TABLE 121

Decrease in reserves in seedlings maintained at high temperatures (from Kuijper, 1910)

Plant	Temperature (°C)	Starch decrease %	Protein decrease %
Lupinus	25–30	0	37
Pisum	35	54	22
Triticum	40	74	12

yeast shows no depression up to 45°C, but at 46° and higher it decreases with exposure time (van Amstel and Iterson; Belehradek, 1935). The greater heat injury when submerged in water has actually been ascribed to an oxygen deficiency (Just, 1877, but see Chap. 26). That starvation can occur at high temperatures follows from the higher temperature optimum for respiration than for photosynthesis—50°C and 30°C respectively in potato leaves (Lundegårdh, 1949). Assimilation reached zero at 45 to 50°C when measured over short periods of time, at 37 to 43°C when measured over longer periods. Other metabolic processes besides photosynthesis may also be more heat sensitive than respiration. A 1-hr exposure to 47°C in Saccharomyces, to 44°C in Torula, reduced O_2 consumption by 40 to 60%, nitrogen assimilation to zero (Van Halteren, 1950). After 2½ hours at room temperature, nitrogen assimilation recommenced, though at a lower rate than the control. The longer the exposure time, the slower the recovery rate and the rate of nitrogen assimilation when it does recommence (Table 122). Uptake of PO_4 was also stopped for 2 to 3 hr after the high temperature exposure.

TABLE 122

Duration of high temperature, recovery time, and rate (on recovery) of nitrogen assimilation in yeast (from van Halteren, 1950)

Duration of high temperature (hr)	Time for recovery of N assimilation (hr)	Rate of N assimilation after recovery ($\gamma/cm^3/2$ hr)
0	0	6.3
¼	½	5.3
½	1	4.2
1	2½	3.8
1½	2½	3.3
2	5	2.5

The production of toxic products at the higher temperatures due to an altered metabolism is also possible. An accumulation of acids has been observed in succulents (Belehradek, 1935), but since these plants are characterized by an acid metabolism and are also the most heat hardy (see Chapter 26), this accumulation seems to do no harm. Phaeophytin has been observed to arise from chlorophyll at high temperatures (Belehradek, 1935).

2. TRANSPIRATIONAL HIGH TEMPERATURE INJURY

Gäumann and Jaag (1936) measured the cuticular transpiration at temperatures of 20 to 50°C (Fig. 37). Their results show how pronounced the increase is at the higher temperatures. The danger of drought injury under these conditions is obvious. The difficulties in distinguishing between the two kinds of injury are considered in Chapter 26.

DIRECT INJURY

1. MICROSCOPE OBSERVATIONS

The direct, nonmetabolic effect of high temperatures is shown by the inability of CO_2 or O_2 supply to increases or decrease the heat injury (Illert, 1924). But such evidence is unnecessary in most cases, since the time for killing is usually short. An understanding of the nature of this direct injury has been sought by microscopic observation.

Sachs (1864) describes a heat solidification of protoplasm that may be reversible on cooling. As the small epidermal strips from young leaves or flower buds of *Cucurbita pepo* were warmed, protoplasmic streaming in the hair cells speeded up, until it became very violent. At higher

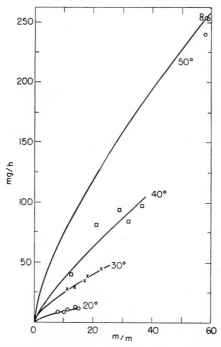

Fig. 37. Cuticular transpiration of *Quercus robur* at different air temperatures (from Gäumann and Jaag, 1936).

temperatures, strands were pulled vigorously into one of the larger proto-plasm masses. Finally, the protoplasm all lay at rest against the cell wall. Five to ten minutes after cooling protuberances gradually began to form, and the network of strands was slowly regenerated. This heat solidification of the protoplasm occurred when the strips were plunged in water at 46 to 47°C for 2 min. But even after exposure to 47–48°C, streaming recommenced within two hours of cooling. In air, higher temperatures had to be used—e.g. 25 min at 50–51°C. The solidification was then reversed only after four hours' cooling. Lepeschkin (1912) states that all layers of the protoplasm including the plasma membrane coagulate simultaneously at the heat killing temperature. Therefore, he determined protoplasmic coagulation by the time when semipermeability of the plasma membrane was lost—i.e. when the colloidally dis-solved pigments of the cell sap were observed to diffuse out under the microscope. But he later (1935) states that protoplasmic coagulation of plasmolyzed cells was recognized first by a rapid decrease in proto-plast volume, and that the injury worked inward from the outer proto-plasm layers (1937). It required a higher temperature for the color to begin to leave the cell. Recovery was not possible after the chloroplasts had begun to coagulate, but the coagulation of the superficial protoplasm layer was reversible. In opposition to Lepeschkin, Bogen (1948) ob-served loss of color from *Rhoeo discolor* cells before any protoplasmic change could be detected. Lepeschkin later (1935) describes four stages of heat coagulation in Spirogyra cells: (1) An imperceptible change in dispersion is detected by an increased permeability to water. The starch grains show just detectible swelling. (2) Starch swells significantly due to a greater increase in permeability, and coagulation of the protoplasm surface begins. There is often a movement of the chloroplast ribbon to-ward the middle of the cell. (3) Complete heat swelling of the starch follows the complete coagulation of the chloroplast. (4) The proteins coagulate completely.

Döring (1932) was able to detect heat swelling of chloroplast starch in living cells and suggests that this may actually injure the protoplasm. He concluded that the tonoplast is more heat hardy than the rest of the protoplasm and that the changes in hardiness under different conditions may not be the same in these two protoplasmic components. Scheibmair (1937) observed the first signs of heat injury in the chloroplasts of mosses. They enlarged and became pale and irregular in contour. At the instant of death, the elaioplasts also changed observably and the whole protoplast contracted in apparent plasmolysis, which was easily distinguished from true plasmolysis by the angular form. Perhaps due to the chloroplast injury, the leaves of some plants (e.g. Oxalis) change from green to yellow on heat killing, though others (e.g. Polygonaceae) fail to show this color change (Illert, 1924).

Dangeard (1951, 1951a, b) attempted to find out how far disorganiza-tion by heat can proceed without causing death. He examined sections of fixed radicles after exposing them to heat killing temperatures for various lengths of time. The chondriosomes were rapidly destroyed, often by less than 1 min. at 55 to 60°C. At lower temperatures, an hour or more was needed. They were rarely destroyed at 42°C or lower. In some cases their destruction was accompanied by the survival of a small percent of the cells, judging survival by their appearance when fixed. Belehradek (1935) reviews many other changes observed by different workers in cells undergoing heat injury—e.g. the formation of granules, vacuolization, protoplasmic contraction. Liberation of lipids has been recorded, even from the cell walls. The nucleus has been found the most heat-sensitive part of the cell, though more hardy in the resting than the dividing state.

2. EXPLANATION OF HEAT INJURY

All these microscopic observations indicate that heat injury is not due to starvation or other metabolic disturbances, for coagulation occurs in too short a time. Since many proteins are denatured at the heat killing temperatures for many plants, this has long been recognized as the obvious explanation of direct heat injury and is accepted as a working hypothesis by even the most recent workers (e.g. Bogen, 1948; Christophersen and Precht, 1952). Direct evidence in its favor is obtained from the reaction times. Lepeschkin (1912) points out that the same logarithmic relation has been found between the heat killing time for protoplasm and coagulation time for protein solutions, though the former is more rapid. From the equation (Chapter 24), the time for protoplasmic coagulation at room temperature can be calculated (Table 123).

TABLE 123
Calculated coagulation times for proteins and plant protoplasm
(from Lepeschkin, 1912)

Material	Temperature (°C)	Coagulation time	Constants	
			a	b
Blood serum	20	42 yr		
Dilute albumin	20	15 yr	80.6	8.2
Concentrated albumin	20	230 yr	53.9	4.2
Tradescantia discolor	20	33 days	79.8	12.8
	0	3 yr		
Beta vulgaris	20	31 hr		
	0	11 days		

The Q_{10} for heat killing of protoplasm is very high, though it varies markedly from plant to plant as well as with the conditions (Table 124). According to Belehradek (1935), it is usually low when the tissues are dry or semidry, or in general when heat hardiness is high, and also at temperatures slightly above the optimum. This lack of constancy has been stated to preclude a single cause of death (Illert, 1924). But the determinations do not always involve simply heat killing. Sometimes, they really measure the acceleration at high temperatures of death that would normally occur at a slow rate even at room temperature—e.g. in the case of excised leaves (Belehradek and Melichar, 1930).

TABLE 124
Temperature coefficients (Q_{10}) for heat killing of plants

Plant	Q_{10}	Temperature range (°C)	Observer
Barley grains (soaked 1 hr)	10	55–70	Goodspeed, 1911
Ceramium tenuisimum	37.6	28–38	Ayres, 1916
Tradescantia discolor	26	40–65	Collander, 1924
Beta vulgaris	71	40–60	Collander, 1924
Brassica oleracea	80	40–60	Collander, 1924
Elodea densa	31	35–55	Collander, 1924
Drapernaldia glomerata	43	35–55	Collander, 1924
Pisum sativum seedlings	118	35–55	Collander, 1924
Elodea canadensis	7.6	22–44	Belehradek and Melichar, 1930
	50	44–65	
American elm	19 (lower slope of curve)	55–68	Lorenz, 1939
	243 (upper slope)		
Catalpa	360	54–65	Lorenz, 1939
Northern white pine	63	54–66	Lorenz, 1939
White spruce	73 (lower slope)	53–69	Lorenz, 1939
	3.6 (upper slope)		Lorenz, 1939
Red pine	66	55–66	Lorenz, 1939
Monterey pine seedlings	28–100	49–55	Baker, 1929

The only two processes known to have as high Q_{10} values as heat killing are the heat coagulation of proteins and the conversion of starch into paste (Lepeschkin, 1935). The actual values for heat killing usually fall within the range for heat coagulation of proteins. The Arrhenius formula gives values for μ of from 50,000 to 132,000, which also falls within the zone for heat coagulation (Lorenz, 1939). Christophersen and Precht (1952) even suggest that the death rate of cells follows the curve for a monomolecular reaction and therefore may be due to the breakdown of a single molecule. But they admit that in the case of bacteria, deviations from the curve for monomolecular reaction are frequent.

Against the explanation of heat killing by protein denaturation is the long recognized fact that many organisms are killed at temperatures too low for the denaturation of known proteins. From such evidence, early investigators (Sachs, 1864; Just, 1877) concluded that protein coagulation cannot be involved. The observed liberation of lipids at high temperatures (Belehradek, 1935) led Heilbrunn to suggest that heat killing may be due to liquefaction of protoplasmic lipids. But Collander (1924) points out that the temperature for denaturation of protoplasmic proteins is unknown. And Lepeschkin (1935) concludes that since the lipids occur in such thin layers in the protoplasm, they would liquefy instantly at a definite temperature and therefore could not account for the high Q_{10} values for heat killing. He believes that lipids are freed as the result, rather than the cause, of death. This seems a more reasonable explanation, since the lipids are oriented with respect to the proteins in the living protoplasm (Frey-Wyssling, 1948). The intermolecular forces should be strong enough to maintain this orientation even above the liquefaction temperature for the free lipids. There can be no doubt that the denaturation is the cause of death when high heat killing temperatures are involved. At very high temperatures, as in the case of dry tissues, the temperature coefficient is low, and the injury is due to a more profound change than denaturation (Lepeschkin, 1937). Similarly, at low heat killing temperatures, indirect metabolic injury must occur. Whether these zones overlap, or whether another intermediate zone exists in which other factors such as lipid liquefaction may play a role, cannot yet be decided with certainty.

Lepeschkin (1935) points to the effects of various factors on heat injury as proof of the protein denaturation theory. Small amounts of acid (e.g. nitric) lowered the heat killing temperature of Spirogyra, and also the heat coagulation temperature of proteins. Very dilute alkalis raised the temperature for both processes. Narcotics, such as alcohol, ether, chloroform, and benzol, lowered the temperature for both processes. Even the protective effect of plasmolyzing solutions against heat injury (Chapter 24) is in accord with the fact that denaturation of proteins occurs at higher temperatures in concentrated than in dilute solutions.

He also points to the effect of salts in lowering the temperature for both processes. But the effect of salts on heat killing (Table 116) is complicated and not agreed on by all workers. Kaho (1921, 1924, 1926) plasmolyzed epidermal strips in single salt solutions and observed them with a horizontal microscope while their temperature was being raised at a constant rate in a water bath. The plasmolyzed protoplasts were seen to expand at a speed depending on the salt used. Shortly before death, the swelling was especially striking. The temperature resulting in rupture of the cells with expulsion of their contents was taken as the heat coagulation temperature. In some salt solutions, no such rupture occurred, and a less sharp coagulation temperature was obtained. The time for initiation of warming to the complete decolorization of the cells averaged 15 minutes.

The anions lowered the heat coagulation temperature more than did the cations, and followed the lyotropic series. For potassium salts, the order was: $CNS > Br > I > NO_3 > Cl > $ tartrate $> CH_3 COO > $ citrate $> SO_4$. The range of temperatures was from $67.5°C$ (for KCNS) to $76.5°C$ (for K_2SO_4). The cations also had some effect in the order: $K, NH_4 > Na, Li, Ca$ (?) $> Mg, Ba, Sr$.

As a general rule, the most rapidly penetrating salts, judging by the rate of protoplast expansion, lowered the heat coagulation the most. This conclusion is also in agreement with the order of permeability found by other workers. Heat coagulation of egg albumin was also found to follow the same series, provided the solutions were acid. $MgSO_4$ gave exceptional results, owing (according to Kaho) to its strong hydrolysis and acidity which enhance coagulation. That the salts are toxic to the cell even in the absence of an injurious high temperature was shown by determining the death rate of the cells in the salt solutions at temperatures from 0 to $36°C$ (Kaho, 1926). Kaho cautions that this heat coagulation of the protoplasm cannot be taken as synonymous with heat injury, since it is only the last link in a chain of phenomena that may cause injury at high temperatures.

Kaho was actually able to raise the heat coagulation temperature with Ca salts, if the correct anion was used. In agreement with these results, Scheibmair (1937) found that a half-hour treatment in a hypotonic solution previous to heating in water resulted in a higher heat killing temperature when $CaCl_2$ was used, a lower one when KCl was used.

Bogen (1948) plunged sections directly into the heated salt solution and determined the heat killing time by loss of vacuole pigment. Monovalent cations of equimolar concentration lowered heat resistance according to their position in the lyotropic series, i.e. $Li > Na > Rb > Cs$. Monovalent anions lowered the heat killing temperature according to their order of adsorption, i.e., $SCN > NO_3 > Br > Cl, C_2O_4 > SO_4$. Multivalent cations did not follow the lyotropic series and he explains their behavior as due to the interference of the oppositely acting adsorption effect, i.e. a discharging of the colloid. Thus, when both monovalent and divalent cations are grouped together, the following is the order of injury: control $<$ Mg $<$ Cs $<$ K $<$ Na $<$ Li $<$ Ca $<$ Ba $<$ Al. When he combined the anion and cation that were both least injurious in their respective series (i.e., $MgSO_4$) he actually obtained an increased heat hardiness. This was the only salt tested that produced an increase.

The change in heat hardiness was proportional to the salt concentration in an exponential manner, i.e. when the concentrations were plotted in a geometric series, a straight line relation was obtained with killing time. Mixtures failed to produce any antagonistic effect. Thus, KCl $+$ $CaCl_2$ produced an additive effect, LiCl $+$ $MgSO_4$, purely a $MgSO_4$ effect.

Lepeschkin (1912, 1935) also found that mechanical agents lower the heat killing temperature. Cutting the tissues produces a sensitization that may last up to 15 hr in the case of beets. Bending of Spirogyra filaments has a similar effect. The farther from the cut or bend a cell is, the less its heat killing temperature is affected. In contrast to Lepeschkin, Scheibmair (1937) found that centrifuging actually raised the heat killing temperature of the moss Plagiochila. In a few cases, however, it was lowered.

Lepeschkin also found that light increased the speed of heat killing. Low concentrations of narcotics raised the heat killing temperature though not affecting protein denaturation. But Scheibmair (1937) was unable to confirm this last result and was able to obtain only a lowering of the heat killing temperature.

Chapter 26.

Heat Hardiness

METHODS OF MEASUREMENT

The two methods originally used by Sachs (1864) are still standard procedure for measuring the heat killing temperature of plants, though more elaborate equipment may nowadays be employed. With the first, potted plants are placed in a heat chamber whose temperature can be controlled and left there at a constant temperature for a standard length of time. They are then transferred to the greenhouse for a period of a week or two, following which the degree of injury is observed. Heyne and Laude (1940), for instance, exposed corn seedlings to 130°F at a relative humidity of 25 to 30% for five hours. With the second method, potted plants are overturned (Sachs, 1864) or small pieces or sections of the plant are plunged in water at a known temperature for a standard length of time, then observed for growth or else microscopically for injury. Sometimes the plant is not allowed to come in contact with the water. Julander (1945), for instance, cut 1½ inch pieces from stolons of range grasses, transferred them in lots of eight into stoppered glass tubes which were then immersed in a constant temperature bath at 48° ± 0.1°C for periods of 0, ½, 1, 2, 4, 8, and 16 hours. The stolon pieces were then planted and recovery was estimated after four weeks.

The first method has the advantage of using the whole plant. But there are definite objections to it. The actual temperatures attained by the tissues are not known, and may be far below those of the surrounding air due to the rapid transpiration at the high temperatures and low relative humidities employed. As evidence for this conclusion, Sapper (1935) found that the plants were able to survive air temperatures as much as 5°C higher in dry than in moist air; and though wilted plants stood higher air temperatures than turgid plants when heated in saturated air, in dry air the relation was reversed. It is possible, therefore, to subject prairie grasses to hot winds at 135 to 145°F without injury, as long as soil moisture is available (Mueller and Weaver, 1942). Even if the plants are heated in still air, some time is needed for temperature equilibrium to be reached, and during this time the tissues are in danger of drought injury, especially at the low relative humidities (e.g. 25 to 30% in Heyne and Laude's tests) that usually prevail. It is not surprising, therefore, that the "heat hardiness" of the plants tested by Heyne and Laude paralleled field drought resistance. Consequently, in order to prevent drought injury during tests by the first method and to obtain plant temperatures identical with the measured air temperatures, Sachs' (1864) original precaution of maintaining 100% relative humidity should be adopted. Any injury produced at the high temperature will then be purely heat injury, as is always true of the second method.

It must be realized, however, that even when the above precaution is taken, the two methods may not always yield exactly the same results. Sachs (1864) found that with the first method, 51°C was the killing temperature, though the plants withstood 49 to 51°C for 10 minutes or more without injury. The same plants, however, were killed if plunged in water at 49 to 51°C for 10 min. According to de Vries (1870), killing occurs at about 2°C lower in water than in air. Yet, in spite of these results, agreement is often surprisingly good. Sapper (1935), for instance, gives a heat killing temperature of 40.5° C for *Oxalis acetosella* exposed for half an hour by the first method; Illert (1924) gives a value of 40°C for 20 min. using the second method on the same species.

The use of tissue pieces enables determinations on individual tissues or even cells. But it has the disadvantage of judging survival by cellular methods instead of by the ability of the plant to continue normal metabolism and growth. In the hands of an untrained observer, cellular methods are dangerous to judge by, particularly if only one criterion is used. Schneider (1925), for instance, was able to obtain plasmolysis-like contraction of the protoplasts in heat killed cells—e.g. moss cells dipped in water at 80°C for half a minute "plasmolyzed" in hypertonic sucrose. This observation was confirmed for guard cells by Weber (1926), but he points out that the "plasmolyzed" cells look abnormal and are not difficult to distinguish from truly plasmolyzed living cells. Schneider, himself, was unable to deplasmolyze and replasmolyze these heat-killed cells, and found that the plasmolyzability was lost in about 10 minutes. As pointed out by Weber, mistaking heat-killed cells for living cells can be avoided by combining vital staining with plasmolysis. Therefore, the observations of men like de Vries (1871), who used several criteria for distinguishing injury, appear fully reliable. Döring (1933) objects, however, that even such methods may fail to distinguish between cells with living protoplasm and those in which only the tonoplast remains functional. But Scheibmair (1937) concluded that even this danger can be avoided by combining vital staining, plasmolysis, observation for abnormalities, and finally deplasmolysis and replasmolysis. It is possible that even with perfectly reliable cellular methods of distinguishing living from dead cells, the second method may still yield slightly higher heat killing temperatures than the first, since plants that are doomed to die after heating (by the first method) may retain full turgor and appear fully healthy for 24 hours (Sachs, 1864). To avoid overlooking such postheating changes, Scheibmair recommends leaving the sections for some time before testing.

A third method, used in the open, is to enclose a shoot in a blackened box, permitting its temperature to rise due to insolation (Rouschal, 1938; Konis, 1949). But neither the temperature nor the time exposed to it can be controlled in this way.

As in the case of frost and drought hardiness, the relative heat hardiness of different species should be compared only when they are in the hardened condition, though few investigators take this precaution. Julander (1945) found little difference between range grass species when they were "unhardened"—i.e. well watered and clipped and grazed. In the hardened condition, however, there were definite differences. Bermuda grass and buffalo grass were the most hardy; they were not killed by even 16 hr at 48°C. Bluestem was intermediate. Slender wheat, smooth brome, and Kentucky bluegrass were the least hardy.

FACTORS RELATED TO HARDINESS

1. ENVIRONMENTAL

The heat hardiness of plants varies markedly with the environment they are adapted to. Those that live in hot, sunny regions are the most hardy; shade and aquatic plants are the least hardy (Table 125). Even larger differences are to be expected when the hardiest plants are tested in their fully hardy natural state instead of being taken from the greenhouse (Sapper, 1935).

In contrast to frost and drought hardiness, heat hardiness is not increased by subjecting the plant to moderate doses of the injurious factor (Sapper, 1935). On the other hand, exposure to low temperature does increase it. Sapper succeeded in obtaining this result by a 2-day exposure to temperatures dropping as low as —4°C, followed by slow thawing and one day in a cool bright room. Similarly, the most frost-hardy spring blooming plants had a heat hardiness equal to that of plants from a sunny region (45 to 50°C).

Sapper also showed that dry cultivation increases heat hardiness by as much as 2°C (Table 126). Wilting alone increased hardiness as much as dry cultivation. This is in agreement with other results on the effect of dehydration (Chapter 24). Similarly, watered bluestem grass was killed by 4 hr at 48°C, droughted bluestem only by 16 hr at the same temperature (Julander, 1945). The effect of moisture is also seen in the frequently observed burn injury to fleshy fruits after long rains when these are followed by hot, sunny weather (Sorauer, 1924; Huber,

TABLE 125

Heat killing temperatures of plants from different habitats (from Sapper, 1935)

Habitat or ecological type	Species	Heat killing temp. (°C), ½-hr exposure
Submerged aquatics	Helodea callitrichoides Vallisneria species	38.5–41.5
Shade	Oxalis acetosella Impatiens parviflora, etc.	40.5–42.5
Partially shaded	Geum urbanum Chelidonium majus Asplenium species	45–46
Very dry and sunny	Alyssum montanum Teucrium montanum Dianthus species Iris chamaeiris Verbascum thapsus, etc.	48–50 or over
Succulents	Sedum species Other succulents	48.5–50 50–54

TABLE 126

Effect of dry cultivation on heat hardiness (from Sapper, 1935)

Species	Heat killing temperature (°C)		Osmotic value at incipient plasmolysis (M sucrose)	
	Sparingly watered	Kept saturated	Sparingly watered	Kept saturated
Melilotus officinalis	46.5	45	0.55–0.60	0.45–0.50
Taraxacum officinale	46	44.5	0.65	0.45
Avena sativa	44.5	< 43.5	0.65	0.40–0.45
Hordeum distichum	46–46.5	< 44	0.80	0.45–0.50
Hieracium pilosella	> 50.5	48.5	0.65–0.75	0.35–0.55
Ceterach officinarum	100–120	47		

1935). Similarly, fungal spores in younger developmental stages with higher water content are more sensitive to heat injury than those in later stages with lower water content (Zobl, 1950). The former become more heat hardy on stepwise, careful drying, in agreement with results using seeds (see Chapter 24).

The effect of light on hardiness is not so easily determined. Five days in the dark increased the heat hardiness of *Oxalis acetosella* (Illert, 1924). In agreement with these results, Sapper (1935) was unable to reduce the heat hardiness of plants by keeping them in the dark for as long as three days. Longer times than this, however, did reduce hardiness. Nevertheless, etiolated young seedlings were more hardy than green, assimilating ones of the same age. In *Hordeum distichum* the heat killing temperatures were 47° and 45° respectively. But sun plants were always hardier than shade plants of the same species, though both were kept thoroughly watered. However, watering alone is unable to maintain the same hydration in the leaves under such different atmospheric conditions. According to Heyne and Laude (1940), even a 1-hr exposure to light increased the heat hardiness of plants previously kept in the dark for 12 to 18 hours; but, as mentioned above, they were probably determining drought rather than heat hardiness.

Nutrient deficiency raised the heat killing temperature of *Oxalis acetosella* (Illert, 1924). In agreement with these results, Sapper (1935) found that excess nitrogen or potassium reduced hardiness, deficiency very effectively raised it (by about 2°C). High nitrogen also reduced the heat hardiness of turf grasses (Carroll, 1943a).

Age may markedly affect heat hardiness. In general, Sachs (1864) found that the blades of young, fully grown leaves were killed first. Younger leaves that were not fully grown and bud parts were more hardy. The most resistant were the old, healthy leaves. De Vries (1870) obtained the same results. According to Illert (1924), older leaves of *Oxalis acetosella* are less heat hardy than younger ones; but the significance of this observation is doubtful, since the leaves were already moribund. Seeds that were allowed to swell in water for 24 hours showed a decreased heat hardiness with age (Table 127), even though no decrease in percent germination of the unheated seeds could be detected. In fruit, heat hardiness increases with ripeness—e.g. from 43°C in unripe grapes to 62°C in ripe grapes (Müller-Thurgau, see Sorauer, 1924). Tree seedlings show an increased hardiness with unfolding of the cotyledons (Huber, 1935). Young leaves of Helodea are less hardy than older ones, but the oldest are the least hardy (Esterak, 1935). On the other hand, Scheibmair (1938) showed that young moss leaves are more hardy than older ones, and younger tip cells hardier than older basal ones. According to Heyne and Laude (1940), 10- to 14-day-old corn seedlings are hardier than older ones. They also noted an exhaustion of the food material in the endosperm by about the fourteenth day. As mentioned above, however, Heyne and Laude may actually have been measuring drought hardiness rather than heat hardiness. Sapper (1935) was unable to detect any difference in heat hardiness between seedlings and older plants. And Baker (1929) concluded that the apparent increase in hardiness of conifer seedlings with age was not protoplasmic but simply due to the development of mechanical protection. According to Bogen (1948), however, younger leaves of *Rhoeo discolor* survive heating for a longer time than older leaves. The same was true of younger basal cells versus older tip cells.

TABLE 127

Relation of heat hardiness to age of wheat grains swollen in distilled water for 24 hr. Germination of untreated seeds unaltered by age (from Porodko, 1926)

Date	Temperature (°C)	Exposure time for killing
Sept. – Oct., 1917	60.4	75 sec
Aug., 1918		45 sec
July, 1917	55	8 min
Nov., 1917		7 min
Dec., 1917		7½ min
Oct., 1918		5 min
Nov., 1917	50	85 min
Aug., 1918		60 min

Many others showed similar hardiness gradients in a single organ that may not be related to age differences. The base of Iris and Anthericum leaves had higher killing temperatures than the tip (de Vries, 1870). In apples, the center may be killed at 50 to 52°C, the outer layers only by temperatures above 52°C (Huber, 1935). According to Belehradek and Melichar (1930), the basal cells of *Helodea canadensis* leaves succumb first, the apical cells show the greatest heat hardiness. But this order was reversed at lower temperatures, and they point out that the gradient may actually be due to the injurious effect of cutting, which is perhaps propagated from the base to the tip. The correctness of this suspicion was later indicated by Esterak (1935), who obtained a gradient in the reverse direction on the same material. The result apparently depended on whether the leaves were removed with forceps before testing, or by excising with scissors as done by Belehradek and Melichar. A real reversal was found by de Visser Smits (1926). Heat hardiness of beet roots decreased from the base to the tip, except at inception of the second growth period, when the gradient was reversed.

From Kaho's results on the effects of salts on heat coagulation (Chapter 25), Lundegårdh (1949) suggests that the heat hardiness of desert plants or succulents from salt soils may be due to the high chloride content of their cell sap. But Kaho, himself, cautioned against applying his results for this last stage of heat killing to heat hardiness. Illert (1924) suggested that increased hardiness may be associated with lowered acid content, but this does not agree with the fact that the most heat-hardy group of higher plants—the succulents—are also among the most acid. According to Zobl (1950), protein content is a factor in the heat hardiness of spores. This is based on nitrogen analyses which showed that the protein content (6.25 $\times$ N content) was three times as great in the heat-hardy bacterial spores as in the less hardy fungal spores.

Evidence of a relation with cell sap concentration has also been produced. The effects of nutrition, low temperature, and moisture found by Sapper (1935) also paralleled the osmotic value (Table 126). But when different species were compared, or even different parts of the same plant, this relation did not hold. Both with respect to their high water contents and low osmotic potentials, the very hardy succulents are exceptional. Julander (1945) found, however, that hardened grasses had about twice as high carbohydrate contents as the unhardened, though there was very little starch. Sucrose accumulated but reducing sugars did not. The substances that accumulated the most were the colloidal carbohydrates, especially levulosans. Since Julander heat-hardened his plants by exposure to drought, these results are not surprising. Sapper (1935), on the other hand, found etiolated lower carbohydrate plants more hardy than the normal green ones.

The relation of cell sap concentration to hardiness is also indicated by the opposite changes in heat hardiness that occur in the guard cells and subsidiary cells (Weber, 1926a). When the stomata are open in the light, the guard cells are more hardy than the subsidiary cells; when they are closed in the dark, the subsidiary cells are more heat hardy. In each case, the more hardy cells are free of starch, but presumably contain sugar, the less hardy contain starch, but probably little or no sugar (Table 128).

Parija and Mallik (1941) incubated seeds at 40 to 60°C for 8 to 120

TABLE 128

Relation between starch content and time survived at 60°C (from Weber, 1926a)

Species	Heating time (sec)	State	Guard cells		Subsidiary cells	
			Starch	Survival	Starch	Survival
Galium mollugo	6	closed	+	dead	—	living
	6–20	open	—	living	+	dead
Rumex patientia	4	closed		dead		living
	4–16	open		living		dead

hr and recorded the percent germination. Oily seeds survived the high temperature better than starchy seeds; and the higher the oil content, the better was the survival. Linseed was an exception, since it showed greater heat hardiness than cottonseed, though the latter had a higher oil content. They ascribe this to the mucilaginous seed coat.

Protoplasmal properties have received little attention with regard to heat hardiness. Scheibmair (1937) observed more rapid rounding up in the hardier, upper marginal cells of mosses on plasmolysis than in the less hardy basal cells. On the other hand, the tip cells, which were just as hardy as the upper marginal ones, never rounded up at all. This latter result, however, must be due to something other than viscosity— perhaps a firmer adhesion with the cell wall. Henkel and Margolin (1948) conclude that two important reasons for the heat hardiness of succulents are high cytoplasmic viscosity and high bound water. According to their measurements, both of these factors are developed to a higher degree in the succulents than in the other xerophytes which are less heat hardy. They state that the bound water in succulents is much higher than in mesophytes—as high as 70% in certain cacti. During flowering, viscosity decreased suddenly but bound water increased and to some extent compensated for the decreased hardiness resulting from viscosity change.

Chapter 27.

The Mechanism of Heat Hardiness

Indirect Injury

If indirect heat injury is due to starvation or any other metabolic abnormality, those plants that are capable of continuing a normal type of metabolism at high temperatures would be hardy. Harder *et al.* (1932) have shown that many plants adapted to high temperatures actually have a much higher compensation point than unadapted plants. In contrast to potato and similar plants (see Chapter 25), these adapted plants are able to assimilate above the compensation point even at temperatures of 45–53°C. Thermophilic blue-green algae show the same phenomenon (Bünning and Herdtle, 1946). Their respiration rises very slowly with temperature, and even at high temperatures, assimilation is in excess. The temperature optimum for growth is also high (40°C). The temperature optima for photosynthesis are the same in tomato and cucumber, yet the latter is more hardy, due to the less steep drop of its photosynthesis curve to the maximum (Lundergårdh, 1949).

Direct Injury

If protein denaturation is the cause of heat injury, there are two possible mechanisms of hardiness: (1) increased stability of the protoplasmic proteins, and (2) increased speed of resynthesis of the proteins.

1. Increased stability of protoplasmic proteins.

Molisch (1926) explains heat hardiness by the different denaturation temperatures of different proteins. Organisms living in hot springs must therefore have proteins that do not coagulate until 55 to 70°C or higher. This may be due to the presence in the protoplasm of substances that inhibit coagulation, just as in blood. The protoplasm may perhaps also be more alkaline. This was also implied by Illert (1924). Bünning and Herdtle (1946) suggest that a decrease in free water reduces the rate of metabolic processes by slowing down diffusion. At the same time protoplasmic stability is increased, and with it, resistance to all sorts of injurious agents. Christophersen and Precht (1953) expand this explanation and repropose the identical theory put forward much earlier by Gortner (1938) to explain frost and drought hardiness. They suggest that metabolism and hardiness are inversely related to each other, the latter being directly related to bound water, or more correctly nonsolvent space. As the solvent space (which is nearly the same as free water) decreases, the transport of substances is decreased and with it metabolism. On the other hand, free water weakens the intermicellar bridges. The thermal oscillations induced by high temperatures can therefore readily break the H and S-S protein bridges. This frees the SH groups, leading to new intra- and intermicellar bonds and loss of the original specific structure. In this way, heat denaturation of the proteins occurs. Bound water, on the other hand, strengthens the protein bridges and opposes high temperature denaturation.

Bogen (1948) attempts to explain his results on the basis of modern knowledge of proteins, particularly the folding of proteins and the structural bonds between them. He assumes that heat hardiness is determined by the stability of the molecular form and that any molecular deformation or tearing of molecular bonds can lead to a structural disturbance and finally to death of the cell. Thus he concludes that heat hardiness is not due simply to the degree of hydration, but to the original order of charges and the hydration centers of individual molecules. Any disturbance of this order may lead to death, since the molecule is thereby deformed and the system of molecular bonds exposed to tensions. In this process, the total water content may be increased, decreased, or unaltered. This, he thinks, may explain "the many contradictory results on the influence of hydration on heat hardiness" (but, as shown above, the results agree very well). Where heat hardiness and hydration do run parallel, it is because they are similarly affected by many factors.

The effects of the monovalent cations, according to Bogen, can be explained only by adsorption which occurs without discharging the colloidal particle. As a result, the imbibition of the protein is increased, the molecular bonds are loosened, and heat hardiness is lowered. The same is true for the monovalent anions, since they are effective in the order of their adsorbability. In both cases, however, Bogen states that it is not the hydration of the colloid as a whole that is involved but the hydration of individual molecules, and even then not equally over the whole molecular surface. Nor is it likely to involve a simple enlargement of the hydration shell about previously existing hydration centers. More likely, new dipole moments are induced under the influence of the ion and new hydration centers are created. Thus, both the charge distribution and the arrangement of the hydration centers are altered. The increased heat hardiness produced by $MgSO_4$ does not involve a change in hydration but is associated with strengthening of the structure. It may bind two protein molecules together and hold them in their original orientation, thereby stabilizing the system of molecular bonds. The effect of pretreatment with water he explains as due to the washing out of ions.

The sole basis for Bogen's theory is the effect of ions on the coagulation temperature of living cells. On the basis of an earlier and very extensive investigation of this relation, Kaho cautioned against drawing any conclusions about heat hardiness from this last stage of heat killing. Furthermore, the order of effectiveness of the ions was basically the same as in Bogen's later results. Kaho pointed out that this order agreed with the order of penetration of the ions into the living cell. Nevertheless, Bogen chooses to conclude that the ion effects are purely due to adsorption on the protoplasmic proteins, which could be true only if they all penetrated at the same rate. Bogen's statement that the many experiments on the effects of hydration on heat hardiness are contradictory, does not agree with the facts (Chapter 25). On the contrary, Bogen's own results fit in with the conclusion from the above that increased total hydration of protoplasm causes decreased heat hardiness, owing perhaps to a more ready unfolding (i.e. denaturation) of the micelles in the presence of ample water. The order of effectiveness of the ions on heat hardiness is the same as the order of their effectiveness on protein swelling (Scarth and Lloyd, 1930). A combination of this effect with the order of penetration of the ions leads to a clear understanding of the results. The protective effect of $MgSO_4$, for instance, follows from its lack of penetration and consequent osmotic dehydration of the protoplasm. Another factor which cannot be ignored is the toxic effect of the unbalanced ions (Kaho, 1926), which must become far more pronounced at the higher temperatures.

2. Increased speed of resynthesis of proteins.

Lepeschkin (1935) found that interrupting the exposure to high temperature at the midpoint by 2 min at 20°C had no effect on the total time needed to produce killing of Spirogyra. When the interruption was for 2⅔ hr at 20°C, however, a longer total time at the high temperature was needed for heat killing. He concludes from this that the protein denaturation is physically and chemically irreversible, but that it can be repaired by physiological activity. Allen (1950) showed that, in the absence of nutrients, thermophilic bacteria die at 55°C just as rapidly as the mesophilic bacteria. Similarly, the enzyme systems of the thermophiles are rapidly inactivated at this temperature. She concluded, therefore, that they can synthesize enzymes and other cell constituents far faster than they are destroyed by heat, and that they have higher co-efficients of enzyme synthesis. According to this concept, heat killing occurs when the speed of resynthesis of an indispensable component (e.g. an enzyme or an intermediate substance) is unable to compensate for its degradation.

Chapter 28.

Hardiness to Dehydration, Heat, and Other Injurious Agents

The close correlation of the hardiness of plants to frost, drought, and osmotic water removal has already been shown (Chapter 23). Since all three forces injure by dehydrating, the hardiness of the plant to them may be called dehydration hardiness. As mentioned earlier (Chapter 25), high temperature may also have a dehydrating effect by increasing the transpiration rate. But direct heat injury is completely independent of dehydration, and when investigating heat injury, precautions must be taken to avoid drought injury (Chapter 26). There is, therefore, no a priori reason to expect a relation between dehydration hardiness and heat hardiness. If, in spite of this, a correlation is found, this should give a clue as to the nature of heat hardiness.

Among the earliest investigators of heat hardiness, Sachs (1864) thought he saw a similarity between cold and heat injury, for both low and high temperatures stopped cytoplasmic streaming before any injury set in. But the more recent evidence is far more convincing. The following similarities have been established:

1. The environmental conditions that induce dehydration hardiness (cold, drought, low nitrogen and sometimes other nutrients) also increase heat hardiness. There is even some evidence that the seasonal change in heat hardiness follows that in dehydration hardiness—i.e. it rises in late autumn (Illert, 1924). Light may sometimes have the same effect on both; e.g. when it induces stomatal opening, the hardiness of the guard cells to both frost and heat increases (Weber, 1926).

2. Factors correlated with dehydration hardiness (e.g. low moisture and high sugar content) have also shown a good correlation with heat hardiness, though in both cases exceptions occur.

3. The order of hardiness of different cells to dehydration parallels the order of heat hardiness. Guard cells (when open) are more hardy than the other epidermal cells to both frost and heat (Weber, 1926). Three kinds of orange peel cells follow the same order of hardiness to both dehydration and heat (Levitt and Nelson, 1942). The three ecological groups of marine algae show the same order of hardiness to dehydration and heat (Biebl, 1952). Even age may induce similar changes in hardiness to both agents, though there are complications and contradictions in both cases (Chapters 8, 19, 26).

Some exceptions have been described. Tumanov (1930) points out that millet is heat resistant though lacking frost hardiness. But no direct measurement was made of millet's heat hardiness. Carroll (1943a) found that the correlation usually held true, but some species showed a different order of hardiness to drought and heat.

That heat (like dehydration) sensitizes the protoplasm to mechanical injury was shown by Lepeschkin (1935) and more recently by Bogen's (1948) observation that the most effective way to reduce heat hardiness is to deplasmolyze the cells at the high temperature. Perhaps this is because the protoplasm solidifies before injury sets in (Sachs, 1864).

On the basis of all these similarities, it seems safe to conclude that the same factors prevent the denaturation of the protoplasmic proteins, whether they are exposed to dehydration or heat injury. According to the mechanical theory, dehydration injury is due to the interaction of two factors: (1) the mechanical weakness of protoplasm which is enhanced by dehydration, and (2) the stresses arising during dehydration. Heat injury may also be conceived of as due to a similar pair of factors: (1) the same mechanical weakness of protoplasm which causes it to succumb to (2) thermally induced oscillations. Thus the mechanical force producing the injury is different, but the protoplasmic properties that enable it to tolerate these forces would be the same. The common denominator might be called protoplasmic cohesion—i.e. the resistance of protein bonds to forces tending to break them and leading to unfolding and denaturation of the molecules.

The only general theory to date that seems capable of explaining this protoplasmic tolerance of forces tending to disrupt it, is the protection of these bonds, perhaps by water bound in hardy protoplasm. This theory was most strongly championed by Gortner during his lifetime. Enthusiasm for it has since waned, not only because of the loss of its champion, but also because the evidence he produced in its favor was unfortunately erroneous (Chapter 10). New evidence produced more recently is less easily discounted (see Chapter 10).

The protection of the proteins from denaturation by bound water may also be visualized in a manner that is in a sense the opposite of Gortner's concept. The bonds within a folded protein molecule must be protected from rupture, for this would lead to unfolding and denaturation of the molecule. This protection may involve a strengthening of these intramolecular bonds as suggested above, But it may just as conceivably be due to a *weakening* of the *inter*molecular bonds. If the latter are too strong to be ruptured by a mechanical stress, the *intra*molecular bonds may give way. On the other hand, if the intermolecular bonds are loosened by the entrance of water molecules, any tension on the protoplasm may simply result in a displacement of the protein molecules relative to each other, and no tension on the intramolecular bonds could arise. This interpretation actually agrees better with the observed stiffening and even rupture of nonhardy protoplasm under conditions of tension that fail to injure hardy protoplasm, and with the increase in quantity of water-soluble protein associated with hardening.

But the similarity between the different kinds of hardiness is not complete. Just as intracellular freezing injury is quite different from the dehydration injury caused by extracellular freezing, so also heat hardiness due to speed of resynthesis of proteins to replace those denatured by heat would in no way be related to dehydration hardiness. But the very existence of the correlation indicates that this resynthesis is not the main factor in the heat hardiness of higher plants.

Since the term hardiness is used for the ability of the plant to survive exposure of its protoplasm to any unfavorable environmental factors, dehydration hardiness and heat hardiness do not exhaust the possibilities. Do plants also vary in their hardiness to radiation and to chemicals such as salts, toxins, etc.? Before attempting to answer this question, it must first be emphasized once more that hardiness is not synonymous with resistance. Nothing can be stated about the plant's hardiness unless it is known just what quantity of radiation or chemical is attained *inside the cell*. As seen above (Chapters 2, 25), the plant cannot long avoid temperature injury by maintaining its temperature above or below that of its enviroment. Nor can it avoid rapid dehydration to the same degree as its environment, if sections of tissue are directly exposed to it. But when a plant is exposed to radiations, the fraction reaching its protoplasm cannot be the same as that incident on its surface and will vary to an unknown degree from plant to plant and from tissue to tissue. When exposed to chemicals, the concentration inside the cell may never become equal to that outside it.

It is not surprising, therefore, that the few investigations of radiation and chemical injury have failed to determine the plant's hardiness, though resistance has been investigated. Linsbauer (1926) observed more rapid injury to guard cells of closed than to those of open stomata when placed in a solution of a leuco dye. The relation paralleled frost hardiness, but Linsbauer points to evidence of a greater permeability in the more readily injured cells. Sergejev and Lebedev (1936) concluded that the resistance of wheat and rye seedlings to salt solutions (NaCl, Na_2SO_4, Na_2CO_3) paralleled their frost hardiness. Unfortunately, however, they showed that their "salt resistant" plants actually absorbed less salt, and therefore their results fail to give any information about salt hardiness.

Biebl (1952, 1952a) uses the term "ecological resistance" for the adaptation of plants to drought, cold, heat, strong light, etc. The three ecological groups of marine algae showed the same relative ecological resistance to all these agents. Thus the species in intertidal locations were less sensitive to strong light than those deeply submerged or shaded. This difference, however, is far more likely to be due to external morphological or color differences than to internal protoplasmic differences, and therefore gives no information about hardiness to strong light. In contrast to this ecological resistance, he speaks of a "nonenvironment, constitutional resistance"—a resistance to substances or influences which play no important role in the life of the plant under normal conditions. Resistance to ultraviolet light bore no relation to the habitat of the plant, and there was no similarity in the resistance to different chemical substances—e.g. H_3BO_3, $ZnSO_4$, $VOSO_4$.

Hardiness to injurious agents other than dehydration and heat is thus an open field that has yet to be investigated. Preliminary results indicate that Maximov's (1929) sweeping generalization (see quotation at beginning of Part II) is too broad and all-inclusive. For though dehydration and heat hardiness go hand in hand, there is no evidence and no a priori reason for expecting that other kinds of hardiness are also included.

References

ABBE, C. 1894. The influence of cold on plants—a resume. *U. S. Dept. Agr. Expt. Sta. Record* **6**: 777-781.

ABBOTT, O. 1923. Chemical changes at beginning and ending of rest period in apple and peach. *Botan. Gaz.* **76**: 167-184.

AHRNS, W. 1924. Weitere Untersuchungen über die Abhängigkeit des gegenseitigen Mengenverhältnisses der Kohlenhydrate im Laubblatt vom Wassergehalt. *Botan. Arch.* **5**: 234-259.

ÅKERMAN, Å. 1919. Über die Bedeutung der Art des Auftauens für die Erhaltung gefrorener Pflanzen. *Botan. Notiser,* pp. 49-64, 105-126.

ÅKERMAN, Å. 1923. The resistance shown by numerous varieties of wheat at Svalöf during the winter of 1921-22. (Abstract) *Intern. Rev. Sci. Practice Agr.* **1** (part 1): 350-353.

ÅKERMAN, Å. 1927. "Studien über den Kältetod und die Kälteresistenz der Pflanzen" pp. 1-232. Berlingska Boktryckeriet, Lund, Swenden.

ÅKERMAN, A., ANDERSSON, G., and LINDBERG, J. E. 1935. Studien über die Winterfestigkeit des Roggens. *Z. Pflanzenzücht.* **6**: 137-168.

ALGERA, L. 1936. Concerning the influence of temperature treatment on the carbohydrate metabolism, the respiration, and the morphological development of the tulip. I-III. *Koninkl. Ned. Akad. Wetenschap. Amsterdam Proc.* **39**: 1-29.

ALLEN, M. B. 1950. The dynamic nature of thermophily. *J. Gen. Physiol.* **33**: 205-214.

ANDERSON, A., and KIESSELBACH, T. A. 1934. Studies on the technic of control hardiness tests with winter wheat. *J. Am. Soc. Agron.* **26**: 44-50.

ANDERSSEN, F. G. 1929. Some seasonal changes in the tracheal sap of pear and apricot trees. *Plant Physiol.* **4**: 459-476.

ANDERSSON, G. 1934. Winterhardiness of rye (trans. title) *Sveriges Utsädesfören. Tidskr.* **44**: 409-416. (*Biol. Abstr.* **11**: 1550, 1937.)

ANDERSSON, G. 1935. Auslese von winterfesten Transgressionen bei Wintergerste durch Gefrierversuche. *Züchter* **7**: 254-260.

ANDERSSON, G. 1944. "Gas Change and Frost Hardening Studies in Winter Cereals," 163 pp. Håkan Ohlssons Boktryckeri, Lund, Sweden.

ANGELO, E., IVERSON, V. E., BRIERLEY, W. G., and LANDON, R. H. 1939. Studies on some factors relating to hardiness in the strawberry. *Minnesota Agr. Expt. Sta. Tech. Bull.* **135**: 1-36.

ANONYMOUS. 1935. Winter injury to fruit and nut varieties in New York State. *New York Agr. Expt. Sta. Circ.* **156**: 1-18.

ANTEVS, E. 1916. Zur Kenntnis der jährlichen Wandlungen der stickstoffreien Reservestoffe der Holzpflanzen. *Arch. Botan.* **14**: No. 16, 1-25.

APELT, A. 1907. Neue Untersuchungen über den Kältetod der Kartoffel. *Beitr. Biol. Pflanz.* **9**: 215-262.

ARAKERI, H. R., and SCHMID, A. R. 1949. Cold resistance of various legumes and grasses in early stages of growth. *Agron. J.* **41**: 182-185.

ARLAND, A. 1931. Krankheitsbefall, Anfälligkeit, Pflanzenernährung, und Winterfestigkeit in ihren Beziehungen untereinander und zur Transpiration. *Arch. Pflanzenbau* **7**: 79-125.

ARLAND, A. 1932. Kalidüngung und Frostschutzwirkung. *Ernähr. Pflanze* **28**: 61-64.

ARREGUIN, B., and BONNER, J. 1949 Experiments on sucrose formations by potato tubers as influenced by temperature. *Plant Physiol.* **24**: 720-737.

ARRHENIUS, O., and SÖDERBERG, E. 1917. Der osmotische Druck der Hochgebirgspflanzen. *Svensk. Botan. Tidskr.* **11**: 373-380.

ASKENASY, E. 1875. Ueber die Temperatur, welche Pflanzen im Sonnenlicht annehmen. *Botan. Z.* **33**: 441-444.

AYRES, A. A. 1916. The temperature coefficient of the duration of life of Ceramium tenuissimum. *Botan. Gaz.* **62**: 65-69. 389-420.

BADALLA, L. 1911. Le svernamento della piante sempreverxi nel clima del Piemonte. *Botan. Centr.* **117**: 456.

BAKER, F. S. 1929. Effect of excessively high temperatures on coniferous reproduction. *J. Forestry* **27**: 949-975.

BAKKE, A. L., RADSPINNER, W. A., and MANEY, T. J. 1920. A new factor in the determination of the hardiness of the apple. *Proc. Am. Soc. Hort. Sci.* **17**: 279-289.

BALDE, H. 1930. Vergleichende chemische und refractometrische Untersuchungen an Weizenkeimlingen unter Berücksichtigung der Frosthärte der untersuchten Sorten. *Angew. Botan.* **12**: 177-211.

BANGA, O. 1936. Physiologische Symptomen van Lage-Temperatuur-Bederf. *Lab. v. Tuinbouwplant.* (Wageningen) **24**: 3-143.

BARINOWA, R. A. 1937. The dynamics of the carbohydrate colloid complex as a factor of drought resistance in sugar beet. *Izvest. Akad. Nauk S.S.S.R. Ser. Biol.* No. **1**: 255-270.

BARTEL, A. T. 1947. Some physiological characteristics of four varieties of spring wheat presumably differing in drought resistance. *J. Agr. Research* **74**: 97-112.

BARTETZKO, H. 1909. Untersuchungen über das Erfrieren von Schimmelpilzen. *Jahrb. wiss. Botan.* **47**: 57-98.

BARULINA, E. I. 1923. The winter resistance of cereals. *Ann. Inst. Agron. Saratov* **1**: 42-57. (*Expt. Sta. Record* **50**: 231-232, 1924.)

BATCHELOR, L. D. 1922. Winter injury to young walnut trees during 1921-22. *Colorado Agr. Expt. Sta. Circ.* **234**: 1-5.

BATES, C. G. 1923. Physiological requirements of Rocky Mountain trees. *J. Agr. Research* **24**: 97-164.

BAUMANN, A. 1902. Schutzwirkung des Kalis gegen Frost. *Arb. deut. Landwirtschges.* **67**: 10-11.

BAYLES, B. B., TAYLOR, J. W., and BARTEL, A. T. 1937. Rate of water loss in wheat varieties and resistance to artificial drought. *J. Am. Soc. Agron.* **29**: 40-52.

BEACH, S. A., and ALLEN, F. W. 1915. Hardiness in the apple as correlated with structure and composition. *Iowa Agr. Expt. Sta. Research Bull.* **21**.

BECK, W. A. 1929. The effect of drought on the osmotic value of plant tissues. *Protoplasma* **8**: 70-126.

BECQUEREL, P. 1907. Recherches sur la vie latente des grains. *Ann. Sci. Nat. Ser.* **9**(5): 193-311.

BECQUEREL, P. 1932. L'anhydrobiose des tubercules des Renoncules dans l'azote liquide. *Compt. rend.* **194**: 1974-1976.

BECQUEREL, P. 1937. La mort par le gel de la cellule végétale dans l'azote liquide à —190°. *Compt. rend.* **204**: 1267-1269.

BECQUEREL, P. 1939. Role de la synérèse dans le mécanisme de la congélation cellulaire. *Chron. Botan.* **5**: 10-11.

BECQUEREL, P. 1949. L'action du froid sur la cellule végétale. *Botaniste* **34**: 57-74.

BECQUEREL, P. 1951. (Apparent death of algae, lichens, and mosses near absolute zero, and role of reversible syneresis for their survival after thaw as a possible explanation of the existence of polar and alpine floras.) *Compt. rend.* **232**(1): 22-25.

BECQUEREL, P. 1953. La cryosynérèse cytonucléoplasmique et sa distinction de la plasmolyse, de la coagulation, et de la solidification du protoplasme congèlé. *Compt. rend.* **237**: 1473.

BECQUEREL, P. 1954. La cryosynérèse cytonucléoplasmique jusqu' aux confins du zero absolu, son role pour la végétation polaire et la conservation de la vie. *8th Congr. Inter. Botan.* **11**: 269-270.

BELEHRADEK, J., and MELICHAR, J. 1930. L'action différente des températures élevées et des températures normales sur la survie de la cellule végétale (Helodea canadensis, Rich.). *Biol. Gen.* **6**: 109-124.

BELEHRADEK, J. 1935. Temperature and living matter. *Protoplasma Monograph.* **8**: 277 pp.

BENNETT, J. P. 1934. The effect of low temperature on the retention of solutes by potato tissues. *11th Meeting Am. Soc. Plant Physiol.*, Pittsburgh.

BEREZNICKAJA, N. I., and OVECKIN, S. K. 1936. The enzymatic activity in winter wheat during winter. *Zbirnik. prats. Agrofiziol.* **1**: 186-197. (*Herbage Abstr.* **8**: 1788, 1938).

BEREZNICKAJA, N. I., and OVECKIN, S. K. 1936a. Activity of enzymes in relation to winter hardiness and phasic development of winter wheat. *Zbirnik. prats. Agrofiziol.* **2**: 67-82. (*Herbage Abstr.* **8**: 1860, 1938.)

BIEBL, R. 1938. Trockenresistenz und osmotische Empfindlichkeit der Meeresalgen verschieden tiefer Standorte. *Jahrb. wiss. Botan.* **86**: 350-386.

BIEBL, R. 1939. Über die Temperaturresistenz von Meeresalgen verschiedener Klimazonen und verschieden tiefer Standorte. *Jahrb. wiss. Botan.* **88**: 389-420.

BIEBL, R. 1942. Borwirkung auf Pisum sativum. *Jahrb. wiss. Botan.* **90**: 731-749.

BIEBL, R. 1952. Ecological and non-environmental constitutional resistance of the protoplasm of marine algae. *J. Marine Biol. Assoc. United Kingdom* **31**: 307-315.

BIEBL, R. 1952a. Resistenz der Meeresalgen gegen sichtbares Licht und gegen kurzwellige UV-Strahlen. *Protoplasma* **41**: 353-377.

BINZ, E. 1939. Untersuchungen über die Dürreresistenz verschiedener Getreidesorten bei Austrocknung des Bodens. *Jahrb. wiss. Botan.* **88**: 470-518.

BLAGOWESTSCHENSKI, A. W. 1926. Der osmotische Wert bei den Gebirgspflanzen Mittelasiens. *Jahrb. wiss. Botan.* **65**: 279-313.

BLANCHARD, K. C. 1940. Water, free and bound. *Cold Spring Harbor Symposia Quant. Biol.* **8**: 1-8.

BLINN, P. K. 1911. Alfalfa. The relation of type to hardiness. *Colorado Bull.* **181**: 1-16.

BLUM, G. 1937. Osmotische Untersuchungen in Java II. Untersuchungen in Trockengebieten Ostjavas. *Ber. schweiz. botan. Ges.* **47**: 400-416.

BOBART, J. 1684. "Philosophical Transactions and Collections to the End of the year 1700." (Abridged and disposed under general heads.) Vol. 2, 4th ed. pp. 155-160, 1731.

BOBKO, E. W., and POPOWA, R. A. 1929. Beiträge zur Frage über die Dürre-und Kälteresistenz der Pflanzen. Mitteilung I. Gebundenes Wasser in den nach der Kälteresistenz verschiedenen Weizensorten. Z. Pflanzenernähr. Düng. u. Bodenk. 13: 24-37.

BOGDANOV, P. 1935. Photoperiodism in species of woody plants. Preliminary contribution. Expt. Sta. Record 73: 22.

BOGEN, H. J. 1948. Untersuchungen über Hitzetod und Hitzeresistenz pflanzlicher Protoplaste. Planta 36(3/4): 298-340.

BOON-LONG, T. S. 1941. Transpiration as influenced by osmotic concentration and cell permeability. Am. J. Botany 28: 333-343.

BOSWELL, V. R. 1923. Dehydration of certain plant tissues. Botan. Gaz. 75: 86-94.

BOSWELL, V. R. 1925. A study of some environmental factors influencing the shooting to seed of wintered-over cabbage. Proc. Am. Soc. Hort. Sci. 22: 380-393. (Biol. Abstr. 1: 1057.)

BOWDEN, W. M. 1940. Diploidy, polyploidy, and winter hardiness relationships in the flowering plants. Am. J. Botany 27: 357-371.

BRADFORD, F. C., and CARDINELL, H. A. 1922. Observations on winter injury. Missouri Agr. Expt. Sta. Research Bull. 56.

BRANDON, D. 1939. Seasonal variations of starch content in the genus Rosa and their relation to propagation by stem cuttings. J. Pomol. Hort. Sci. 17: 233-235.

BRAUN-BLANQUET, J. 1931. Zur Frage der "Physiologischen Trockenheit" der Salzböden. Ber. schweiz. botan. Ges. 40: 33-39.

BRIERLEY, W. G., and LANDON, R. H. 1938. A study of the winter respiration of the strawberry plant. Proc. Am. Soc. Hort. Sci. 36: 480-482.

BRIERLEY, W. G., and LANDON, R. H. 1939. The effect of ice upon the survival of strawberry plants. Proc. Am. Soc. Hort. Sci. 37: 557-563.

BRIERLEY, W. G., and LANDON, R. H. 1946. A study of cold resistance of the roots of the Latham red raspberry. Proc. Am. Soc. Hort. Sci. 47: 215-218.

BRIERLEY, W. G., and LANDON, R. H. 1946a. Some relationships between rest period, rate of hardening, loss of cold resistance and winter injury in the Latham raspberry. Proc. Am. Soc. Hort. Sci. 47: 224-234.

BRIGGS, D. R., and SIMINOVITCH, D. 1949. The chemistry of the living bark of the black locust tree in relation to frost hardiness. II. Seasonal variations in the electrophoresis pattern of the water-soluble proteins of the bark. Arch. Biochem. 23: 18-28.

BRIGINEC, N., and TREGUBENKO, M. 1939. On bound water in plant tissues. Kolloid-Z. 5: 95-103. (Herbage Abstr. 10: 275, 1940.)

BROWN, H. T., and ESCOMBE, F. 1897. The influence of very low temperatures on the germinative power of seeds. Proc. Roy. Soc. 62: 160-165.

BROWN, R. T., and POTTER, G. F. 1949. Relation of fertilizers to cold injury to tung trees occurring at Lucedale, Mississippi in March 1948. Proc. Am. Soc. Hort. Sci. 53: 109-113.

BUCHINGER, A. 1929. Der Einfluss hoher Anfangstemperaturen auf die Keimung, dargestellt an Trifolium pratense. Jahrb. wiss. Botan. 71: 149-153.

BÜNNING, E., and HERDTLE, H. 1946. Physiologische Untersuchungen an thermophilen Blaualgen. Z. Naturforsch. 1(2): 93-99.

BUGAEVSKY, M. F.   1939.   Dynamics of vegetable cell decay due to low temperature. *Compt. rend. acad. sci. U.R.S.S.* **22**: 131-134.

BUGAEVSKY, M. F.   1939a.   Contribution to the study of causes of death in root crops subjected to low temperatures. *Compt. rend. acad. sci. U.R.S.S.* **25**: 527-530.

BUHLERT, H.   1906.   Untersuchungen über das Auswintern des Getreides. *Landwirtsch. Jahrb.* **35**: 837-887.

BURR, G. O.   1936.   *13th Ann. Meeting Soc. Plant. Physiol.*, Atlantic City.

BUTLER, O. R., SMITH, T. O., and CURRY, B. E.   1917.   Physiology of the apple. Distribution of food materials in the tree at different periods of vegetation. *New Hampshire Agr. Expt. Sta. Tech. Bull.* **13**: 1-21.

CAJLACHJAN, M. H.   1935.   On the permeability of the plasma in the leaves of spring and winter wheats. *Compt. rend. acad. sci. U.R.S.S.* **2**: 158-160.

CALDWELL, J. S.   1913.   The relation of environmental conditions to the phenomenon of permanent wilting in plants. *Physiol. Research* **1**: 1-56.

CALVERT, J.   1935.   Drought resistance in wheat. The "bound" and "free" water of expressed sap from wheat leaves in relation to time and soil moisture. *Protoplasma* **24**(4): 505-524.

CAMARGO, T. DE ALMEIDA.   1921.   Chemical changes in coffee leaves killed by cold. Escola Agr. "Luis de Queiroz" Piracicaba. *Brazil. Boll.* **8**: 1-17, 1921. (E.S.R. **48**: 222, 1923.)

CANDOLLE, A. DE   1838.   Sur les éffets du froid rigoureux du mois de Janvier 1838 dans les environs de Génève. *Verhandl. schweiz. naturforsch. Ges.* **23**: 123.

CANDOLLE, C. DE.   1895.   Sur la vie latente des graines. *Bibl. Univ. Arch. sci. phys. nat.* [3] **33**: 497-512.

CAROLUS, R. L.   1930.   Effect of seasonal temperatures on chemical composition of kale. *Proc. Am. Soc. Hort. Sci.* **27**: 502-508.

CARRICK, D. B.   1920.   Resistance of the roots of some fruit species to low temperature. *Cornell Mem.* **36**: 613-661.

CARRICK, D. B.   1929.   The effect of freezing on the catalase activity of apple fruits. *Cornell Mem.* **122**: 1-18.

CARROLL, J. C.   1943.   Atmospheric drought tests of some pasture and turf grasses. *J. Am. Soc. Agron.* **35**: 77-79.

CARROLL, J. C.   1943a.   Effects of drought, temperature, and nitrogen on turf grasses. *Plant Physiol.* **18**: 19-36.

CARROLL, J. C., and WELTON, F. A.   1939.   Effect of heavy and late applications of nitrogenous fertilizer on the cold resistance of Kentucky bluegrass. *Plant Physiol.* **14**: 297-308.

CASPARY, R.   1854.   Auffallende Eisbildung auf Pflanzen. *Botan. Ztg.* **12**: 665-674; 681-690; 697-706.

CASPARY, R.   1857.   Bewirkt die Sonne Risse in Rinde und Holz der Bäume? *Botan. Ztg.* **15**: 153-156; 329-335; 345-350; 361-371.

CAVALLERO, 1888, 1891.   Cited by Abbe, 1894.

CHAMBERS, R., and HALE, H. P.   1932.   The formation of ice in protoplasm. *Proc. Roy. Soc.* **B110**: 337-352.

CHANDLER, R. C.   1937.   The nature of "bound" water in plant sap and some effects of nutrition and temperature thereon. Dissertation, Univ. of Calif.

CHANDLER, R. C. 1941. Nature of bound water in colloidal systems. *Plant Physiol.* **16**: 273-291.

CHANDLER, R. C. 1941a. Bound water in plant sap and some effects of temperature and nutrition thereon. *Plant Physiol.* **16**: 785-798.

CHANDLER, W. H. 1913. The killing of plant tissue by low temperature. *Missouri Agr. Expt. Sta. Research Bull.* **8**.

CHANDLER, W. H. 1914. Sap studies with horticultural plants. *Missouri Agr. Expt. Sta. Research Bull.* **14**: 491-552.

CHANDLER, W. H. 1919. Winter injury in New York state during 1917-1918. *Proc. Am. Soc. Hort. Sci.* **15**: 18-24.

CHANDLER, W. H. 1945. "Trees in Two Climates." U. of California Press, Berkeley.

CHANDLER, W. H., and HILDRETH, A. C. 1935. Evidence as to how freezing kills plant tissue. *Proc. Am. Soc. Hort. Sci.* **33**: 27-35.

CHIBNALL, A. C. 1939. "Protein Metabolism in the Plant." Yale U. P., New Haven.

CHOMIEL, M. 1710. Sur les arbres morts par la gelée de 1709. Histoire de l'Academie Royal des Sciences (Avec les memoires, etc.), pp. 59-61.

CHRIST, H. 1911. Die Vegetation unter dem Einfluss des trockenen Sommers 1911 im nördlichen Jura. *Ber. schweiz. botan. Ges.* **20**: 254-258.

CHRISTOFF, M. A. 1939. Untersuchungen über die Kältefestigkeit der Wintergerste. *Z. Pflanzenzücht.* **23**: 47-90.

CHRISTOPHERSEN, J., and PRECHT, H. 1952. Untersuchungen zum Problem der Hitzeresistenz. II. Untersuchungen an Hefezellen. *Biol. Zentr.* **71**(11/12): 585-601.

CHRISTOPHERSEN, J., and PRECHT, H. 1953. Die Bedeutung des Wassergehaltes der Zelle für Temperaturanpassungen. *Biol. Zentr.* **72** (1/2): 104-119.

CHU, CHIEN-REN. 1936. Der Einfluss des Wassergehaltes der Blätter der Waldbäume auf ihre Saugkräfte und ihren Turgor. *Flora* **130**: 384-437.

CIVINSKIJ, V. 1934. Capacity of cotton to withstand cold. *Compt. rend. acad. sci. U.R.S.S.* **1**: 149-150.

CLEMENTS, H. F. 1937. Studies in drought resistance of the soy bean. *Research Studies State Coll. Washington* **5**(1): 1-16.

CLEMENTS, H. F. 1937a. Studies in the drought resistance of the sunflower and potato. *Botan. Dept. State. Coll. Washington Contrib.* No. **59**: 81-98.

CLEMENTS, H. F. 1938. Mechanisms of freezing resistance in the needles of *Pinus ponderosa* and *Pseudotsuga mucronata*. *Research Studies State Coll. Washington* **6**(1): 3-45.

COCKERHAM, G. 1930. Some observations on cambial activity and seasonal starch content in sycamore (*Acer pseudoplatanus*). *Proc. Leeds Phil. Lit. Soc.* **2** (Part 2): 64-80.

COHN, F., and DAVID, G. 1871. Wirkung der Kälte auf Pflanzenzellen. *Naturforscher.* No. **39**: 316.

COLLANDER, R. 1924. Beobachtungen über die quantitativen Beziehungen zwischen Tötungsgeschwindigkeit und Temperatur beim Wärmetod pflanzlicher Zellen. *Soc. Sci. Fennica Commentationes O. Biol.* **1**(7): 1-12.

COLLANDER, R., and BÄRLUND, H. 1933. Permeabilitätsstudien an *Chara ceratophylla*. II. Die Permeabilität für Nichtelektrolyte. *Acta botan. Fennica* **11**: 1-114.

COLLISON, R. C., and HARLAN, J. D. 1934. Winter injury of Baldwin apple trees and its relation to previous tree performance and nutritional treatment. *New York (Geneva) Agr. Expt. Sta. Bull.* **647**: 1-13.

CONSTANTINESCU, E. 1933. Weitere Beiträge zur Physiologie der Kälteresistenz bei Wintergetreide. *Planta* **21**: 304-323.

COOK, C. W. 1943. A study of the roots of Bromus inermis in relation to drought resistance. *Ecology* **24**: 169-182.

COOPER, J. R., and WIGGANS, C. B. 1929. A study on the effect of commercial fertilizers on the performance of peach trees. *Arkansas Agr. Expt. Sta. Bull.* **239**: 1-62.

COUTURIER, A. 1903. Frost and potash fertilisers. *J. Agr. prat.* [n.s.] **6**: 118-119. (*Expt. Sta. Record* **15**: 236, 1903-04.)

COVILLE, F. V. 1920. The influence of cold in stimulating the growth of plants. *J. Agr. Research* **20**: 151-160.

CRAFTS, A. S. 1935. Physiological problems connected with the use of sodium chlorate in weed control. *Plant Physiol.* **10**: 699-711.

CRÉPIN, C., ALABOUVETTE, L., MÉNERET, G., and CHEVALIER, R. 1929. Étude sur la résistance au froid du blé et de l'avoine. *Ann. sci. agron.* [6] **46**: 661-718.

CRESCINI, F., and TETTAMANZI, A. 1929. Sulla resistenza del grano alle bassa temperature. *Italia Agr.* **66**: 546-552. (*Biol. Abstr.* **6**: 15613, 1932).

CURTIS, O. F. 1938. Wallace and Clum "leaf temperatures": A critical analysis with additional data. *Am. J. Botany* **25**: 761-771.

CZAPEK, F. 1901. Der Kohlenhydrat-Stoffwechsel der Laubblätter in Winter. *Ber. deut. botan. Ges.* **19**: 120-127.

DALMER, M. 1895. Über Eisbildung in Pflanzen mit Rücksicht auf die anatomische Beschaffenheit derselben. *Flora* **80**: 436-444.

DANGEARD, P. 1951. Observations sur la résistance des radicules de diverses plantes à des températures entre 40 et 60°. *Compt. rend.* **232**: 913-915.

DANGEARD, P. 1951a. Observations sur la destruction du chondriome par la chaleur. *Compt. rend.* **232**: 1274-1276.

DANGEARD, P. 1951b. Observations sur la résistance des radicules à des températures entre 40 et 60°. *Botaniste (Paris)* **35** (1/6): 237-243.

DANIEL, L. 1928. Résistance au froid des descendants de l'Artemisia absinthium greffée sur le Chrysanthemum frutescens. *Botaniste* **20**: 255-257.

DÄNIKER, A. U. 1923. Biologische Studien über Baum- und Waldgrenze, insbesondere über die klimatischen Ursachen und deren Zusammenhänge. *Vierteljahrsschr. naturforsch. Ges. Zurich* **68**: 3-102.

D'ARBAUMONT, J. 1901. Sur l'évolution de la chlorophylle et de l'amidon dans la tige de quelques végétaux ligneux. *Ann. sci. nat. Ser. 8 Botan.* **14**: 125-212.

D'ARSONVAL, M. 1901. La pression osmotique et son rôle de défense contre le froid dans la cellule vivante. *Compt. rend.* **133**: 84-86.

DARWIN, E. 1800. *Phytologia*, 275-276.

DAY, W. R., and PEACE, T. R. 1934. The experimental production and the diagnosis of frost injury on forest trees. *Oxford Forest Mem.* **16**: 1-60. (*Biol. Abstr.* **9**: 5667, 1935.)

DAY, W. R., and PEACE, T. R. 1937. The influence of certain accessory factors on frost injury to forest trees. II. Temperature conditions before freezing. III. Time factors. *Forestry* **11**: 13-29.

DAY, W. R., and PEACE, T. R. 1937a. The influence of certain accessory factors on frost injury to forest trees. IV. Air and soil conditions. *Forestry* **11**: 92-103.

DELACROIX, G. 1908. "Maladies des plantes cultivées. Maladies non parasitaire, *in* "Encyclopodie Agricole," p. 123. Ballière, Paris.

DE LONG, W. A. 1924. Pentosan content in relation to hardiness of the apple. Master's Thesis. McGill University.

DE LONG, W. A., BEAUMONT, J. H., and WILLAMAN, J. J. 1930. Respiration of apple twigs in relation to winter hardiness. *Plant Physiol.* **5**: 509-534.

DETMER, W. 1886. Über Zerstörung der Molekularstructur des Protoplasmas der Pflanzenzellen. *Botan. Ztg.* **44**: 513-524.

DE VISSER SMITS, D. 1926. Einfluss der Temperatur auf die Permeabilität des Protoplasmas bei *Beta vulgaris*. L. *Rec. trav. botan. néerl.* **23**: 104-199.

DE VRIES, H. 1870. Matériaux pour la connaissance de l'influence de la température sur les plantes. *Arch. néerl. sci.* **5**: 385-401.

DE VRIES, H. 1871. Sur la mort des cellules végétales par l'effet d'une température élevée. *Arch. néerl. sci.* **6**: 245-295.

DEXTER, S. T. 1932. Studies of the hardiness of plants: a modification of the Newton pressure method for small samples. *Plant Physiol.* **7**: 721-726.

DEXTER, S. T. 1933. Effect of several environmental factors on the hardening of plants. *Plant Physiol.* **8**: 123-139.

DEXTER, S. T. 1933a. Decreasing hardiness of winter wheat in relation to photosynthesis, defoliation, and winter injury. *Plant Physiol.* **8**: 297-304.

DEXTER, S. T. 1934. Salt concentration and reversibility of ice formation as related to the hardiness of winter wheat. *Plant Physiol.* **9**: 601-618.

DEXTER, S. T. 1934a. Respiratory rate and enzyme activity as related to the hardened condition of plants. *Plant Physiol.* **9**: 831-837.

DEXTER, S. T. 1935. Growth, organic nitrogen fractions and buffer capacity in relation to hardiness of plants. *Plant Physiol.* **10**: 149-158.

DEXTER, S. T. 1935a. Salt concentration and reversibility of ice-formation as related to the hardiness of alfalfa. *Plant Physiol.* **10**: 403-407.

DEXTER, S. T. 1937. The winterhardiness of weeds. *J. Am. Soc. Agron.* **29**: 512-517.

DEXTER, S.T. 1941. Effects of periods of warm weather upon the winter hardened condition of a plant. *Plant Physiol.* **16**: 181-188.

DEXTER, S. T. 1942. Seasonal variations in drought resistance of exposed rhizomes of quack grass. *J. Am. Soc. Agron.* **34**: 1125-1136.

DEXTER, S. T., TOTTINGHAM, W. E., and GRABER, L. F. 1930. Preliminary results in measuring the hardiness of plants. *Plant Physiol.* **5**: 215-223.

DEXTER, S. T., TOTTINGHAM, W. E., and GRABER, L. F. 1932. Investigations of hardiness of plants by measurement of electrical conductivity. *Plant Physiol.* **7**: 63-78.

DILLMAN, A. C. 1941. Cold tolerance in flax. *J. Am. Soc. Agron.* **33**: 787-799.

DIXON, H. H., and ATKINS, W. R. G. 1912. Variations in the osmotic pressure of the sap of Ilex aquifolium. *Sci. Proc. Roy. Dublin Soc.* **13**: 229-238.

DIXON, H. H., and ATKINS, W. R. G. 1912a. Variations in the osmotic pressure of the sap of Hedera helix. *Sci. Proc. Roy. Dublin Soc.* **13**: 239-246.

DIXON, H. H., and ATKINS, W. R. G. 1913. On osmotic pressure in plants. I. Methods of extracting sap from plant organs. *Sci. Proc. Roy. Dublin Soc.* **13**: 422-433.

DIXON, H. H., and ATKINS, W. R. G. 1915. V. Seasonal variations in the concentration of the cell sap of some deciduous and evergreen trees. *Sci. Proc. Roy. Dublin Soc.* **14**: 445-461.

DODONOVA, E. V., and IVANOV, N. I. 1939. A study of biochemical characters of spring and winter wheats. *Selek. Semenovod.* No. 2/3, 16-21. *Herbage Abstr.* **10**: 298, 1940.)

DÖRING, H. 1932. Beiträge zur Frage der Hitzeresistenz pflanzlicher Zellen. *Planta* **18**: 405-434.

DÖRR, M. 1941. Temperaturmessungen an Pflanzen des Frauensteins bei Mödling. *Botan. Centr. Beih.* **60**(a): 679-728.

DOMIEN, F. 1949. Influence de la deshydratation sur las respiration des feuilles de végétaux aeriens. *Rév. gén. botan.* **56**: 285-317.

DORSEY, M. J. 1934. Ice formation in the fruit bud of the peach. *Proc. Am. Soc. Hort. Sci.* **31**: 22-27.

DORSEY, M. J., and BUSHNELL, J. W. 1920. The hardiness problem. *Proc. Am. Soc. Hort. Sci.* **17**: 210-224.

DORSEY, M. J., and STRAUSBAUGH, P. D. 1923. Winter injury to plum during dormancy. *Botan. Gaz.* **76**: 113-142.

DOYLE, J., and CLINCH, P. 1926. The pentosan theory of cold resistance applied to conifers. *Sci. Proc. Roy. Dublin Soc.* **18**: 219-235.

DOYLE, J., and CLINCH, P. 1926a. The dehydration rates of conifer leaves in relation to pentosan content. *Sci. Proc. Roy. Dublin Soc.* **18**: 265-275.

DOYLE, J., and CLINCH, P. 1927. Seasonal changes in conifer leaves, with special reference to enzymes and starch formation. *Proc. Roy. Irish Acad.* **B37**: 373-414.

DUHAMEL DE MONCEAU, H. L. 1741. Observations Botanico-Météorologiques pour l'année 1740. *Mem. Math. Phys. Acad. Roy. Sci.* (*Paris*) pp. 149-171.

DUHAMEL DE MONCEAU, H. L. 1758. "La physique des arbres." Part 2: pp. 343-354, Paris.

DU HAMEL, H. L., and DE BUFFON, G. L. L. 1740. Observations des différents effets que produisent sur les Végétaux les grandes gelées d'Hiver et les petites gelées du Printemps. 1737. *Mem. Math. Phys. Acad. Roy. Sci.* (*Paris*) pp. 273-298.

DUMAS, L. 1903. Frosts and potash fertilisers. *J. Agr. prat.* [n.s.] **6**: 226. (*Expt. Sta. Record* **15**: 348, 1903-04).

DUNN, S. 1930. The relation of hydrophilic colloids to hardiness in the apple, as shown by the dye adsorption test. *New Hampshire Agr. Expt. Sta. Tech. Bull.* **44**.

DUNN, S. 1933. Relation of hydrophilic colloids to hardiness in cabbage, brussels sprouts and alfalfa plants as shown by the dye adsorption test. *Plant Physiol.* **8**: 275-286.

DUNN, S. 1935. Dye adsorption. *New Hampshire Agr. Expt. Sta. Bull.* **284**: 13-14.

DUNN, S. 1937. Factors affecting cold resistance in plants. *Plant Physiol.* **12**: 519-526.

DUNN, S. 1937a. Value of the dye-adsorption test for predetermining the degree of hardiness. *Plant Physiol.* **12**: 869-874.

DUNN, S., and BAKKE, A. L. 1926. Adsorption as a means of measuring relative hardiness in the apple. *Plant Physiol.* **1**: 165-177.

DUTROCHET, M. 1839. Recherches sur la température propre des végétaux. *Ann. sci. nat.* [2] **12**: 77-84.

DUTROCHET, M. 1840. Récherches sur la chaleur propre des êtres vivants à basse température. *Ann. sci. nat.* [2] **13**: 5-49, 65-85.

EATON, F. M., and ERGLE, D. R. 1948. Carbohydrate accumulation in the cotton plants at low moisture levels. *Plant Physiol.* **23**: 169-187.

EBIKO, K., and WATANABE, Y. 1935. Studies on the refractive indices of expressed juice in wheat seedlings. *Saghalien Central Expt. Sta. Repts.* [1] No. **5**: 127-147. (*Expt. Sta. Record* **77**: 762, 1937.)

EGGERT, R. 1944. Cambium temperatures of peach and apple trees in winter. *Proc. Am. Soc. Hort. Sci.* **45**: 33-36.

EGGERT, R. 1946. The construction and installation of thermocouples for biological research. *J. Agr. Research* **72**: 341-355.

EHLERS, J. H. 1915. The temperature of leaves of *Pinus* in winter. *Am. J. Botany* **2**: 32-70.

EIBL, A. 1926. Osmotische und Saugkraftmessungen an Kulturpflanzen. *Fortschr. Landwirtsch.* **1**: 661-669.

EIBL, A. 1927. Osmotische und Saugkraftmessungen an Kulturpflanzen. *Fortschr. Landwirtsch.* **2**: 123-124.

ELLET, W. B., and WOLFE, T. K. 1921. The relation of fertilisers to Hessian fly injury and winterkilling of wheat. *J. Am. Soc. Agron.* **13**: 12-14.

EREMEJEV, G. N. 1938. Drought resistance and dehydration resistance of plants. *Compt. rend. sci. U.R.S.S.* **18**: 195-198.

ESTERAK, K. B. 1935. Resistenz- Gradienten in Elodea Blättern. *Protoplasma* **23**: 367-383.

EWART, A. J. 1898. The action of cold and of sunlight upon aquatic plants. *Ann. Botany (London)* **12**: 363-397.

EWART, M. H., SIMINOVITCH, D., and BRIGGS, D. R. 1953. Studies on the chemistry of the living bark of the black locust tree in relation to frost hardiness. VI. Amylase and phosphorylase systems of the bark tissues. *Plant Physiol.* **28**: 629-644.

FABRICIUS, L. 1906. Untersuchungen über den Stärke- und Fettgehalt der Fichte auf der oberbayerischen Hochebene. *Botan. Centr.* **102**: 29-30.

FAMINTZIN, A., and BORODIN, J. 1867. Über transitorische Stärkebildung bei der Birke. *Botan. Ztg.* **25**: 385-387.

FIELD, C. P. 1939. Low temperature injury to fruit blossom. I. On the damage caused to fruit blossom by varying degrees of cold. *Ann. Rept.* (26th year) 1938. *East Malling Research Station*, pp. 127-138.

FISCHER, A. 1888. Glycose als Reservestoff der Laubhölzer. *Botan. Ztg.* **46**: 405-417.

FISCHER, A. 1891. Beiträge zur Physiologie der Holzgewächse. *Jahrb. wiss. Botan.* **22**: 73-160.

FISCHER, H. W. 1911. Gefrieren und Erfrieren, eine physico-chemische Studie. *Beitr. Biol. Pflanz.* **10**: 133-234.

FITTING, H. 1911. Die Wasserversorgung und die osmotischen Druckverhältnisse der Wüstenpflanzen. *Z. Botan.* **3**: 209-275.

FITTING, H. 1915. Untersuchungen über die Aufnahme von Salzen in die lebende Zelle. *Jahrb. wiss. Botan.* **56**: 1-64.

FRANK, B. 1879. Die Pflanzenkrankheiten. *In* "Handbuch der Botanik" (A. von Schenk, ed.), Vol. 1, pp. 327-570. Eduard Trewendt, Breslau.

FRANK, B. 1895. "Die Krankheiten der Pflanzen," 2nd ed., Vol. 1, pp. 177-216. Eduard Trewendt, Breslau.

FRECKMAN. 1934. Can we reduce or prevent frost injury on moors (transl. title). *Mitt. Ver. Förd. Moorkult. Deut. Reiche* **52**: 117-124. (*Expt. Sta. Record,* **74**: 159, 1936.)

FREY-WYSSLING, A. 1948. "Submicroscopic Morphology of Protoplasm and its Derivatives." Elsevier, New York.

FRISCHENSCHLAGER, B. 1937. Versuche über die Keimstimmung an einigen Gemüsearten. *Die Gartenwissenschaft.* **11**: 159-166.

FRITZSCHE, G. 1933. Untersuchungen über die Gewebetemperaturen von Strand-pflanzen unter dem Einfluss der Insolation. *Botan. Centr. Beih.* **50**(1): 251-322.

FUCHS, W. H. 1930. Weiteres zur Bestimmung der Kälteresistenz des Winter-weizens durch indirekte Methoden. *Arch. Pflanzenbau* **3**: 692-722.

FUCHS, W. H. 1932. Zur Prüfung der Kälteresistenz der Wintergetreide. *Fortschr. Landwirtsch.* **7**: 106-110.

FUCHS, W. H. 1934. Beiträge zur Züchtung kältefester Winterweizen. *Z. Zücht. Reihe A Pflanzenzücht.* **19**: 309-323.

FUCHS, W. H. 1935. Worauf beruht die Erhöhung der Kälteresistenz durch reich-liche Kaliernährung. *Ernähr. Pflanze* **31**: 233-234.

FUCHS, W. H. 1935a. Der Anteil des Zuckers am osmotischen Wert bei Weizen. *Planta* **23**: 340-348.

FUCHS, W. H. 1935b. Die Veränderung der Struktur und Reaktion der Zelle bei Abkühlung. *Kuhn-Arch.* **39**: 1-40.

FUJIMURA, J., and SANO, T. 1939. Seasonal changes in the starch reserves of Kaki trees. *J. Hort. Assoc.* (*Japan*) **10**: 20-26. (*Biol. Abstr.* **14**: 5520, 1940.)

FUKUDA, Y. 1932. A study of the conditions of completely frozen plant cells, with special reference to resistance to cold. *Botan. Mag.* (*Tokyo*) **46**: 239-246.

FUKUDA, Y. 1933. Hygronastic curling and uncurling movement of the leaves of *Rhododendron micranthum* Turez; with respect to temperature and resistance to cold. *Japan. J. Botany* **6**: 191-224.

FURLINGER, H. 1938. Harnstoff-Permeabilität der Epidermis etiolierter und ergrünender Blätter. *Protoplasma* **31**: 277-285.

GAIL, F. W. 1926. Osmotic pressure of cell sap and its possible relation to winter killing and leaf fall. *Botan. Gaz.* **81**: 434-445.

GARCIA, F., and RIGNEY, J. W. 1914. Hardiness of fruitbuds and flowers to frost. *New Mexico Agr. Expt. Sta. Bull.* **89**: 1-52.

GARDNER, F. E. 1929. Composition and growth initiation of dormant Bartlett pear shoots as influenced by temperature. *Plant Physiol.* **4**: 405-434.

GARDNER, V. R. 1935. The susceptibility of flower buds of the Montmorency cherry to injury from low temperature. *J. Agr. Research* **50**: 563-572.

GARDNER, V. R. 1944. Winter hardiness in juvenile and adult forms of certain conifers. *Botan. Gaz.* **105**: 408-410.

GASSNER, G. 1918. Beiträge zur physiologischen Charakteristik sommer- und winterannueller Gewächse, insbesondere der Getreidepflanzen. *Z. Botan.* **10**: 417-480.

GASSNER, G.   1929.   Die experimentelle Bestimmung der Frosthärte von Getreide-pflanzen. *Züchter* **1**: 257-264.

GASSNER, G., and GOEZE, G.   1931.   Zur Frage der Frosthärtebestimmung durch refractometrische Untersuchung von Pflanzenpresssäften. *Phytopathol. Z.* **4**(4): 387-413.

GASSNER, G., and GRIMME, C.   1913.   Beiträge zur Frage der Frosthärte der Getreidepflanzen. *Ber. deut. botan. Ges.* **31**: 507-516.

GÄUMANN, E., and JAAG, O.   1936.   Untersuchungen über die pflanzliche Tran-spiration. *Ber. schweiz. botan. Ges.* **45**: 411-518.

GEFFKEN, K.   1936.   Zur Bestimmungsmethodik biologisch wichtiger Kohlenhydrate in Pflanzenmaterial. *Botan. Arch.* **36**: 345-376.

GEHENIO, P. M., and LUYET, B. J.   1939.   A study of the mechanism of death by cold in the plasmodium of the myxomycetes. *Biodynamica* **55**: 1-22.

GERRETSEN, F. C.   1939.   Cold-resistance and manganese deficiency. *Nieuwe Vel-bode* No. **31**; 1939. *Korte meded. Ridjkslandbouwproefsta.* (Groningen) No. **92**: 3. (*Herbage Abstr.* **9**: 1089, 1939.)

GESLIN, H.   1939.   La lutte contre les gelées et les seuils de résistance des princi-pales cultures fruitières. *Ann. epiphyt. et phytogenet.* **5**: 7-16. (*Biol. Abstr.* **14**: 3663. 1940.)

GETMAN, F. H., and DANIELS, F.   1937.   "Outlines of Theoretical Chemistry." Wiley, New York.

GIBBS, R. D.   1940.   Studies in tree physiology. II. Seasonal changes in the food reserves of field birch (*Betula populifolia* Marsh.) *Can. J. Research* **C18**: 1-9.

GICKLHORN, J.   1936.   Gradienten des Erfrierens von Laubblättern. *Protoplasma* **26**: 90-96.

GLADWIN, F. E.   1917.   Winter injury of grapes. New York (*Geneva*) *Agr. Expt. Sta. Bull.* **433**.

GÖPPERT, H. R.   1830.   Über die Wärme-Entwickelung in den Pflanzen, deren Gefrieren und die Schutzmittel gegen dasselbe. Max and Comp, Berlin, Breslau.

GÖPPERT, H. R.   1871.   Höhe der Kältegrade, welche die Vegetation überhaupt erträgt. *Botan. Ztg.* **29**: 49-58, 65-76.

GÖPPERT, H. R.   1871a.   Wenn stirbt die durch Frost getödtete Pflanze, zur Zeit des Gefrierens oder im Moment des Aufthauens? *Botan. Ztg.* **29**: 399-402.

GÖPPERT, H. R.   1883.   "Über das Gefrieren. Erfrieren der Pflanzen und Schutz-mittel dagegen. Altes und Neues," Enke, Stuttgart, pp. 1-87.

GOETZ, A., and GOETZ, S. S.   1938.   Vitrification and crystallization of protophyta at low temperatures. *Am. Phil. Soc. Proc.* **79**: 361-388.

GOLDSMITH, G. W., and SMITH, J. H. C.   1926.   Some physico-chemical properties of spruce sap and their seasonal and altitudinal variation. *Colorado Coll. Publ. Gen. Ser.* No. **137**, *Colorado Coll. Publ. Sci. Ser.* **13**: 13-71.

GOLICINSKII, D. A.   1939.   The significance of age (time of sowing) on winter hardiness in winter wheat under different conditions of wintering. *Trudy Belorusck. Seljskohoz. Inst.* **8**: (30): 67-68. (*Herbage Abstr.* **10**: 183, 1940.)

GOLUS, B. M.   1935.   Changes of the plasma permeability induced by temperature effects. *Compt. rend. acad. sci. U.R.S.S.* **11**: 304-306.

GOLUS, B. M.   1938.   Permeability of plasma as a factor of resistance to cold. *Compt. rend. acad. sci. U.R.S.S.* **18**: 363-366.

GOODALE, G. L.   1885.   "Gray's Botanical Textbook," Vol. 2. Physiological botany. Ivison, Blakeman, Taylor, New York.

GOODSPEED, T. H. 1911. The temperature coefficient of the duration of life of barley grains. *Botan. Gaz.* **51**: 220-224.

GORKE, H. 1906. Über chemische Vorgänge beim Erfrieren der Pflanzen. *Landwirtsch. Versuchs Sta.* **65**: 149-160.

GORTNER, R. A. 1929, 1938. "Outlines of Biochemistry." Wiley, New York.

GORTNER, R. A., and GORTNER, W. A. 1934. The cryoscopic method for the determination of "bound water". *J. Gen. Physiol.* **17**: 327-339.

GOVOROV, L. 1923. The diverse characters of winter and spring forms of cereals in connection with the problem of hardiness in winter crops. *Bull. Appl. Botan. Genet. Plant Breeding* (*Leningrad*) **13**:525-559. (*Biol. Abstr.* **15**: 1177. 1926.)

GRABER, L. F., NELSON, N. T., LUEKEL, W. A., and ALBERT, W. B. 1927. Organic food reserves in relation to the growth of alfalfa and other perennial herbaceous plants. *Wisconsin Agr. Expt. Sta. Research Bull.* **80**: 1-128.

GRAHLE, A. 1933. Vergleichende Untersuchungen über strukturelle und osmotische Eigenschaften der Nadeln verschiedener Pinus-Arten. *Jahrb. wiss. Botan.* **78**: 203-294.

GRAINGER, J., and ALLEN, A. L. 1937. The internal temperatures of fruit-tree buds. *Ann. Appl. Biol.* **23**: 1-10. (*Biol. Abstr.* **11**: 2996. 1937.)

GRANDFIELD, C. O. 1943. Food reserves and their translocation to the crown buds as related to cold and drought resistance in alfalfa. *J. Agr. Research* **67**: 33-47.

GRANHALL, I. 1943. Genetical and physiological studies in interspecific wheat crosses. *Hereditas* **29**: 269-380.

GRANHALL, I. 1950. Frost resistance problems in fruit tree breeding. *Proc. 7th Intern. Botan. Congr., Stockholm*, pp. 201-202.

GREATHOUSE, G. A. 1932. Effects of the physical environment on the physicochemical properties of plant saps, and the relation of these properties to leaf temperature. *Plant Physiol.* **7**: 349-390.

GREATHOUSE, G. A. 1935. Unfreezable and freezable water equilibrium in plant tissues as influenced by sub-zero temperatures. *Plant Physiol.* **10**: 781-788.

GREATHOUSE, G. A. 1938. Conductivity measurements of plant sap. *Plant Physiol.* **13**: 553-569.

GREATHOUSE, G. A., and STUART, N. W. 1934. A study of the physical and chemical properties of red clover roots in the cold hardened and unhardened condition. *Univ. Maryland Agr. Sta. Bull.* **370**.

GREATHOUSE, G. A., and STUART, N. W. 1934a. A study of the physical and chemical properties of red clover roots in the cold hardened and unhardened condition. *11th Ann. Meeting Am. Soc. Plant Physiol.*, Pittsburgh.

GREATHOUSE, G. A., and STUART, N. W. 1936. Seasonal changes in the physical and chemical properties of foreign and domestic red clover plants. *12th Ann. Meeting Am. Soc. Plant Physiol. Atlantic City.*

GREATHOUSE, G. A., and STUART, N. W. 1936a. Hydration studies in fresh and dried red clover roots and shoots with reference to physical properties and chemical composition of tissue. *Plant Physiol.* **11**: 873-880.

GREATHOUSE, G. A., and STUART, N. W. 1937. Enzyme activity in cold hardened and unhardened red clover. *Plant Physiol.* **12**: 685-702.

GREBNITZKY, A. 1884. Über die jährliche Periode der Stärkespeicherung in den Zweigen unserer Bäume. *Botan. Centr.* **18**: 157.

GREELEY, A. W. 1901. On the analogy between the effect of loss of water and lowering of temperature. *Am. J. Physiol.* **6**: 122-128.

GROLLMAN, A. 1931. The vapour pressures of aqueous solutions with special reference to the problem of the state of water in biological fluids. *J. Gen. Physiol.* **14**: 661-683.

GROVES, J. F. 1917. Temperature and life duration of seeds. *Botan. Gaz.* **63**: 169-189.

GUTTENBERG, H. R. VON. 1907. Anatomisch-physiologische Untersuchungen über das immergrüne Laubblatt der Mediterranflora. *Engler's Botan. Jahrb.* **38**: 383-444.

GUTTENBERG, H. R. VON. 1907. Studien über das Verhalten des immergrünen Laubblattes der Mediterranflora zu verschiedenen Jahreszeiten. *Planta* **4**: 726-779.

GUTTENBERG, H. R. VON. 1928. F. A. Preising's Untersuchungen über den Kohlenhydratstoffwechsel immergrüner Blätter im Laufe eines Jahres. *Planta* **6**: 801-808.

HAAS, A. R. C., and HALMA, F. F. 1928. Physical and chemical characteristics of expressed citrus leaf sap and their significance. *Botan. Gaz.* **85**: 457-461.

HAAS, A. R. C., and HALMA, F. F. 1931. Sap concentration and inorganic constituents of mature citrus leaves. *Hilgardia* **5**: 407-424.

HABERLANDT, F. 1875. Wissenschaftlich-Praktische Untersuchungen auf dem Gebiete des Pflanzenbaues. Herausg. v. F. Haberlandt.

HABERLANDT, G. 1876. Über den Einfluss des Frostes auf die Chlorophyllkörner. *Österr. Botan. Z.* **26**: 249-255.

HABERLANDT, G. 1877. Über den Einfluss des Frostes auf die Chlorophyllkoerner. *Bull. soc. botan. France* **24** (Rev. Bibl.): 148.

HABERLANDT, G. 1878. Untersuchungen über die Winterfärbung ausdauernder Blätter. Sitzungsber. der kais. Akad. d. Wissensch. zu Wien 1876). *Just's Botan. Jahresber.* **4**: 895-897. (1876).

HABERLANDT, G. 1882. Vergleichende Anatomie des assimilatorischen Gewebesystems der Pflanzen. *Jahrb. wiss. Botan.* **13**: 74-188.

HAFEKOST, G. 1930. Zur Theorie der Saugkraftmessungen an Kulturpflanzen im Keimlingsstadium. *Biol. Generalis* **6**: 633-650.

HALES, S. 1727. "Vegetable Staticks," pp. 321-322. Wand J. Innys, London.

HALSTED, B. D. 1889. An investigation of apple twigs. *Iowa Agr. Expt. Sta. Bull.* **4**: 104-132.

HANNIG, E. 1912. Untersuchungen über die Verteilung des osmotischen Drucks in der Pflanze in Hinsicht auf die Wasserleitung. *Ber. deut. botan. Ges.* **30**: 194-204.

HARDER, R. 1925. Über die Assimilation von Kälte und Warmeindividuen der gleichen Pflanzenspezies. *Jahrb. wiss. Botan.* **64**: 169-200.

HARDER, R. 1930. Beobachtungen über die Temperatur der Assimilationsorgane sommergrüner Pflanzen der algerischen Wüste. *Z. Botan.* **23**: 703-744.

HARDER, R., FILZER, P., and LORENZ, A. 1932. Über Versuche zur Bestimmung der Kohlensäureassimilation immergrüner Wüstenpflanzen während der Trockenzeit in Beni Unif (algerische Sahara). *Jahrb. wiss. Botan.* **75**: 45-194.

HARRIS, J. A., and POPENOE, W. 1916. Freezing point lowering of the leaf sap of the horticultural types of *Persea americana*. *J. Agr. Research* **7**: 261-268.

HÄRTEL, O. 1940. Physiologische Studien an Hymenophyllaceen. II. Wasser-haushalt und Resistenz. *Protoplasma* **34**: 489.

HARVEY, R. B. 1918. Hardening process in plants and developments from frost injury. *J. Agr. Research* **15**: 83-112.

HARVEY, R. B. 1922. Varietal differences in the resistance of cabbage and lettuce to low temperatures. *Ecology* **3**: 134-139.

HARVEY, R. B. 1923. Relation of the color of bark to the temperature of the cambium in winter. *Ecology* **4**: 391-394.

HARVEY, R. B. 1926. "Plant Physiological Chemistry," pp. 187-9, 200. Century, New York.

HARVEY, R. B. 1930. Time and temperature factors in hardening plants. *Am. J. Botany* **17**: 212-217.

HARVEY, R. B. 1930a. Length of exposure to low temperature as a factor in the hardening process in tree seedlings. *J. Forestry* **28**: 50-53.

HARVEY, R. B. 1935. An Annotated Bibliography of the Low Temperature Rela-tions of Plants." Burgess, Minneapolis.

HAUCK, L. 1929. Untersuchungen über den Einfluss der Bodenfeuchtigkeit auf die Saugkraft der Pflanzen. *Botan. Arch.* **24**: 458-491.

HAUSER, J. 1930. *Mezögazclasagi Kulatasok* **3**: 143-149. (*Biol. Abstr.* **6**: 4811. 1932.)

HAWKINS, L. A. 1922. The effect of low temperature storage and freezing on fruits and vegetables. *Am. J. Botany* **9**: 551-556.

HAYES, H. K., and AAMODT, O. S. 1927. Inheritance of winter hardiness and growth habit in crosses of Marquis with Minhardi and Minturki wheats. *J. Agr. Research* **35**: 223-236.

HAYES, H. K., and GARBER, R. J. 1919. Breeding small grains in Minnesota. Part I. Technic and results with wheat and oats. *Minnesota Agr. Expt. Sta. Bull.* **182**.

HEDLUND, T. 1917. Über die Möglichkeit, von der Ausbildung des Weizens im Herbst auf die Winterfestigkeit der verschiedenen Sorten zu schliessen. *Botan. Centr.* **135**: 222-224.

HEINRICHER, E. 1896. Über die Widerstandsfähigkeit der Adventivknospen von *Cystopderis bulbifera* (L.) Bernhardi gegen das Austrocknen. *Ber. deut. botan. Ges.* **14**: 234-244.

HENKEL, P. A., and KOLOTOVA, S. S. 1938. Presowing hardening and frost resist-ance in plants. *Zbirnik prisv. Pam. Ljubimenka* (*Kiev*) pp. 195-206. (*Herbage Abstr.* **9**: 628, 1939.)

HENKEL, P. A., and MARGOLIN, K. P. 1948. Reasons of resistance of succulents to high temperatures. *Botan. Zhur. S.S.S.R.* **33** (1): 55-62.

HENRICI, M. 1945. The effect of wilting on the direct assimilates of lucerne and other fodder plants. *S. African J. Sci.* **41**: 204-212.

HENRICI, M. 1946. Effect of excessive water loss and wilting on the life of plants. *Union S. Africa Dept. Agr. and Forestry Sci. Bull.* **256**: 1-22.

HERMBSTÄDT, S. F. 1808. Über die Fähigkeit der lebenden Pflanzen im Winter Wärme zu erzeugen. *Ges. Naturforsch. Freunde zu Berlin zweiter Jahrgang.* pp. 316-319.

HERTEL, W. 1939. Beiträge zur Kenntnis masshafter Beziehungen im Wasser-haushalt der Pflanzen. I. Untersuchungen über die Grundlagen der Mess-methodik und einige Messergebnisse. *Flora* **133**: 143-214.

HEYNE, E. G., and LAUDE, H. H. 1940. Resistance of corn seedlings to high temperatures in laboratory tests. *J. Am. Soc. Agron.* **32**: 116-126.

HILBRIG, H. 1900. Ueber den Einfluss supramaximaler Temperatur auf das Wachstum der Pflanzen. Inaug. Diss. Universität Leipzig, pp. 1-17.

HILDRETH, A. C. 1926. Determination of hardiness in apple varieties and the relation of some factors to cold resistance. *Minnesota Agr. Expt. Sta. Tech. Bull.* **42**.

HIRAI, T., YAMAMOTO, M., and KOSHIMIZU, Y. 1950. Studies on the snowblight diseases of winter cereals with special reference to the mechanism of physiological weakening of the plants under snow-cover. *Tôhoku Agr. Expt. Sta.* 1-21.

HIRANO, E. 1931. Relative abundance of stomata in Citrus and related genera. *Botan. Gaz.* **92**: 296-310.

HOAGLAND, D. R. 1940. Salt accumulation by plant cells, with special reference to metabolism and experiments on barley roots. *Cold Spring Harbor Symposia Quant. Biol.* **8**: 181-194.

HODGSON, R. W. 1933. Resistance to low winter temperatures of subtropical fruit plants. *Proc. Am. Soc. Hort. Sci.* **30**: 349-354.

HÖFLER, K. 1942. Über die Austrocknungsfähigkeit des Protoplasmas. *Ber. deut. botan. Ges.* **60**: (94)-(107).

HÖFLER, K. 1942a. Über die Austrocknungsgrenzen des Protoplasmas. *Anz. Akad. Wiss. Wien. Math. naturw. Kl.* **79**: 56-59.

HÖFLER, K. 1944. Über Trockenhärtung des Protoplasmas. *Rundschau deut. botan. Ges.* **1944** (1): 2.

HÖFLER, K. 1945. Über Trockenhärtung und Härtungsgrenzen des Protoplasmas einiger Lebermoose. *Anz. Akad. Wiss. Wien. Math. naturw. Kl.* **82**: 5-8.

HÖFLER, K. 1950. Über Trockenhärtung des Protoplasmas. *Ber. deut. botan. Ges.* **63** (1): 3-10.

HÖFLER, K., MIGSCHE, H., and ROTTENBERG, W. 1941. Über die Austrocknungsresistenz landwirtschaftlicher Kulturpflanzen. *Forschungsdienst* **12**: 50-61.

HOFFMAN, H. 1857. "Witterung und Wachsthum, oder Grundzüge der Pflanzenklimatologie," pp. 312-334. Leipzig.

HOFFMAN, H. 1867. Zur Naturgeschichte der Hefe. Bot. Untersuchungen aus dem phys. Lab. der Landwirt. Lehranst. in Berlin. Herausg. v. H. Karsten. I: 341-368.

HOFFMAN, H. 1883. Über das Erfrieren der Pflanzen. Oberhessische Gessellschaft für Natur- und Heilkunde (Giessen) 22 (Sitzungsberichte): 354-356.

HOFMEISTER, L. 1938. Verschiedene Permeabilitätsreihen bei einer und derselben Zellsorte von *Rannunculus repens*. *Jahrb. wiss. Botan.* **86**: 401-419.

HOGETOP, K. 1930. Untersuchungen über den Einfluss der Temperatur auf Keimung und Lebensdauer der Kartoffelknolle. *Botan. Arch.* **30**: 351-413.

HOLLE, H. 1915. Untersuchungen über Welken, Vertrocknen und Wiederstraffwerden. *Flora* **108**: 73-126.

HOOKER, H. D. 1920. Pentosan content in relation to winter hardiness. *Proc. Am. Soc. Hort. Sci.* **17**: 204-207.

HOOKER, H. D. 1920b. Seasonal changes in chemical composition of apple spurs. *Missouri Agr. Expt. Sta. Research Bull.* **40**: 1-51.

HOPKINS, E. F. 1924. Relation of low temperatures to respiration and carbohydrate changes in potato tubers. *Botan. Gaz.* **78**: 311-325.

Hopp, R. 1947. Internal temperatures of plants. *Proc. Am. Soc. Hort. Sci.* **50**: 103-108.

Horn, T. 1923. Das gegenseitige Mengenverhältnis der Kohlenhydrate im Laubblatt in seiner Abhängigkeit vom Wassergehalt. *Botan. Arch.* **3**: 137-173.

Horsfall, F., Jr., and Vinson, C. G. 1938. Hardiness investigations with the apple. *Missouri Agr. Expt. Sta. Research Bull.* **289**: 3-24.

Huber, B. 1932. Einige Grundfragen des Wärmehaushalts der Pflanzen I. Die Ursache der hohen Sukkulenten-Temperaturen. *Ber. deut. botan. Ges.* **50**: (68)-(76).

Huber, B. 1935. Der Wärmehaushalt der Pflanzen. *Naturw. u. Landwirtsch.* **17**: 148 pp.

Hunter, J. 1775. Experiments on animals and vegetables, with respect to the power of producing heat. *Phil. Trans. Roy. Soc.* **65**: 446-458.

Hunter, J. 1779. Of the heat of animals and vegetables. *Phil. Trans. Roy. Soc.* **68**: 7-49.

Ibraginov, B. B. 1931. Cause of death of plants from frost, and the nature of cold hardiness in wheat seed. *Wiss. Ber. Biol. Fak. Tomsker. Staats. Univ.* **1**: 71-96.

Iljin, W. S. 1923. Der Einfluss des Wassermangels auf die Kohlenstoffassimilation durch die Pflanzen. *Flora* **116**: 360-378.

Iljin, W. S. 1923a. Einfluss des Welkens auf die Atmung der Pflanzen. *Flora* **116**: 379-403.

Iljin, W. S. 1927. Über die Austrocknungsfähigkeit des lebenden Protoplasmas der vegetativen Pflanzenzellen. *Jahrb. wiss. Botan.* **66**: 947-964.

Iljin, W. S. 1929. Der Einfluss der Standortsfeuchtigkeit auf den osmotischen Wert bei Pflanzen. *Planta* **7**: 45-58.

Iljin, W. S. 1929a. Standortsfeuchtigkeit und der Zuckergehalt in den Pflanzen. *Planta* **7**: 59-71.

Iljin, W. S. 1930. Die Ursache der Resistenz von Pflanzenzellen gegen Austrocknung. *Protoplasma* **10**: 379-414.

Iljin, W. S. 1930a. Der Einfluss des Welkens auf den Ab- und Aufbau der Stärke in der Pflanze. *Planta* **10**: 170-184.

Iljin, W. S. 1931. Austrocknungsresistenz des Farnes Notochlaena Marantae R. Br. *Protoplasma* **13**: 322-330.

Iljin, W. S. 1933. Über Absterben der Pflanzengewebe durch Austrocknung und über ihre Bewahrung vor dem Trockentode. *Protoplasma* **19**: 414-442.

Iljin, W. S. 1933. Über den Kältetod der Pflanzen und seine Ursachen. *Protoplasma* **20**: 105-124.

Iljin, W. S. 1934. The point of death of plants at low temperatures. *Bull. assoc. russe recherches sci. Prague. Sect. sci. nat. math.* **1** (6), No. 4: 135-160.

Iljin, W. S. 1934a. Kann das Protoplasma durch den osmotischen Druck des Zellsaftes zerdrückt werden? *Protoplasma* **20**: 570-585.

Iljin, W. S. 1935. The relation of cell sap concentration to cold resistance in plants. *Bull. assoc. russe recherches sci. Prague, Sect. sci. nat. math.* **3** (8) No. 13: 33-55.

Iljin, W. S. 1935a. Lebensfähigkeit der Pflanzenzellen in trockenem Zustand. *Planta* **24**: 742-754.

Iljin, V., Nazarova, P., and Ostrovskaja, M. 1916. Osmotic pressure in roots and in leaves in relation to habitat moisture. *J. Ecol.* **4**: 160-173.

ILLERT, H. 1924. Botanische Untersuchungen über Hitzetod und Stoffwechsel-gifte. *Botan. Arch.* **7**: 133-141.

IMPERIAL BUREAU PLANT BREEDING AND GENETICS 1939. Bibliography on cold resistance in plants.

IRELAND, J. C. 1939. Seasonal sugar variations in alfalfa. *Plant Physiol.* **14**: 381-384.

IRMSCHER, E. 1912. Über die Resistenz der Laubmoose gegen Austrocknung und Kälte. *Jahrb. wiss. Botan.* **50**: 387-449.

ISAAC, W. E. 1933. Some observations and experiments on the drought resistance of *Pelvetia canaliculata*. *Ann. Botany (London)* **47**: 343-348.

ISHIBE, O. 1935. The seasonal changes in starch and fat reserves of some woody plants. *Mem. Coll. Sci. Kyoto Imp. Univ. Ser. B.* **11**, No. 1: 1-53.

IVANOFF, S. S. 1951. The use of activated oat seeds in the study of winter-hardiness. *Botan. Gaz.* **113**: 90-94.

IVANOV, S. M. 1931. Determination of the frost resistance of plants from the changes induced by frost injury in the electrical conductivity of the sap. *Bull. Appl. Botan. Genet. Plant Breeding* **27**: 283-307. (*Biol. Abstr.* **9**: 4694, 1935.)

IVANOV, S. M. 1939. Activity of growth process—principal factor in frost resistance of citrus plants. *Compt. rend. acad. sci. U.R.S.S.* **22**: 277-281.

IVANOV, S. M. 1939a. Importance of temperature conditions in the hardening of citrus plants. *Compt. rend. acad. sci. U.R.S.S.* **25**: 440-443.

IVANOV, S. M. 1939b. Influence of light intensity on the hardening of citrus plants. *Compt. rend. acad. sci. U.R.S.S.* **25**: 444-446.

IWANOFF, L. 1924. Über die Transpiration der Holzgewächse im Winter I. *Ber. deut. botan. Ges.* **42**: 44-49; II. 210-218.

JANSSEN, G. 1929. Effect of date of seeding of winter wheat upon some physiological changes of the plant during the winter season. *J. Am. Soc. Agron.* **21**: 168-200.

JANSSEN, G. 1929a. Effect of date of seeding of winter wheat on plant development and its relationship to winter hardiness. *J. Am. Soc. Agron.* **21**: 444-466.

JANSSEN, G. 1929b. Physical measurements of the winter wheat plant at various stages in its development. *Plant Physiol.* **4**: 477-491.

JENSEN, I. J. 1925. Winter wheat studies in Montana with special reference to winter killing. *J. Am. Soc. Agron.* **17**: 630-631.

JOHNSTON, E. S. 1919. An index of hardiness in peach buds. *Am. J. Botany* **6**: 373-379.

JOHNSTON, E. S. 1922. Undercooling of peach buds. *Am. J. Botany* **9**: 93-98.

JOHNSTON, E. S. 1923. Moisture relations of peach buds during winter and spring. *Maryland Agr. Expt. Sta. Bull.* **255**: 59-86.

JONES, C. H., and BRADEE, J. L. 1933. The carbohydrate contents of the maple tree. *Vermont Agr. Expt. Sta. Bull.* **358**: 1-147.

JOSLYN, M. A., and DIEHL, H. C. 1952. Physiological aspects of low temperature preservation of plant products. *Ann. Rev. Plant Physiol.* **3**: 149-170.

JULANDER, O. 1945. Drought resistance in range and pasture grasses. *Plant Physiol.* **20**: 573-599.

JUST, L. 1877. Ueber die Einwirkung hoher Temperaturen auf die Erhaltung der Keimfähigeit der Samen. *Beitr. Biol. Pflanz.* **2**: 311-348.

248 REFERENCES

KABANOV, P. G. 1938. Winter hardiness of winter wheat in relation to weather conditions during autumn. *Soc. zern. Hoz.* No. **1**: 19-30. (*Herbage Abstr.* **9**: 631, 1939.)

KÄRCHER, H. 1931. Über die Kälteresistenz einiger Pilze und Algen. *Planta* **14**: 515-516.

KAHO, H. 1921. Über die Beeinflussung der Hitzekoagulation des Pflanzenprotoplasmas durch Neutralsalze. I. *Biochem. Z.* **117**: 87-95.

KAHO, H. 1924. Über die Beeinflussung der Hitzekoagulation des Pflanzenplasmas durch die Salze der Erdalkalien VI. *Biochem. Z.* **151**: 102-111.

KAHO, H. 1926. Über den Einfluss der Temperatur auf die koagulierende Wirkung einiger Alkalisalze auf das Pflanzenplasma VIII. *Biochem. Z.* **167**: 182-194.

KALTWASSER, J. 1938. Assimilation und Atmung von Submersen als Ausdruck ihrer Entquellungsresistenz. *Protoplasma* **29**: 498-535.

KARSTEN, H. 1861. Über die Wirkung plötzlicher, bedeutender Temperaturveränderungen auf die Pflanzenwelt. *Botan. Ztg.* **19**: 289-292.

KEANE, J. F. 1953. Comparative efficiency of some compounds containing the amide group in protecting tissues against freezing injury. *Biodynamica* **7** (142): 157-169.

KENCH, J. E. 1939. The seasonal cycles of ash, carbohydrate, and nitrogenous constituents in the terminal shoots of apple trees and the effects of five vegetatively propagated rootstocks on them. III. Nitrogenous constituents. *J. Pomol. Hort. Sci.* **16**: 346-363.

KENNARD, W. D. 1949. Defoliation of Montmorency sour cherry trees in relation to winter hardiness. *Proc. Am. Soc. Hort. Sci.* **53**: 129-133.

KENWAY, C. B., and PETO, H. 1939. Researches on drought resistance in spring wheat. I. A machine for measuring the resistance of plants to artificial drought. *Can. J. Research* **C17**: 294-296.

KENWAY, C. B., PETO, H. B., and NEATBY, K. W. 1942. Researches on drought resistance in spring wheat. II. The effect of time of day on survival of plants during exposure to artificial drought. *Can. J. Research* **C20**: 397-402.

KERNER VON MARILAUN, A. 1894. The Natural History of Plants. Vol. 1, Part 2 (translated by F. W. Oliver) pp. 539-557. Holt, New York.

KESSLER, W. 1935. Über die inneren Ursachen der Kälteresistenz der Pflanzen. *Planta* **24**: 312-352.

KESSLER, E., and RUHLAND, W. 1938. Weitere Untersuchungen über die inneren Ursachen der Kälteresistenz. *Planta* **28**: 159-204.

KESSLER, W., and RUHLAND, W. 1942. Über die inneren Ursachen der Kälteresistenz der Pflanzen. *Forschungsdienst. Sonderheft* **16**: 345-351.

KIESSELBACH, T. A., and RATCLIFF, J. A. 1918. Freezing injury of seed corn. *Nebraska Agr. Expt. Sta. Bull.* **163**: 1-16.

KILLIAN, C. 1947. Le deficit de saturation hydrique chez les plantes Sahariennes. *Rév. gén. botan.* **54**: 81-101.

KIMBALL, D. A. 1927. Effect of the hardening process on the water content of some herbaceous plants. *Proc. Am. Soc. Hort. Sci.* **24**: 64-69.

KIRCHOFF, F. 1915. Über das Verhalten von Stärke und Gerbstoff in den Nadeln unserer Koniferen im Laufe des Jahres. *Botan. Centr.* **128**: 154-155.

KISSELEW, N. N. 1927. Zur Frage des Stärkeabbaues beim Welken der Blätter. *Planta* **4**: 606-616.

KISSELEW, N. N. 1928. Der Temperatureinfluss auf die Stärkehydrolyse in Meso-phyll- und Schliesszellen. *Planta* **6**: 135-161.

KISSELEW, N. N. 1935. Dürreresistenz und Saugkraft der Pflanzen. *Planta* **23**: 760-773.

KLAGES, K. H. 1926. Relation of soil moisture content to resistance of wheat seedlings to low temperatures. *J. Am. Soc. Agron.* **18**: 184-193.

KLAGES, K. H. 1926a. Metrical attributes and the physiology of hardy varieties of winter wheat. *J. Am. Soc. Agron.* **18**: 529-566.

KLEMM, P. 1895. Desorganisationserscheinungen der Zelle. *Jahrb. wiss. Botan.* **28**: 627-700.

KNEEN, E., and BLISH, M. J. 1941. Carbohydrate metabolism and winter hardi-ness of wheat. *J. Agr. Research* **62**: 1-26.

KNOWLTON, H. E., and DORSEY, M. J. 1927. A study of the hardiness of the fruit buds of the peach. *West Virginia Expt. Sta. Bull.* **211**: 1-28.

KOKKONEN, P. 1927. Über das Verhältnis der Winterfestigkeit des Roggens zur Dehnbarkeit und Dehnungsfestigkeit seiner Wurzeln. *Acta forest. fennica* **33**: 5-45.

KOLOMYCEV, G. G. 1936. Winter hardiness and earliness of wheats. *Compt. rend. acad. sci. U.R.S.S.* **12**: 351-356.

KONIS, E. 1949. The resistance of maquis plants to supramaximal temperatures. *Ecology* **30** (4): 425-429.

KONIS, E. 1950. On the temperature of *Opuntia* joints. *Palestine J. Botany Jeru-salem Ser.* **5** (1): 46-55.

KOPERZINSKII, V. V. 1939. The effect of fertilizers on winter hardiness in clover. *Himiz. Soc. Zembed* pp. 25-33 (*Herbage Abstr.* **10**: 185, 1940).

KOPERZINSKII, V. V. 1939a. The significance of partial proteolysis of proteins in clover roots for winter hardiness in the plants. *Biohimiya* **4**: 404-410. (*Herb-age Abstr.* **10**: 186, 1940.)

KORSTIAN, C. F. 1924. Density of cell sap in relation to environmental conditions in the Wasatch Mountains of Utah. *J. Agr. Research* **28**: 845-907.

KOSTIUCHENKO, I. W. 1938. Winter hardiness of plants as influenced by yaroviza-tion of ripening seed grains. *Compt. rend. acad. sci. U.R.S.S.* **18**: 589-592. (*Biol. Abstr.* **14**: 9223, 1940.)

KOSTIUCHENKO, I. W. 1939. The effects of low temperatures in the extreme north on winter wheat. *Selek. Semenovod.* 22-24. (*Herbage Abstr.* **10**: 181, 1940.)

KOVPAK, F. K. 1939. Intervarietal crossing and increase in frost resistance in win-ter wheats. *Jarovizacijai* pp. 53-58 (*Herbage Abstr.* **10**: 174, 1940).

KRAMER, P. J. 1937. Photoperiodic stimulation of growth by artificial light as a cause of winter killing. *Plant Physiol.* **12**: 881-883.

KRASAN, F. 1869. Bemerkungen über den Einfluss der Temperatur auf die Lebens-erscheinungen der Pflanzen. *Oest. Botan. Z.* **19**: 14-15.

KRASSINSKY, N. 1929. Über jahreszeitliche Änderungen der Permeabilität des Protoplasmas. *Protoplasma* **9**: 622-631.

KRAUS, G. 1875. Über die winterliche Färbung grüner Pflanzentheile. *Bull. soc. botan. France* **22** (Rev. bibl.): 31-32.

KREUTZ, H. 1930. Beitrag zum Problem der Winterfestigkeit der Pferdebohne (*Vicia faba*). *Pflanzenbau, Pflanzenschutz, Pflanzenzucht* **6**: 375-377. (*Biol. Abstr.* **6**: 19824, 1932.)

KUCKUCK, H. 1933. Über die Entstehung von Wintergersten aus Kreuzung von Sommergersten und über die Beziehung der Winterfestigkeit zum Winter-Sommertyp. *Z. Zücht. Reihe A. Pflanzenzucht.* **18**: 259-290.

KÜHNE, W. 1864. "Untersuchungen über das Protoplasma und die Contractilität," pp. 100-102. Leipzig.

KUKSA, I. N. 1939. The effect of mineral nutrition on winter hardiness and yield of winter wheat. *Himiz. Soc. Zemled* No. 1: 70-79. (*Herbage Abstr.* 9: 635, 1939.)

KUKSA, I. N. 1939a. The effect of mineral nutrition on phasic development of plants. *Sovet. Agron.* No. 8: 55-60. (*Herbage Abstr.* 10: 793, 1940.)

KUIJPER, J. 1910. Ueber den Einfluss der Temperatur auf die Atmung höhere Pflanzen. *Rec. trav. botan. neerl.* 7: 131-240.

KUNISCH, H. 1880. Über die tödliche Einwirkung niederer Temperaturen auf die Pflanzen. Inaug. Diss. Breslau. 55 pp.

KYLIN, H. 1917. Über die Kälteresistenz der Meeresalgen. *Ber. deut. botan. Ges.* 35: 370-384.

LACIS, AGR. H. 1930. Minerals leicits ka kalija mesolsanas lidzeklis. *Lauksaimniecibas Menesraksts. Riga* 8: 506-513. (*Biol. Abstr.* 5: 24571, 1931.)

LAL, K. N., and MALHOTRA, O. N. 1949. Studies in crop physiology: cell size characteristics of sugar-cane varieties in relation to drought resistance. *Botan. Gaz.* 111: 193-210.

LANGLET, O. 1934. Om variationen hos tallen (*P. silvestris* L.) och dess samband med klimatet. *Svenska Skog. Tidskr.* 32: 87-110. (*Biol. Abstr.* 9: 12236, 1935.)

LAUDE, H. H. 1937. Cold resistance of winter wheat, rye, barley, and oats in transition from dormancy to active growth. *J. Agr. Research* 54: 899-917.

LAUDE, H. H. 1937a. Comparison of the cold resistance of several varieties of winter wheat in transition from dormancy to active growth. *J. Agr. Research* 54: 919-926.

LAUDE, H. H. 1939. Diurnal cycle of heat resistance in plants. *Science* 89: 556-557.

LAUE, E. 1938. Untersuchungen an Pflanzenzellen in Dampfraum. *Flora* 132: 193-224.

LEBEDINCEV, E. 1930. Untersuchungen über die wasserbindenden Kräfte der Pflanzen im Zusammenhang mit ihrer Dürre-und Kälteresistenz. *Protoplasma* 10: 53-81.

LE CONTE, J. 1852. Observations sur la congélation des végétaux et sur les causes qui permettent à certaines plantes de supporter de très grands froids. *Bibl. Univ. Geneve Arch. sci. phys. nat.* 20: 161-165.

LEPESCHKIN, W. W. 1912. Zur Kenntnis der Einwirkung supramaximaler Temperaturen auf die Pflanze. *Ber. deut. botan. Ges.* 30: 703-714.

LEPESCHKIN, W. W. 1924. "Kolloidchemie des Protoplasmas." Springer, Berlin.

LEPESCHKIN, W. W. 1935. Zur Kenntnis des Hitzetodes des Protoplasmas. *Protoplasma* 23: 349-366.

LEPESCHKIN, W. W. 1937. Zell-Nekrobiose und Protoplasma-Tod. *Protoplasma Monographien* 12.

LEVITT, J. 1933. The physiology of cold resistance in plants. M.S. Thesis. McGill Univ.

LEVITT, J. 1939. The relation of cabbage hardiness to bound water, unfrozen water, and cell contraction when frozen. *Plant Physiol.* 14: 93-112.

LEVITT, J. 1941. "Frost Killing and Hardiness of Plants." Burgess, Minneapolis.

LEVITT, J. 1951. Frost, drought, and heat resistance. *Ann. Rev. Plant Physiol.* **2**: 245-268.

LEVITT, J. 1954. Investigations of the cytoplasmic particulates and proteins of potato tubers. II. Nitrogen, phosphorus, and carbohydrate contents. *Physiol. Plantarum* **7**: 117-123.

LEVITT, J. 1954a. Investigations of the cytoplasmic particulates and proteins of potato tubers. III. Protein synthesis during the breaking of the rest period. *Physiol. Plantarum* **7**: 597-601.

LEVITT, J. 1954b. The role of carbohydrates in frost resistance. *8th Intern. Congr. Botan.* **11**: 278-280.

LEVITT, J., and NELSON, R. C. 1942. The relative resistance of morphologically different orange-peel cells to various injury factors. *Biodynamica* **4**: 57-64.

LEVITT, J., and SCARTH, G. W. 1936. Frost-hardening studies with living cells. *Can. J. Research* **C14**: 267-305.

LEVITT, J., and SIMINOVITCH, D. 1940. The relation between frost resistance and the physical state of protoplasm. I. *Can. J. Research* **C18**: 550-561.

LEWIS, F. J., and TUTTLE, G. M. 1920. Osmotic properties of some plant cells at low temperatures. *Ann. Botany (London)* **34**: 405-416.

LEWIS, F. J., and TUTTLE, G. M. 1923. On the phenomena attending seasonal changes in the organisation in leaf cells of *Picea canadensis*. (Mill.) B.S.P. *New Phytologist* **22**: 225-232.

LIDFORSS, B. 1896. Zur Physiologie und Biologie der wintergrünen Flora. *Botan. Centr.* **68**: 33-44.

LIDFORSS, B. 1907. Die wintergrüne Flora. *Lunds. Univ. Årsskr.* [N.F.] **2**: 1-76.

LIDFORSS, B. 1909. Die wintergrüne Flora. *Botan. Centr.* **110**: 291-293.

LINDLEY, J. 1842. Observations upon the effects produced on plants by the frost which occurred in England in the winter of 1837-38. (Read in 1838). *Trans. Hort. Soc. (London)* [2] **3**: 225-315.

LINDNER, J. 1915. Über den Einfluss günstiger Temperaturen auf gefrorene Schimmelpilze. (Zur Kenntnis der Kältereresistenz von Aspergillus niger. *Jahrb. wiss. Botan.* **55**: 1-52.

LINSBAUER, K. 1926. Beobachtungen an Spaltöffnungen. *Planta* **2**: 530-536.

LIPMAN, C. B. 1936. The tolerance of liquid air temperatures by dry moss protonema. *Bull. Torrey Botan. Club* **63**: 515-518.

LIPMAN, C. B. 1936a. Normal viability of seeds and bacterial spores after exposure to temperatures near the absolute zero. *Plant Physiol.* **11**: 201-205.

LIPMAN, C. B. 1937. Tolerance of liquid air temperatures by spore-free and very young cultures of fungi and bacteria growing on agar media. *Bull. Torrey Botan. Club* **64**: 537-546.

LIPMAN, C. B., and LEWIS, G. N. 1934. Tolerance of liquid-air temperatures by seeds of higher plants for sixty days. *Plant Physiol.* **9**: 392-394.

LIVINGSTON, B. E. 1903. "The Role of Diffusion and Osmotic Pressure in Plants." Univ. Chicago Press, Chicago.

LIVINSTON, B. E. 1911. Light intensity and transpiration. *Botan. Gaz.* **52**: 417-438.

LIVINGSTON, J. E., and SWINBANK, J. C. 1950. Some factors influencing the injury to winter wheat heads by low temperatures. *Agron. J.* **42**: 153-157.

LOCKETT, M. C., and LUYET, B. J. 1951. Survival of frozen seeds of various water contents. *Biodynamica* **7** (134): 67-76.

LORENZ, R. W. 1939. High temperature tolerance of forest trees. *Univ. Minnesota Agr. Expt. Sta. Tech. Bull.* **141**: 1-25.

LOEWENSTEIN, A. 1903. Über die Temperaturgrenzen des Lebens bei der Thermalalge Mastigocladus laminosus Cohn. *Ber. deut. botan. Ges.* **21**: 317-323.

LOTT, R. V. 1926. Correlation of chemical composition with hardiness in brambles. *Missouri Agr. Expt. Sta. Research Bull.* **95**.

LUEG, H. 1929. Die Bedeutung verschiedener Untersuchungsmethoden zur Bestimmung der relativen Winterfestigkeit von Winterweizensorten. *Arch. Pflanzenbau* **1**: 725-803.

LUNDEGÅRDH, H. 1914. Einige Bedingungen der Bildung und Auflösung der Stärke. *Jahrb. wiss. Botan.* **53**: 421-463.

LUNDEGÅRDH, H. 1924. Der Temperaturfaktor bei Kohlensäureassimilation und Atmung. *Biochem. Z.* **154**: 195-234.

LUNDEGÅRDH, H. 1949. "Klima und Boden," 3rd ed. Fischer, Jena.

LUSENA, C. V., and COOK, W. H. 1953. Ice propagation in systems of biological interest. I. Effect of membranes and solutes in a model cell system. *Arch. Biochem. and Biophys.* **46**: 232-240.

LUTZ, J. M. 1935. The influence of rate of thawing on freezing injury of apples, potatoes, and onions. *Proc. Am. Soc. Hort. Sci.* **33**: 227-233.

LUYET, B. J. 1937. The vitrification of organic colloids and of protoplasm. *Biodynamica* **29**: 1-14.

LUYET, B. J. 1940. "Life and Death at Low Temperatures," Monograph No. 1. Biodynamica, Normandy, Missouri.

LUYET, B. J. 1951. Survival of cells, tissues and organisms after ultrarapid freezing. "Freezing and Drying" (R. J. C. Harris, ed.), pp. 3-23. Institute of Biology, London.

LUYET, B. J. 1954. Le mécanisme du gel et la résistance au froid. *8th Intern. Congr. Botany* **11**: 259-267.

LUYET, B. J., and CONDON, H. M. 1938. Temperature relationships and ice-water proportions during death by freezing in plant tissues. *Biodynamica* **37**: 1-8.

LUYET, B. J., and Galos, G. 1940. The effect of the rate of cooling on the freezpoint of living tissues. *Biodynamica* **3** (65): 157-169.

LUYET, B. J., and GEHENIO, P. M. 1937. The double freezing point of living tissues. *Biodynamica* **30**: 1-23.

LUYET, B. J., and GEHENIO, P. M. 1938. The lower limit of vital temperatures, a review. *Biodynamica* **33**: 1-92.

LUYET, B. J., and SISTER GRELL, M. 1936. A study with the ultracentrifuge of the mechanism of death in frozen cells. *Biodynamica* **23**: 1-16.

LUYET, B. J., and HODAPP, E. L. 1938. On the effect of mechanical shocks on the congelation of subcooled plant tissues. *Protoplasma* **30**: 254-257.

LUYET, B. J., and THOENNES, G. 1938a. The survival of plant cells immersed in liquid air. *Science* **88**: 284-285.

LUYET, B. J., and THOENNES, G. 1938b. Démonstration des propriétés isotropiques de masses cellulaires vitrifiées à la température de l'air liquide. *Compt. rend.* **206**: 2002.

M. A. O. 1937. Determination of winter hardiness by germinating seeds in sugar and salt solutions. *Herbage Revs.* **5**: 161.

McALISTER, D. F. 1944. Determination of soil drought resistance in grass seedlings. *J. Am. Soc. Agron.* **36**: 324-336.

MACFAYDEN, A. 1900. On the influence of the temperature of liquid air on bacteria. *Proc. Roy. Soc.* **66**: 180-182, 339-340.

McGEE, J. M. 1916. The effect of position upon the temperature and dry weight of joints of Opuntia. *Carnegie Inst. Wash. Yearbook* **15**: 73-74.

McROSTIE, G. P. 1939. The thermal death point of corn from low temperatures. *Sci. Agr.* **19**: 687-699.

MADER, W. 1927. Messungen des osmotischen Wertes bei Grenzplasmolyse bei floristisch verschiedenen Winterweizen- und Wintergerstesorten. *Fortschr. Landwirtsch.* **2**: 409-412.

MÄDE, A., and ULLRICH, H. 1941. Temperaturuntersuchungen an erfrierenden Blättern. Ein Beitrag zur Frage der Frostresistenzforschung in der Pflanzenzüchtung. *Umschau Wiss. u. Tech.* **45**: 43-45.

MAGISTAD, O. C., and TRUOG, E. 1925. Influence of fertilizers in protecting corn against freezing. *J. Am. Soc. Agron.* **17**: 517-526.

MAGNESS, J. R., REGEIMBAL, L. O., and DEGMAN, E. S. 1932. Accumulation of carbohydrates in apple foliage, bark, and wood as influenced by moisture supply. *Proc. Am. Soc. Hort. Sci.* **29**: 246-252.

MAKI, T. E., MARSHALL, H., and OSTROM, C. E. 1946. Effects of napthaleneacetic-acid sprays on the development and drought resistance of pine seedlings. *Botan. Gaz.* **107**: 297-312.

MALHOTRA, R. C. 1931. Part I. Oil synthesis at various elevations of the Himalayas and its physiological influence on the protoplasm of *Cedrus odoratus*. *J. Indian Botan. Soc.* **10**: 293-310.

MALTE, M. O. 1919. Sugar content and its relation to winter hardiness. *Agr. Gaz. Can.* **6**: 329-331.

MANEY, T. J. 1931. Correlation of bound water in apple wood with hardiness. *Ann. Rept. Iowa Agr. Expt. Sta.*, pp. 97-98.

MARK, J. J. 1936. The relation of reserves to cold resistance in alfalfa. *Iowa Agr. Expt. Sta. Research Bull.* **208**: 305-335.

MARTIN, J. F. 1932. The cold resistance of Pacific Coast spring wheats at various stages of growth as determined by artificial refrigeration. *J. Am. Soc. Agron.* **24**: 871-880.

MARTIN, J. H. 1927. Comparative studies of winter hardiness in wheat. *J. Agr. Research* **35**: 493-534.

MATRUCHOT, L., and MOLLIARD, M. 1900. Sur certains phénomènes présentés par les noyaux sous l'action du froid. *Compt. rend.* **130**: 788-791.

MATRUCHOT, L., and MOLLIARD, M. 1901. Sur l'identité des modifications de structure produites dans les cellules végétales par le gel, la plasmolyse, et la fanaison. *Compt. rend.* **132**: 495-498.

MATRUCHOT, L., and MOLLIARD, M. 1902. Modifications produites par le gel dans la structure des cellules végétales. *Rev. gen. botan.* **14**: 401-419, 463-482, 522-533.

MAXIMOV, N. A. 1908. Zur Frag über das Erfrieren der Pflanzen. *J. botan. ed. Sect. Botan. Soc. imp. Nat. St. Petersburg* 32-46. (*Botan. Centr.* **110**: 597-598, 1909.)

MAXIMOV, N. A. 1912. Chemische Schutzmittel der Pflanzen gegen Erfrieren. *Ber. deut. botan. Ges.* **30**: 52-65, 293-305, 504-516.

MAXIMOV, N. A. 1914. Experimentelle und kritische Untersuchungen über das Gefrieren und Erfrieren der Pflanzen. *Jahrb. wiss. Botan.* **53**: 327-420.

MAXIMOV, N. A. 1929. Internal factors of frost and drought resistance in plants. *Protoplasma* **7**: 259-291.

MAXIMOV, N. A. 1934. The theoretical significance of vernalization. *Imp. Bur. Plant Genet. Herbage Plants Bull.* **16**: 1-14.

MAXIMOV, N. A. 1929. "The Plant in Relation to Water." Allen and Unwin, London.

MAXIMOV, N. A. 1929a. Physiological nature of drought resistance of plants. *Proc. Intern. Congr. Plant Sci.* **2**: 1169-75.

MAXIMOV, N. A., and KRASNOSELSKY-MAXIMOV, T. A. 1924. Wilting of plants in its connection with drought resistance. *J. Ecol.* **12**: 95-110.

MEADER, E. N., DAVIDSON, O. W., and BLAKE, M. A. 1945. A method for determining the relative cold hardiness of dormant peach fruit buds. *J. Agr. Research* **70**: 283-302.

MEGEE, C. R. 1935. A search for factors determining winter hardiness in alfalfa. *J. Am. Soc. Agron.* **27**: 685-698.

MEINDL, T. 1934. Weitere Beiträge zur protoplasmatischen Anatomie des Helodea-Blattes. *Protoplasma* **21**: 362-393.

MER, E. 1876. De la constitution et des fonctions des feuilles hivernales. *Bull. soc. botan. France* **23**: 231-238.

MER, E. 1877. Recherches sur les causes des colorations diverses qui apparaissent dans les feuilles en automne et en hiver. *Bull. soc. botan. France* **24**: 105-115.

MER, E. 1879. De la répartition de l'amidon dans les rameaux des plantes ligneuses. Des causes qui y président. De son influence sur la ramification. *Bull. soc. botan. France* [2] **26**: 44-53.

MER, E. 1891. Repartition hivernale de l'amidon dans les plantes ligneuses. *Compt. rend.* **112**: 964-966.

MER, E. 1898. Des variations qu'éprouve la réserve amylacée des arbres aux diverses époques de l'année. *Bull. soc. botan. France* **45**: 290-309.

MEYEN, F. J. F. 1841. "Pflanzen-Pathologie," pp. 313, 323. von Esenbeck, Berlin.

MEYER, A. 1918. Die angebliche Fettspeicherung immergrüner Laubblätter. *Ber. deut. botan. Ges.* **36**: 5-10.

MEYER, B. S. 1928. Seasonal variations in the physical and chemical properties of the leaves of the pitch pine, with especial reference to cold resistance. *Am. J. Botany* **15**: 449-470.

MEYER, B. S. 1932. Further studies on cold resistance in evergreens, with special reference to the possible role of bound water. *Botan. Gaz.* **94**: 297-321.

MEZ, C. 1905. Neue Untersuchungen über das Erfrieren eisbeständiger Pflanzen. *Flora* **94**: 89-123.

MICHAELIS, P. 1934. Ökologische Studien an der alpinen Baumgrenze. IV. Zur Kenntnis des winterlichen Wasserhaushaltes. *Jahrb. wiss. Botan.* **80**: 169-247.

MICHAELIS, P. 1934a. Ökologische Studien an der alpinen Baumgrenze. V. Osmotischer Wert und Wassergehalt während des Winters in den verschieden Hohenlagen. *Jahrb. wiss. Botan.* **80**: 337-362.

MICHAELIS, G. P. 1935. Ökologische Studien an der alpinen Baumgrenze. *Botan. Centr. Beih.* **52**(b): 333-377.

MICHEL-DURAND, E. 1919. Variation des substances hydrocarbonées dans les feuilles. *Rev. gén. botan.* **31**: 145-156; 196-204.

MIEHE, H. 1907. Thermoidium sulfureum n.g. n. sp., ein neuer Wärmepilz. *Ber. deut. botan. Ges.* **25**: 510-515.

MIGAHID, AHMED MOHAMED. 1938. Binding of water in relation to drought resistance. Fouad I. Univ. Fac. Sci. No. 18: 5-28.

MILLER, E. C. 1939. A physiological study of the winter wheat plant in different stages of its development. Kansas Agr. Expt. Sta. Tech. Bull. 47.

MILTHORPE, F. L. 1950. Changes in the drought resistance of wheat seedlings during germination. Ann. Botany (London) 14: 79-89.

MITRA, S. K. 1921. Seasonal changes and translocation of carbohydrate materials in fruit spurs and two-year-old seedlings of apple. Ohio J. Sci. 21: 89-99.

MIX, A. J. 1916. Sun-scald of fruit trees, a type of winter injury. Cornell Univ. Agr. Expt. Sta. Bull. 382: 237-284.

MIYAKE, K. 1902. On the starch of evergreen leaves and its relation to photosynthesis during the winter. Botan. Gaz. 33: 321-340.

MÖBIUS, M. 1907. Die Erkältung der Pflanzen. Ber. deut. botan. Ges. 25: 67-70.

MOHL, H. VON 1848. Über das Erfrieren der Zweigspitzen mancher Holzgewächse. Botan. Ztg. 6: 6-8.

MOLISCH, H. 1896. Das Erfrieren von Pflanzen bei Temperaturen über dem Eispunkt. Sitzber. Kaiserlichen Akad. Wiss. Wien. Math.-naturw. Kl. 105: 1-14.

MOLISCH, H. 1897. "Untersuchungen über das Erfrieren der Pflanzen," pp. 1-73. Fischer, Jena.

MOLISCH, H. 1911. Das Erfrieren der Pflanze. Schriften Ver. Verbreit. naturw. Kent. Wien. 51: 141-176.

MOLISCH, H. 1921. Über den Einfluss der Transpiration auf das Verschwinden der Stärke in den Blättern. Ber. deut. botan. Ges. 39: 339-344.

MOLISCH, H. 1926. "Pflanzenbiologie in Japan." Fischer, Jena.

MOLL, J. W. 1880. Quelques observations concernant l'influence de la gelée sur les plantes toujours vertes. Arch. néerl. sci. exact nat. 15: 345-348. (Summarized in Der Naturforsch. 14, No. 9: 85-86, 1881.)

MOLZ, F. J. 1926. A study of suction force by the simplified method. I. Effect of external factors. Am. J. Botany 13: 433-463.

MONTFORT, C., and HAHN, H. 1950. Atmung und Assimilation als dynamische Kennzeichen abgestufter Trockenresistenz bei Farnen und höheren Pflanzen. Planta 38: 503-515.

MORETTI, A. 1953. (Physiological effects of winter treatments of chemicals upon grape-vine). Riv. frutticolt. viticolt. ed orticolt. 15: 2-25.

MOROSOV, A. S. 1939. Effect of temperature on the reversible activity of invertase in forage grasses as dependent on their cold and heat resistance. Compt. rend. acad. sci. U.R.S.S. 23: 949-951.

MORREN, C. 1838. Observations anatomiques sur la congélation des organes des végétaux. Bull. acad. roy. sci. belles-lettres Bruxelles 5: 65-66, 93-111.

MOSCHKOV, B. S. 1935. Photoperiodismus und Frosthärte ausdauernder Gewächse. Planta 23: 774-803.

MOSCHKOV, B. S. 1939. Relationship between photoperiodism and drought resistance of perennial plants. Compt. rend. acad. sci. U.R.S.S. 22: 184-186.

MOTHES, K. 1928. Die Wirkung des Wassermangels auf den Eiweissumsatz in höheren Pflanzen. Ber. deut. botan. Ges. 46 (42 Generalversammlung): 59-67.

MUDRA, A. 1932. Zur Physiologie der Kälteresistenz des Winterweizens. Planta 18: 435-478.

MULAY, A. S. 1932. Seasonal changes in the composition of the non-protein nitrogen in the current year's shoots of Bartlett pear. Plant. Physiol. 7: 107-118.

Müller, G. 1939. Untersuchungen über die Kältefestigkeit von Pflaumensorten. *Z. Pflanzenzucht.* **23**: 91-144.

Mueller, I. M., and Weaver, J. E. 1942. Relative drought resistance of seedlings of dormant prairie grasses. *Ecology* **23**: 387-398.

Müller-Thurgau, H. 1880. Über das Gefrieren und Erfrieren der Pflanzen. *Landwirtsch. Jahrb.* **9**: 133-189.

Müler-Thurgau, H. 1882. Über Zuckeranhäufung in Pflanzentheilen in Folge niederer Temperatur. *Landwirtsch. Jahrb.* **11**: 751-828.

Müller-Thurgau, H. 1886. Über das Gefrieren und Erfrieren der Pflanzen. II. Theile. *Landwirtsch. Jahrb.* **15**: 453-610.

Müller-Thurgau, H. 1894. Über die Wirkung des Frühjahrsfrostes und die Behandlung der dadurch beschädigten Reben. *Schweiz. Z. Obst. u. Weinbau Obstrundschaw* **3**: 117-121.

Münch, E. 1928. Frostgefährdung wintergrüner Gehölze. *Mitt. deut. dendrolog. Ges.* **40**: 175-184.

Münch, E. 1913. Hitzeschäden an Waldpflanzen. *Naturw. Z. Forst. u. Landwirtsch.* **11**: 557-562.

Münch, E. 1914. Nochmals Hitzeschäden an Waldpflanzen. *Naturw. Forst. u. Landwirtsch.* **12**: 169-188.

Münch, E., and Liske, F. 1926. Die Frostgefährdung der Fichte in Sachsen. *Tharandt. forst. Jahrb.* **77**: 97-115, 129-148, 161-176, 197-221.

Nägeli, C. 1861. Ueber die Verdunstung an der durch Korksubstanz geschützten Oberfläche von lebenden und todten Pflanzentheilen. *Sitzber. math. phys. Kl. bayer. Akad. Wiss. München* **1**: 238-264.

Nägeli, C. 1861a. Über die Wirkung des Frostes auf die Pflanzenzellen. *Sitzber. math. phys. Kl. bayer. Akad. Wiss. München* **1**: 264-271.

Nau. 1809. Hat man bis jetzt durch Versuche und Beobachtungen eine eigenthümliche Wärme in den Gewächsen erwiesen? *Ann. Wetterauischen Ges. für ges. Naturk.* **1**: 27-36.

Neger, F. W. 1915. Die Stärke-ökonomie der grünen Pflanze. *Naturw. Z. Forst-u. Landwirtsch.* **13**: 1.

Newton, R. 1922. A comparative study of winter wheat varieties with especial reference to winter killing. *J. Agr. Sci.* **12**: 1-19.

Newton, R. 1924. Coloidal properties of winter wheat plants in relation to frost resistance. *J. Agr. Sci.* **14**: 178-191.

Newton, R. 1924a. The nature and practical measurement of frost resistance in winter wheat. *Univ. Alberta Coll. Agr. Research Bull.* No. **1**: 1-53.

Newton, R., and Anderson, J. A. 1931. Respiration of winter wheat plants at low temperatures. *Can. J. Research* **5**: 337-354.

Newton, R., and Brown, W. R. 1926. Seasonal changes in the composition of winter wheat plants in relation to frost resistance. *J. Agr. Sci.* **16**: 522-538.

Newton, R., and Brown, W. R. 1931. Frost precipitation of proteins of plant juice. *Can. J. Research* **5**: 87-110.

Newton, R., and Brown, W. R. 1931. Catalase activity of wheat leaf juice in relation to frost resistance. *Can. J. Research* **5**: 333-336.

Newton, R., and Martin, W. M. 1930. Physico-chemical studies on the nature of drought resistance in crop plants. *Can. J. Research* **3**: 336-427.

NEWTON, R., BROWN, W. R. and ANDERSON, J. A. 1931. Chemical changes in nitrogen fractions of plant juices on exposure to frost. *Can. J. Research* **5**: 327-332.

NIKLEWSKI, B. 1906. Untersuchungen über die Umwandlung einiger stickstoffreier Reservestoffe während der Winterperiode der Bäume. *Beitr. Botan. Centr.* **19** (erste Abt.): 68-117.

NILSSON-EHLE, H. 1913. Zur Kenntnis der Erblichkeitsverhältnisse der Eigenschaft Winterfestigkeit beim Weizen. *Z. Pflanzenzücht* **1**: 3-12.

NIZENJKOV, N. P. 1939. Electrometric method of determining cold and drought resistance in crops. *Doklady Vsesoyuz. Akad. Sel'skokhoz. Nauk.* **1939**: 11-18. (*Herbage Abstr.* **10**: 187, 1940.)

NOACK, K. 1920. Der Betriebstoffwechsel der thermophilen Pilze. *Jahrb. wiss. Botan.* **59**: 413-466.

NORDHAUSEN, M. 1916. Über die Saugkraft transpirierender Sprosse. *Ber. deut. botan. Ges.* **34**: 619-639.

NORDHAUSEN, M. 1919. Die Saugkraftleistungen abgeschnittener transpirierender Sprosse. *Ber. deut. botan. Ges.* **37**: 443-449.

NORTHEN, H. T. 1943. Relationship of dissociation of cellular proteins by incipient drought to physiological processes. *Botan. Gaz.* **104**: 480-485.

NOVIKOV, V. A. 1928. Cold resistance of plants, II. *J. Exptl. Landwirtsch. Südosten Eur-Russlands* **6**: 71-100.

NOVIKOV, V. A. 1934. On the problem of hardiness of seedlings of alfalfa varieties. *Compt. rend. acad. sci. U.R.S.S.* **4**: 483-486.

NOVIKOV, V. A., and MOHOVA, M. L. 1936. The effect of wilting on winter hardiness. Symposium of paper from the *Central Plant Breeding Sta. Sojuz.* No. 1, H. **1**: 149-152, Tashkent, 1936. (*Herbage Abstr.* **7**: 239, 1937.)

OBERDIECK, J. G. C. 1872. Beobachtungen über das Erfrieren vieler Gewächse und namentlich unserer Obstbäume in kalten Wintern. *Ver. deut. Pom. Vereinsbl. für seine Mitglieder für 1871-72, Ravensburg*, pp. 1-108.

OHLWEILER, W. W. 1912. The relation between the density of the cell saps and the freezing points of leaves. *Missouri Botan. Garden 23rd Rept.*, pp. 101-131.

OKNINA, E. Z., and MARKOVICH, A. A. 1951. (Means of increasing resistance to cold in Rosa gallica). *Izvest. Akad. Nauk S.S.S.R. Ser. Biol.* **1951**: 107-114.

ONODA, N. 1937. Mikroskopische Beobachtungen über das Gefrieren einiger Pflanzenzellen in flüssigem Paraffin. Botanisches Institut der Kaiserlichen Universität zu Kyoto.

ONODERA, J., and TAKASAKI, T. 1930. Osmotic pressure of plant juice and cold resistance in some winter crops, and meteorological factors influencing their cold resistance. *Proc. Crop Sci. Soc (Japan)* **2**: 142-152. (*Biol. Abstr.* **8**: 402, 1934.)

OPPENHEIMER, H. 1927. Osmotische und Saugkraftmessungen an unseren Kulturpflanzen. *Landwirtsch. Fortschr.* **2**: 215-219.

OPPENHEIMER, H. R. 1932. Zur Kenntnis der hochsommerlichen Wasserbilanz mediterraner Gehölze. *Ber. deut. Botan. Ges.* **50A**: 185-245.

OVERTON, E. 1899. Beobachtungen und Versuche über das Auftreten von rothem Zellsaft bei Pflanzen. *Jahrb. wiss. Botan.* **33**: 171-177.

PANTANELLI, E. 1918. Sur la resistanza delle piante al freddo. *Atti reale acad. Italia Mem. classe sci. fis. mat. e nat.* **27**: 126-130, 148-153. (*Biol. Abstr.* **2**: 1135, 1919.)

PANTANELLI, E. 1919. Alterazione del ricambio e della permeabilita cellulare a temperature prossime al congelamento. *Atti reale acad. Italia Mem. classe sci. fis. mat. e nat.* **28**: 205-209. (*Biol. Abstr.* **6**: 1312, 1920.)

PANTANELLI, E. 1920. Influenza della nutrizione e dell'attivita radicale sul colasso e il disseccamento prodotti dal freddo. *Atti reale acad. Italia Mem. classe sci. fis. mat. e nat.* **29**: 66-71. (*Biol. Abstr.* **7**: 2155, 1921.)

PARIJA, P., and MALLIK, P. 1941. Nature of the reserve food in seeds and their resistance to high temperature. *J. Indian Botan. Soc.* **19**: 223-230.

PARIJA, P., and PILLAY, K. P. 1945. Effect of pre-sowing treatment on the drought resistance in rice. *Proc. Natl. Acad. Sci. (India)* **15B** (1): 6-14.

PARKER, J. 1952. Desiccation in conifer leaves: Anatomical changes and determination of the lethal level. *Botan. Gaz.* **114**: 189-198.

PAYEN, M. 1838. Phénomènes resultant de la congélation des pommes de terre. *Compt. rend.* **6**: 344-347.

PELTIER, G. L. 1931. Control equipment for the study of hardiness in crop plants. *J. Agr. Research* **43**: 177-182.

PELTIER, G. L., and KIESSELBACH, T. A. 1934. The comparative cold resistance of spring small grains. *J. Am. Soc. Agron.* **26**: 681-686.

PELTIER, G. L., and TYSDAL, H. M. 1931. Hardiness studies with 2-year-old alfalfa plants. *J. Agr. Research* **43**: 931-955.

PELTIER, G. L., and TYSDAL, H. M. 1932. A method for the determination of comparative hardiness in seedling alfalfas by controlled hardening and artificial freezing. *J. Agr. Research* **44**: 429-444.

PENTZER, W. T., and HEINZE, P. H. 1954. Post harvest physiology of fruits and vegetables. *Ann. Rev. Plant Physiol.* **5**: 205-224.

PETIT-THOUARS, A. DU. 1817. "Le verger Francais ou traité général de la culture des arbres fruitiers, etc.," pp. 6-45. Paris.

PETRIE, A. H. K., and WOOD, J. G. 1938. Studies on the nitrogen metabolism of plants. I. The relation between the content of proteins, amino acids and water in the leaves. *Ann. Botany (London)* **2**: 33-60.

PETTINGER, N. A., HENDERSON, R. G., and WINGARD, S. A. 1932. Some nutritional disorders in corn grown in sand cultures. *Phytopathology* **22**: 33-51.

PFEIFFER, M. 1933. Frostuntersuchungen an Fichtentrieben. *Tharandt. forst. Jahrb.* **84**: 664-695.

PFEFFER, W. 1903. "The Physiology of Plants," Vol. 2, pp. 232-247. Oxford, New York.

PICTET, R. 1893. De l'emploi méthodique des basses températures en biologie. *Bibl. Univ. Arch. Sci. Phys. nat.* [3] **30**: 293-314.

PINKHOF, M. 1929. Untersuchungen über die Umfallkrankheit der Tulpen. *Rec. trav. botan. néerl.* **26**: 135-288.

PISEK, A. 1950. Frosthärte und Zusammensetzung des Zellsaftes bei *Rhododendron ferrugineum, Pinus cembra* und *Picea excelsa. Protoplasma* **39**: 129-146.

PISEK, A. 1953. Wie schützen sich die Alpenpflanzen gegen Frost? *Umschau Wiss. u. Tech.* 21.

PISEK, A., and BERGER, E. 1938. Kutikulare Transpiration und Trockenresistenz isolierter Blätter und Sprosse. *Planta* **28**: 124-155.

PISEK, A., and CARTELLIERI, E. 1932. Zur Kenntnis des Wasserhaushaltes der Pflanzen I. Sonnenpflanzen *Jahrb. wiss. Botan.* **75**: 195-251. II. Schatten-pflanzen. *Ibid.* **75**: 643-678.

PISEK, A., and CARTELLIERI, E. 1939. Zur Kenntnis des Wasserhaushaltes der Pflanzen. IV. Bäume und Straucher. *Jahrb. wiss. Botan.* **88**: 22-68.

PISEK, A., and LARCHER, W. 1954. Zusammenhang zwischen Austrocknungs-resistenz und Frosthärte bei Immergrünenpflanzen. *Protoplasma* **44**: 30-46.

PISEK, A., SOHM, H., and CARTELLIERI, E. 1935. Untersuchungen über osmotischen Wert und Wassergehalt von Pflanzen und Pflanzengesellschaften der alpinen Stufe. *Beitr. Botan. Centr.* **52**: 634-675.

PLATT, A. W. 1937. The effect of soil moisture, hardening, endosperm condition and variety on the frost reaction of wheat, oat and barley seedlings. *Sci. Agr.* **17**: 616-626.

PLATT, A. W., and DARROCH, J. G. 1942. The seedling resistance of wheat varieties to artificial drought in relation to grain yield. *Sci. Agr.* **22**: 521-527.

PLINY. 1855-1856. "Natural History" (J. Bostock and H. T. Riley, transls.), Vols. 3 and 4. London.

POJARKOVA, A. 1924. Winterruhe, Reservestoffe, und Kälteresistenz bei Holz-pflanzen. *Ber. deut. botan. Ges.* **42**: 420-429.

POPOV, V. P. 1937. The roles of combined water in frost resistance of winter wheat. *Compt. rend. acad. sci. U.R.S.S.* **14**: 49-52.

PORODKO, T. M. 1926. Über die Absterbegeschwindigkeit der erhitzten Samen. *Ber. deut. botan. Ges.* **44**: 71-80.

PORODKO, T. M. 1926a. Einfluss der Temperatur auf die Absterbegeschwindigkeit der Samen. *Ber. deut. botan. Ges.* **44**: 80-84.

POTAPOV, P. E. 1939. Respiration intensity in winter wheat, as an index of winter hardiness. *Soc. Zern. Hoz.* **1938**: 11-128. (*Herbage Abstr.* **10**: 178, 1940.)

POTAPOV, P. E. 1939a. Intensity of respiration in relation to winter hardiness of winter wheat. *Selek. Semenovod.* **1**: 25-27. (*Herbage Abstr.* **9**: 632, 1939.)

POTTER, G. F. 1924. Experiments on the resistance of apple roots to low tempera-tures. *New Hampshire Agr. Expt. Sta. Tech. Bull.* **27**.

PREISING, F. A. 1930. Untersuchungen über den Kohlenhydratstoffwechsel des im-mergrünen Laubblattes im Laufe eines Jahres. *Botan. Arch.* **30**: 231-306.

PRESTON, J. F., and PHILLIPS, F. J. 1911. Seasonal variation in the food reserves of trees. *Forestry Quart.* **9**: 232-243.

PRICE, W. A. 1916. Starch in apple trees. *Ohio J. Sci.* **16**: 356-359.

PRILLIEUX, E. 1869. Sur la formation de glaçons a l'intérieur des plantes. *Ann. sci. nat. Paris Ser. 5* **12**: 125-134.

PRILLIEUX, E. 1872. Coloration en bleu des fleurs de quelques orchidées sous l'influence de la gelée. *Bull. soc. botan. France* **19**: 152-155.

PRINGSHEIM, E. 1906. Wasserbewegung und Turgorregulation in welkenden Pflanzen. *Jahrb. wiss. Botan.* **43**: 89-144.

QUISENBERRY, K. S., and BAYLES, B. B. 1939. Growth habit of some winter wheat varieties and its relation to winter hardiness and earliness. *J. Am. Soc. Agron.* **31**: 785-789.

QUISENBERRY, K. S., and CLARK, J. A. 1929. Breeding hard red winter wheats for winter hardiness and high yield. *U.S. Dept. Agr. Tech. Bull.* **136**: 1-28.

RABE, F. 1905. Über die Austrocknungsfähigkeit gekeimter Samen und Sporen. *Flora* **95**: 253-324.

RAHEJA, P. C. 1951. Recent physiological investigations on drought resistance in crop plants. *Indian J. Agr. Sci.* **21**: 335-346.

RAO, K. SUBBA, RAO, M. BHIMASENA, and RAO, B. SANJIVA. 1949. Drought resistance of plants in relation to hysteresis in sorption. I. Hydration and dehydration of the leaves of certain drought resistant and drought sensitive plants. *Proc. Natl. Inst. Sci. (India)* **15** (2): 41-49.

RAO, K. SUBBA, RAO, M. BHIMASENA, and RAO, B. SANJIVA. 1949a. Drought resistance of plants in relation to hysteresis in sorption. II. Adaptability of the Ragi plant to varying conditions of soil drought. *Proc. Natl. Inst. Sci. (India)* **15** (2): 51-58.

REA, M. W., and SMALL, J. 1927. The hydrion concentration of plant tissues VI. Stem tissue reactions throughout the year. *Protoplasma* **2**: 428-459.

REIN, R. 1908. Untersuchungen über den Kältetod der Pflanzen. *Z. Naturforsch* **80**: 1-38.

RENNER, O. 1911. Experimentelle Beiträge zur Kenntis der Wasserbewegung. *Flora* **103**: 171-247.

RENNER, O. 1932. Zur Kenntnis des Wasserhaushaltes javanischer Kleinepiphyten. *Planta* **18**: 215-287.

REUM, J. A. 1835. "Pflanzenphysiologie, oder das Leben Wachsen und Verhalten der Pflanzen," pp. 168-169. Arnoldische Buchhandlung. Dresden u. Leipzig.

RICHTER, A. 1910. Zur Frage über den Tod von Pflanzen infolge niedriger Temperatur. *Zentr. Bakteriol. Parasitenk. Abt. II* **28**: 617-624.

RIGG, G. B., and CAIN, R. A. 1929. A physico-chemical study of the leaves of three medicinal plants in relation to evergreenness. *Am. J. Botany* **16**: 40-57.

RIKHTER, A. A. 1927. Cold resistance of plants. I. Dynamics of soluble carbohydrates in wheat and rye during the winter. *J. Exptl. Landwirtsch. Südosten Eur. Russl.* **4**: 326-345. (*Biol. Abstr.* **3**: 17818, 1929.)

RIVERA, V., and CORNELI, E. 1931. Rassegna die casi fitopatologici osservati nel 1929 (danni da freddo e da crittogame). *Riv. patol. vegetale* **21**: 65-100. (*Biol. Abstr.* **6**: 12786, 1932.)

ROBBINS, W. J., and PETSCH, K. F. 1932. Moisture content and high temperature in relation to the germination of corn and wheat grains. *Botan. Gaz.* **93**: 85-92.

ROBERTS, D. W. A. 1950. Qualitative and quantitative determinations of the wheat leaf carbohydrates. *Can. J. Research* **C28**: 754-779.

ROBERTS, R. H. 1922. The development and winter injury of cherry blossom buds. *Wisconsin Agr. Expt. Sta. Research Bull.* **52**.

ROBERTS, R. H. 1937. Blossom bud development and winter hardiness. *Am. J. Botany* **24**: 683-685.

ROBERTSON, A. H. 1927. Thermophilic and thermoduric microorganisms, with special reference to species isolated from milk. *New York Agr. Expt. Sta. Tech. Bull.* **130**.

ROEMER, T., RUDORF, W., and LUEG, H. 1928. Das Refraktometer als Hilfsmittel zur Bestimmung der Winterfestigkeit bei Winterweizen. *Fortschr. Landwirtsch.* **3**: 408-409.

ROGERS, W. S. 1949. Frost damage to fruit: a note on the present position of research in England. *Ann. Rept. East Malling Research Sta. 1948* pp. 128-130.

ROSA, J. T. 1920. Pentosan content in relation to hardiness of vegetable plants. *Proc. Am. Soc. Hort. Sci.* **17**: 207-210.

ROSA, J. T. 1921. Investigation on the hardening process in vegetable plants. *Missouri Agr. Expt. Sta. Research Bull.* **48**.

ROSENBERG, O. 1896. Die Stärke der Pflanzen im Winter. *Botan. Centr.* **66**: 337-340.

ROUSCHAL, E. 1938. Zum Wärmehaushalt der Macchienpflanzen. *Österr. Botan. Z.* **87**: 42-50.

ROUSCHAL, E. 1939. Der sommerliche Wasserhaushalt der Macchienpflanzen. *Jahrb. wiss. Botan.* **87**: 436-523.

ROUSCHAL, E. 1939a. Beiträge zum winterliche Wasserhaushalt von *Cheiranthus cheiri* und anderen wintergrünen Gartenpflanzen. *Österr. Botan. Z.* **88**: 148-154.

RUBEL, E. 1906. Lichtmessungen unter Schnee. *Verhandl. Schweiz. naturforsch. Ges.* **89**: 68.

RUDORF, W. 1938. Keimstimmung und Photoperiode in ihrer Bedeutung für die Kälteresistenz. *Züchter* **10**: 238-246.

RUSSELL, W. 1914. De la survie des tissus végétaux après le gel. *Compt. rend.* **158**: 508-510.

RUSSOW, E. 1883. I. Ueber Tüpfelbildung und Inhalt der Bastparenchym- und Bastrahlzellen der Dikotylen und Gymnospermen. II. Ueber den Inhalt der parenchymatischen Elemente der Rinde vor und während des Knospenaustriebes und Beginns der Cambiumthätigkeit in Stamm und Wurzel der einheimischen Lignosen. *Botan. Centr.* **13**: 271-275.

RUSSOW, E. 1884. Über das Schwinden und Wiederauftreten der Stärke in der Rinde der einheimischen Holzgewächse. *Sitzber. Dorpater Naturforsch. Ges.* **6**: 492-494.

SABLON, L. DU. 1904. Recherches physiologiques sur les matières de reserves des arbres. *Rev. gén. botan.* **16**: 341-368; 386-401.

SABLON, L. DU. 1906. Recherches physiologiques sur les matières de réserves des arbres. (Deuxième Mémoire). *Rev. gén. Botan.* **18**: 5-25; 82-96.

SACHS, J. 1860. Krystallbildungen bei dem Gefrieren und Veränderung der Zellhäute bei dem Aufthauen saftiger Pflanzentheile, mitgetheilt von W. Hofmeister *Ber. Verhandl. kgl. sächs. Ges. Wiss. Leipzig. Math. phys. Kl.* **12**: 1-50.

SACHS, J. 1864. Ueber die obere Temperatur-Grenze der Vegetation. *Flora* **47**: 5-12, 24-29, 33-39, 65-75.

SACHS, J. 1873. Grundzüge der Pflanzenphysiologie. Separatabdruck des dritten Buchs der dritten Auflage des Lehrbuchs der Botanik. Engelmann, Leipzig.

SALMON, S. C. 1917. Why cereals winterkill. *J. Am. Soc. Agron.* **9**: 353-380.

SALMON, S. C. 1933. Resistance of varieties of winter wheat and rye to low temperature in relation to winter hardiness and adaptation. *Kansas Agr. Expt. Sta. Tech. Bull.* **35**: 1-66.

SALMON, S. C., and FLEMING, F. L. 1918. Relation of the density of cell sap to winter hardiness in small grains. *J. Agr. Research* **13**: 497-506.

SALTYKOVSKIJ, M. I. 1935. Determination of frost resistance of winter wheat and rye in grain. *Compt. rend. acad. sci. U.R.S.S.* **3**(8): 321-324.

SALTYKOVSKIJ, M. I. 1936. Cold resistance of the first generation of wheat hybrids. *Compt. rend. acad. sci. U.R.S.S.* **3** (12): 235-238.

SALTYKOVSKIJ, M. I. 1939. Cold resistance of wheat x wheatgrass hybrids of the first generation. *Doklady Vsesoyuz. Akad. Sel'skokhoz Nauk.* 15-18. (*Herbage Abstr.* **10**: 180, 1940.)

SALTYKOVSKIJ, M. I., and SAPRYGINA, E. S. 1935. The frost-resistance of winter cereals at different stages of development. *Compt. rend. acad. sci. U.R.S.S.* **4** (9): 99-103.

SALTYKOVSKIJ, M. I., and SAPRYGINA, E. S. 1939. On selecting pairs in crossing and breeding winter hardy wheat. *Compt. rend. acad. sci. U.R.S.S.* **25**: 766-769.

SAPPER, I. 1935. Versuche zur Hitzeresistenz der Pflanzen. *Planta* **23**: 518-556.

SAPRYGINA, E. S. 1935. Frost resistance of spring wheats. (On the effect of length of the "light" stage on the hardiness of wheats). *Compt. rend. acad. sci. U.R.S.S.* **3** (8): 325-328.

SATTLER, H. 1929. Beiträge zur Kenntnis des N-Stoffwechsels wintergrüner Pflanzen. *Planta* **9**: 315-333.

SAULESCU, N. 1931. Die Winterfestigkeit einiger F_1- Winterweizenbastarde. *Züchter* **3**: 300-302.

SAUSSURE, T. DE. 1827. De l'influence du dessèchement sur la germination de plusieurs grains alimentaires. *Ann. Sci. Nat.* [1] **10**: 68-93.

SAVELJEV, S. I. 1939. Application of phosphorus and potassium fertilizers by instalments in the autumn as a method of increasing frost resistance and yield in winter wheat. *Soc. Zern. Hoz.* **1938**: 28-35. (*Herbage Abstr.* **10**: 184, 1940.)

SAYRE, J. D. 1932. Methods of determining bound water in plant tissue. *J. Agr. Research* **44**: 669-688.

SAXE, A. I. 1938. Study of winter wheat varieties in respect of the resistance to frost and soil drought. *Izvest. Akad. Nauk S.S.S.R. Ser. Biol.* **5-6**: 187-215. (*Herbage Abstr.* **9**: 1466, 1939.)

SCARTH, G. W. 1941. Dehydration injury and resistance. *Plant Physiol.* **16**: 171-179.

SCARTH, G. W. 1944. Cell physiological studies of frost resistance. *New Phytologist* **43**: 1-12.

SCARTH, G. W., and LEVITT, J. 1937. The frost-hardening mechanism of plant cells. *Plant Physiol.* **12**: 51-78.

SCARTH, G. W., and LLOYD, F. E. 1930. "Elementary Course in General Physiology." Wiley, New York.

SCARTH, G. W., LEVITT, J., and SIMINOVITCH, D. 1940. Plasmamembrane structure in the light of frost-hardening changes. *Cold Spring Harbor Symposia Quant. Biol.* **8**: 102-109.

SCHACHT, H. 1857. "Lehrbuch der Anatomie und Physiologie der Gewächse," pp. 525-529. Berlin.

SCHAFFNIT, E. 1910. Studien über der Einfluss niederer Temperaturen auf die pflanzliche Zell. *Mitt. Kaiser-Wilhelm Inst. Landwirtsch. Bromberg* **3**: 93-144.

SCHAFFNIT, E. 1911. Über den Einfluss niederer Temperaturen auf die pflanzliche Zelle. *Z. Allgem. Physiol.* **12**: 323-336.

SCHAFFNIT, E. 1913. Winterkilling of wheat (tr. title). *Jahresb. Kaiser Wilhelm Inst. Landwirtsch. Bromberg* 21-23. (*Expt. Sta. Record.* **33**: 51-52, 1915.)

SCHAFFNIT, E., and LÜDTKE, M. 1931. Beiträge zur Kenntnis von Kältewirkungen auf die pflanzliche Zelle (II. Mitteilung). *Phytopathol. Z.* **4** (4): 328-386.

SCHAFFNIT, E., and WILHELM, A. F. 1932. Kühlversuche mit verschieden ernährten Pflanzen und Untersuchungen über deren Stoffwechselphysiologie. *Phytopathol. Z.* **5**: 505-566.

SCHANDER, R., and SCHAFFNIT, E. 1919. Untersuchungen über das Auswintern des Getreides. *Landwirtsch. Jahrb.* **52**: 1-66.

SCHEIBMAIR, G. 1937. Hitzeresistenz-Studien an Moos-Zellen. *Protoplasma* **29**: 394-424.

SCHELLENBERG, H. C. 1905. Über Hemicellulosen als Reservestoffe bei unseren Waldbäumen. *Ber. deut. botan. Ges.* **23**: 36-45.

SCHIMPER, A. F. W. 1903. "Plant Geography Upon a Physiological Basis," pp. 38-42. Oxford, New York.

SCHLÖSSER, L. 1936. Frosthärte und Polyploidie. *Züchter* **8**: 75-80.

SCHMETZ, L. 1925. Untersuchungen über den Einfluss einiger Aussenfaktoren auf den Stärkeabbau in Laubblättern. *Botan. Arch.* **10**: 16-33.

SCHMIDT, C. 1909. Über Stärke- und Fettbäume. *Botan. Ztg.* **67**. Jahrg. II. Abt. 129-131.

SCHMIDT, H. 1939. Plasmazustand und Wasserhaushalt bei *Lamium maculatum. Protoplasma* **33**: 25-43.

SCHMIDT, H., DUWALD, K., and STOCKER, O. 1940. Plasmatische Untersuchungen an dürreempfindlichen und dürreresistenten Sorten landwirtschaftlicher Kulturpflanzen. *Planta* **31**: 559-596.

SCHNEIDER, E. 1925. Über die Plasmolyse als Kennzeichen lebender Zellen. *Z. wiss. Mikroskop.* **42**: 32-54.

SCHNEIDER, G. W., and CHILDERS, N. F. 1941. Influence of soil moisture on photosynthesis, respiration, and transpiration of apple leaves. *Plant Physiol.* **16**: 565-583.

SCHNEIDER-ORELLI, O. 1910. Versuche über die Widerstandsfähigkeit gewisser Medicago-Samen (Wollkletten) gegen hohe Temperaturen. *Flora* **100**: 305-311.

SCHÖPF, J. D. 1788. Ueber die Temperatur der Pflanzen. *Naturforsch.* (*Halle*) **23**: 1-36.

SCHOLANDER, P. F., FLAGG, W., HOCK, R. J., and IRVING, L. 1953. Studies on the physiology of frozen plants and animals in the Arctic. *J. Cellular Comp. Physiol.* **42**: 1-56.

SCHRATZ, E 1931. Vergleichende Untersuchungen über den Wasserhaushalt von Pflanzen im Trockengebiete des südlichen Arizona. *Jahrb. wiss. Botan.* **74**: 153-290.

SCHRIBAUX, E. 1929. Influence des engrais sur la résistance au froid du seigle d'hiver. *Compt. rend. acad. agr. France* **15**: 571-574.

SCHRÖDER, D. 1909. Über den Verlauf des Welkens und die Lebenszähigkeit der Laubblätter. Inaug. Dissertation, Gottingen.

SCHRÖDER, G. 1886. Über die Austrocknungsfähigkeit der Pflanzen. Inaug. Dissertation, Tübingen, pp. 1-51.

SCHROEDER, H., and HORN, T. 1922. Das gegenseitige Mengenverhältnis der Kohlenhydrate im Laubblatt in seiner Abhängigkeit vom Wassergehalt. *Biochem. Z.* **130**: 165-198.

SCHÜBLER, G. 1827. Beobachtungen über die Temperatur der Vegetabilien und einige damit verwandte Gegenstände. *Ann. Physik u. Chem.* **10**: 581-592.

Schübler, G. 1829. Untersuchungen über die Temperaturveränderungen der Vegetabilien und verschiedene damit in Beziehung stehende Gegenstände. Eine Inaugural Dissert. unter dem Präsid. v. G. Schübler im Juli 1829 der öffent. Prüfung vorgelegt von W. Neuffer von Esslingen.

Schulz, C. H. 1823. "Die Natur der lebendigen Pflanze," Erster Theil, p. 577. Berlin.

Schulz, E. 1888. Ueber Reservestoffe in immergrünen Blättern unter besonderer Berücksichtigung des Gerbstoffes. *Flora* **46**, N.R. or 71: 223-241, 248-258.

Schumacher, E. 1875. II. Beiträge zur Morphologie und Biologie der Hefe. *Sitzber. Akad. Wiss. Wien Math. Naturw. Kl. Abt. I* **70**: 157-188.

Schwartze, C. D. 1937. Rest period responses and cold resistance in the red raspberry in relation to the breeding of hardy varieties. *Research Studies State Coll. Washington* **5**: 42.

Scott, D. H., and Cullinan, F. P. 1946. Some factors affecting the survival of artificially frozen fruit buds of peach. *J. Agr. Research* **73**: 207-236.

Seelhorst, C. von. 1910. I. Über den Trockensubstanzgehalt junger Weizenpflanzen verschiedener Varietät. *J. Landwirtsch.* **58**: 81-82.

Seemann, J. 1942. Über die Bedeutung der Unterkühlung für die Selektion frostresistenter Bohnenpflanzen. *Züchter* **14**: 258-264.

Seible, D. 1939. Ein Beitrag zur Frage der Kälteschäden an Pflanzen bei Temperaturen über dem Gefrierpunkt. *Beitr. Biol. Pflanz.* **26**: 289-330.

Seifriz, W. 1936. "Protoplasm." McGraw-Hill, New York.

Sellschop, Jacq. P. F., and Salmon, S. C. 1928. The influence of chilling above the freezing point on certain crop plants. *J. Agr. Research* **37**: 315-338.

Senebier, J. 1800. "Physiologie Végétale," Vol. 3, pp. 282-304. Genève.

Senn, G. 1922. Untersuchungen über die Physiologie der Alpenpflanzen. *Verhandl. schweiz. naturforsch. Ges.* **103**: 154-168.

Sergeev, L. I., and Lebedev, A. M. 1936. Theory of physiologic resistance of cultivated cereals. *Botan. Zhur. S.S.S.R.* **21**: 131-152. (*Biol. Abstr.* **11**: 18285, 1937.)

Sergejev, L. I., and Lebedev, A. M. 1936a. Beiträge zu einer physiologischen Resistenztheorie der Kulturgräser. *Planta* **25**: 84-103.

Sergeyev, L. I., and Sergeyeva, K. A. 1939. Effect of ions of aluminum and phosphoric acid on biological properties of plant protoplasm. *Compt. rend. acad. sci. U.R.S.S.* **22**: 626-629.

Sergeyev, L. I., and Sergeyeva, K. A. 1939a. Ionic action as a means of controlling resistance and growth of plants. *Compt. rend. acad. sci. U.R.S.S.* **22**: 630-632.

Sergejev, L. I., Lebedev, A. M., and Akifjeva, A. A. 1935. Correlation of frost resistance and resistance to soil salination. *Compt. rend. acad. sci. U.R.S.S.* **4**(9): 157-160.

Sestakov, V. E. 1936. Frost resistance of winter crops during the light stage. *Compt. rend. acad. sci. U.R.S.S.* **3**(12): 395-398.

Sestakov, V. E. 1938. Study of winter hardiness of winter crops in relation to the choice of parental pairs for crossing. *Selek. Semenovod.* No. **10**: 10-13. (*Herbage Abstr.* **9**: 634, 1939.)

Sestakov, E., and Sergeev, L. I. 1936. Changes in the permeability of protoplasm and the dynamics of frost resistance of winter cereals in connection with their passage through the light stage. *Compt. rend. acad. sci. U.R.S.S.* **4**(13): 25-28.

SESTAKOV, V. E., and SERGEEV, L. I. 1937. Changes in frost resistance and in the properties of cell protoplasm in winter wheat during the photo-stage. *Botan. Zhur. S.S.S.R.* **22**: 351-363. (*Herbage Abstr.* **8**: 234, 1938.)

SESTAKOV, V. E., and SMIRNOVA, A. D. 1936. Temperature hardening and the differentiation of the embryonic spike in winter wheats during the light stage of development. *Compt. rend. acad. sci. U.R.S.S.* **3**(12): 399-403.

SHERWOOD, L. V. 1937. A physiological study of cold tolerance in corn. *J. Am. Soc. Agron.* **29**: 1022-1030.

SHIRLEY, H. L., and MEULI, L. J. 1939. The influence of moisture supply on drought resistance of conifers. *J. Agr. Research* **59**: 1-29.

SHIRLEY, H. L., and MEULI, L. J. 1939a. The influence of soil nutrients on drought resistance of two-year-old pine. *Am. J. Botany* **26**: 355-360.

SHMELEV, I. K. 1935. Frost resistance of fruit trees. *Bull. Appl. Botany Genet. Plant Breeding* (*Leningrad*) *Ser. 3* No. **6**: 263-277. (*Expt. Sta. Record* **75**: 343, 1936.)

SHULL, C. A. 1916. Measurements of the surface forces in soils. *Botan. Gaz.* **62**: 1-31.

SHUTT, F. T. 1903. On the relation of moisture content to hardiness in apple twigs. *Trans. Roy. Soc. Can. II* **9**(4): 149-153.

SILKETT, V. W., MEGEE, C. R., and RATHER, N. C. 1937. The effect of late summer and early fall cutting on crown bud formation and winter hardiness of alfalfa. *J. Am. Soc. Agron.* **29**: 53-62.

SIMINOVITCH, D. 1940-1941. Abstracts American Society of Plant Physiologists (Philadelphia).

SIMINOVITCH, D., and BRIGGS, D. R. 1949. The chemistry of the living bark of the black locust tree in relation to frost hardiness. I. Seasonal variations in protein content. *Arch. Biochem.* **23**: 8-17.

SIMINOVITCH, D., and BRIGGS, D. R. 1953. Studies on the chemistry of the living bark of the black locust in relation to its frost hardiness. III. The validity of plasmolysis and desiccation tests for determining the frost hardiness of bark tissue. *Plant Physiol.* **28**: 15-34.

SIMINOVITCH, D., and BRIGGS, D. R. 1953a. Studies on the chemistry of the living bark of the black locust tree in relation to frost hardiness. IV. Effects of ringing on translocation, protein synthesis and the development of hardiness. *Plant Physiol.* **28**: 177-200.

SIMINOVITCH, D., and BRIGGS, D. R. 1954. Studies on the chemistry of the living bark of the black locust in relation to its frost hardiness. VII. A possible direct effect of starch on the susceptibility of plants to freezing injury. *Plant Physiol.* **29**: 331-337.

SIMINOVITCH, D., and LEVITT, J. 1941. The relation between frost resistance and the physical state of protoplasm. II. *Can. J. Research* **C19**: 9-20.

SIMINOVITCH, D., and SCARTH, G. W. 1938. A study of the mechanism of frost injury to plants. *Can. J. Research* **C16**: 467-481.

SIMINOVITCH, D., WILSON, C. M., and BRIGGS, D. R. 1953. Studies on the chemistry of the living bark of the black locust in relation to its frost hardiness. V. Seasonal transformation and variations in the carbohydrates: starch-sucrose interconversions. *Plant Physiol.* **28**: 383-400.

SIMONIS, W. 1947. CO_2—Assimilation und Stoffproduktion trocken gezogener Pflanzen. *Planta* **35**: 188-224.

SIMONIS, W. 1952. Untersuchungen zum Dürreeffekt. I. Morphologische Struktur, Wasserhaushalt, Atmung und Photosynthese feucht und trocken gezogener Pflanzen. *Planta* **40**: 313-332.

SINNOTT, E. W. 1918. Factors determining character and distribution of food re-reserve in woody plants. *Botan. Gaz.* **66**: 162-175.

SINZ, E. 1914. Beziehungen zwischen Trockensubstanz und Winterfestigkeit bei verschiedenen Winterweizen-Varietäten. *J. Landwirtsch.* **62**: 301-335.

SISAKJAN, N. M., and RUBIN, B. A. 1939. The action of low temperature on the reversibility of enzymatic reaction in relation to winter hardiness of plants. *Biokhimiya* **4**: 149-153. (*Herbage Abstr.* **9**: 1486, 1939.)

SISAKJAN, N. M., and RUBIN, B. A. 1939a. Influence of salts on enzymic activity in a living cell under low temperature conditions. *Compt. rend. acad. sci. U.R.S.S.* **25**: 298-301.

SKINNER, J. J., and REED, C. A. 1925. Fertilizers, cover crops, soil conditions. *Am. Nutrition J.* **22**: 90-93. (*Expt. Sta. Record* **53**: 538, 1925.)

SMIRNOVA, A. D., and SESTAKOV, V. E. 1938. Changes in nitrogen content in relation to carbohydrate accumulation and frost resistance in winter wheat during the photo-stage. *Trudy Konferents Pocrored. Fiziol. Saratov.* **2**: 325-333. (*Herbage Abstr.* **9**: 178, 1939.)

SMITH, A. M. 1915. The respiration of partly dried plant organs. *Brit. Assoc. Advance Sci. Rept.* page 725.

SMITH, T. J. 1942. Responses of biennial sweet clover to moisture, temperature, and length of day. *J. Am. Soc. Agron.* **34**: 865-876.

SMITH, W. H. 1954. Non-freezing injury in plant tissues with particular reference to the detached plum fruit. *8th Intern. Congr. Botany* **11**: 280-285.

SMITH, W. W., and TINGLEY, M. A. 1940. Frost rings in fall fertilized McIntosh apple trees. *Proc. Am. Soc. Hort. Sci.* **37**: 110-112.

SNELL, K. 1932. Die Beschleunigung der Keimung bei der Kartoffelknolle. *Ber. deut. botan. Ges.* **52A**: 146-161.

SOLOMÉ, O. 1803. Observations sur la température interne des végétaux comparée a celle de l'atmosphère. *Ann. chim.* (30 Brumaire an x^e) **40**: 113-122.

SORAUER, P. 1884. Wirkungen künstlicher Froste. *Ber. deut. botan. Ges.* **2**: 22-25.

SORAUER, P. 1906. Die mechanischen Wirkungen des Frostes. *Ber. deut. botan. Ges.* **24**: 43-54.

SORAUER, P. 1907. Blitzspuren und Frostspuren. *Ber. deut. botan. Ges.* **25**: 157-164.

SORAUER, P. 1908, 1924, 1933. "Handbuch der Pflanzenkrankheiten," Vol. 1. Parey, Berlin.

SOSA, A., and SOSA-BOURDOUIL, C. 1936. Variations dans la composition du Bouleau (Betula alba L.) au cours de la végétation d'une année. *Bull. soc. chim. biol.* **18**: 918-925.

SPRANGER, E. 1941. Das Erfrieren der Pflanzen über 0° mit besonderer Berücksichtigung der Warmhauspflanzen. *Gartenbauwiss.* **16**: 90-128.

STARK, A. L. 1936. Unfrozen water in apple shoots as related to their winter hardiness. *Plant Physiol.* **11**: 689-711.

STARKOV, P. A. 1931. Cold resistance of winter wheat. (Izdamie Sortsemtresta) *Stavropal. Kavkazkis*, 16 pp. (*Biol. Abstr.* **8**: 11718, 1934.)

STEEL, T. A., WALDO, G. F., and BROWN, W. S. 1934. Conditions affecting cold resistance in strawberries. *Proc. Am. Soc. Hort. Sci.* **32**: 434-439.

STEINBAUER, G. 1926. Difference in resistance to low temperature shown by clover varieties. *Plant Physiol.* **1**: 281-286.

STEINBRINCK, C. 1900. Zur Terminologie der Volumänderungen pflanzlicher Gewebe und organischer Substanzen bei wechselndem Flüssigkeitsgehalt. *Ber. deut. botan. Ges.* **18**: 217-224.

STEINBRINCK, C. 1903. Versuche über die Luftdurchlässigkeit der Zellwände von Farn- und Selaginella-Sporangien, sowie von Moosblättern. *Flora* **92**: 102-131.

STEINBRINCK, C. 1906. Über Schrumpfungs- und Kohäsionsmechanismen von Pflanzen. *Biol. Centr.* **26**: 657-677; 721-744.

STEINER, M. 1933. Zum Chemismus der osmotischen Jahresschwankungen einiger immergrüner Holzgewächse. *Jahrb. wiss. Botan.* **78**: 564-622.

STEINMETZ, F. H. 1926. Winter hardiness in alfalfa varieties. *Minnesota Agr. Expt. Sta. Tech. Bull.* **38**.

STEINMETZ, F. H., and HILBORN, M. T. 1937. A histological evaluation of low temperature injury to apple trees. *Maine Agr. Expt. Sta. Bull.* **388**: 1-32.

STILES, W. 1930. On the cause of cold death of plants. *Protoplasma* **9**: 459-466.

STOCKER, O. 1928. Der Wasserhaushalt der ägyptischen Wüsten- und Salzpflanzen. *Botan. Abhandl.* No. **13**.

STOCKER, O. 1929. Das Wasserdefizit von Gefässpflanzen in verschiedenen Klimazonen. *Planta* **7**: 382-387.

STOCKER, O. 1942. Untersuchungen über die physiologischen Grundlagen der Dürreresistenz landwirtschaftlicher Kulturpflanzen. *Forschungsdienst* **16**: 275-279.

STOCKER, O. 1947. Probleme der pflanzlichen Dürreresistenz. *Naturwissenschaften* **34**: 362-371.

STOCKER, O. 1947a. Beiträge zu einer Theorie der Dürreresistenz. *Planta* **35**: 445-466.

STOCKER, O. 1951. Kälte- und dürrefeste Pflanzen. *Umschau Wiss. u. Tech.* Heft 22/20.

STOCKER, O., REHM, S., and SCHMIDT, H. 1943. Der Wasser- und Assimilationshaushalt dürreresistenter und dürreempfindlicher Sorten landwirtschaftlicher Kulturpflanzen. I. Hafer, Gerste, und Weizen. *Jahrb. wiss. Botan.* **91**: 1-53. II. Zuckerrüben *Ibid.* 278-330.

STOKLASA, J. 1936. The increase of physiological combustion in the presence of potassium and phosphorus and the prevention of freezing of plants (trans. title) *Ernähr. Pflanze* **32**: 27-31, 40. (*Expt. Sta. Record* **75**: 313-314, 1936.)

STRAHOV, A. D., and TIUNOVA, K. P. 1937. The effect of fertilisers on wintering of wheats, their further development and yield. *Trudy Timirjazev seljkohoz. Akad.* **2**: 3-47. (*Herbage Abstr.* **9**: 629, 1939.)

STRAIB, W. 1946. Beiträge zur Frosthärte des Weizens. *Züchter* **17/18**: 1-12.

STRAUSBAUGH, P. D. 1921. Dormancy and hardiness in the plum. *Botan. Gaz.* **71**: 337-357.

STRÖMER, M. 1749. Gedanken über die Ursache warum die Bäume bei starkem Winter erfrieren, wobei die Möglichkeit solchem vorzubeugen erwiesen wird. *Der Kgl. Schwed. Akad. Wiss. Abhandl. Nat. Haushalt. u. Mech. auf die Jahre 1739 und 1740* (*Aus dem Schwed. übersetzt*) **I**: 116-121.

STRUGGER, S. 1934. Beiträge zur Physiologie des Wachstums. I. Zur protoplasmaphysiologischen Kausalanalyse des Streckungswachstums. *Jahrb. wiss. Botan.* **79**: 406-471.

STUART, N. W. 1938. Cold hardiness of some apple understocks and the reciprocal influence of stock and scion on hardiness. *Proc. Am. Soc. Hort. Sci.* **35**: 386-389.

STUCKEY, I. H., and CURTIS, O. F. 1938. Ice formation and the death of plant cells by freezing. *Plant Physiol.* **13**: 815-833.

SUDDS, R. H., and MARSH, R. S. 1943. Winter injury to trunks of young bearing apple trees in West Virginia following a fall application of nitrate of soda. *Proc. Am. Soc. Hort. Sci.* **42**: 293-297.

SULAKADZE, T. S. 1939. Amounts of ice in frozen winter plants. *Compt. rend. acad. Sci. U.R.S.S.* **23**: 373-375.

SUNESON, C. A., and PELTIER, G. L. 1934. Cold resistance adjustments of field hardened winter wheats as determined by artificial freezing. *J. Am. Soc. Agron.* **26**: 50-58.

SUNESON, C. A., and PELTIER, G. L. 1934a. Effect of stage of seedling development upon the cold resistance of winter wheats. *J. Am. Soc. Agron.* **26**: 687-692.

SUNESON, C. A., and PELTIER, G. L. 1938. Effect of weather variants on field hardening of winter wheat. *J. Am. Soc. Agron.* **39**: 769-778.

SUROZ, J. 1891. Oel als Reservestoff der Bäume. *Botan. Centr. Beih.* **1**: 342-343.

SVIHLA, R. D., and OSTERMAN, E. 1943. Growth of orchid seeds after dehydration from the frozen state. *Science* **98**: 23.

SWARBRICK, T. 1927. Studies in the physiology of fruit trees. I. The seasonal starch content and cambial activity in one to five-year-old apple branches. *J. Pomol. Hort. Sci.* **6**: 137-156.

SWINGLE, C. F. 1933. The exosmosis method of determining injury, as applied to apple rootstock hardiness studies. *Proc. Am. Soc. Hort. Sci.* **29**(1932): 380-383.

TADROS, T. M. 1936. The osmotic pressure of Egyptian desert plants in relation to water supply. *Egypt. Univ. Bull. Fac. Sci.* No. **7**: 1-35.

TAGUCHI, R. 1940. Untersuchungen über die jahreszeitliche Aenderung des Wasser- und Reservestoffgehaltes der Stengel and Wurzeln vom Maulbeerbaum. *Japan. J. Botany* **11**: 34.

TAVCAR, A. 1930. Winterfestigkeit und genetisch bedingte Tieflage der Vegetationspunkte an Getreidepflanzen. *Z. Pflanzenzücht.* **15**: 63-74.

TETLEY, U. 1931. A cytological study of the effect of freezing temperatures on some plant tissues. *Dept. Sci. Ind.* (*Brit.*) *Research Food Invest. Board Rept.* pp. 105-106. (*Expt. Sta. Record* **68**: 328, 1933.)

THIEL, H. 1874. *Jahresber. u. Fortschr. Chem. Bod. Luft u. Düng.* 13-15 Jahrgang (1870-1872). 198-199.

THISELTON-DYER, W. 1899. The influence of the temperature of liquid hydrogen on the germinative power of seeds. *Proc. Roy. Soc.* **65**: 361-368.

THODAY, D. 1921. On the behavior during drought of leaves of two Cape Species of Passerina, with some notes on their anatomy. *Ann. Botany* (*London*) **35**: 585-601.

THODAY, D. 1922. On the organisation of growth and differentiation in the stem of the sunflower. *Ann. Botany* (*London*) **36**: 489-510.

THOMAS, W. 1927. Nitrogenous metabolism of *Pyrus malus*. III. *Plant Physiol.* **2**: 109-137.

THOUIN, A. 1806. Observations sur l'effet des gelées précoces qui ont eu lieu les 18, 19 et 20 vendémiaire an XIV (11, 12, et 13 Octobre 1805). *Ann. Muséum hist. nat.* tome septieme: 85-114.

THREN, R. 1934. Jahreszeitliche Schwankungen des osmotischen Wertes verschiedener ökologischer Typen in der Umgebung von Heidelberg. Mit einen Beitrag zur Methodik der Pressaftuntersuchung. *Z. Botan.* **26**: 448-526.

TIMOFEJEVA, M. 1935. Frost resistance of winter cereals in connection with phasic development and hardening of plants. *Compt. rend. acad. sci. U.R.S.S.* **1**: 64-67.

TINGLEY, M. A., SMITH, W. W., PHILLIPS, T. G., and POTTER, G. F. Experimental production of winter injury to the trunks of apple trees by applying nitrogenous fertilizers in the autumn. *Proc. Am. Soc. Hort. Sci.* **36**:(1938): 177-180.

TISCHLER, G. 1905. Über die Beziehungen der Anthocyanbildung zur Winterhärte der Pflanzen. *Botan. Centr. Beih. Abt. I* **18**: 452-471.

TODD, G. W., and LEVITT, J. 1951. Bound water in *Aspergillus niger*. *Plant Physiol.* **26**: 331-336.

TOTTINGHAM, W. E., SHANDS, R. G., and DELWICKE, E. D. 1931. Test of Chibnall's method of extraction for investigating winter hardiness of plants. *Plant Physiol.* **6**: 167-176.

TRAUB, H. P. 1927. Regional and seasonal distribution of moisture, carbohydrates, nitrogen, and ash in 2-3 year portions of apple twigs. *Minnesota Agr. Expt. Sta. Tech. Bull.* **53**: 1-67.

TREVIRANUS, L. C. 1838. "Physiologie der Gewächse," Vol. 2, Book 10, pp. 672-708. Bonn.

TUMANOV, I. I. 1927. Ungenügende Wasserversorgung und das Welken der Pflanzen als Mittel zur Erhöhung ihrer Dürreresistenz. *Planta* **3**: 391-480.

TUMANOV, I. I. 1930. Welken und Dürreresistenz. *Arch. Pflanzenbau* **3**: 389-419.

TUMANOV, I. I. 1931. Das Abhärten winterannueller Pflanzen gegen niedrige Temperaturen. *Phytopathol. Z.* **3**: 303-334.

TUMANOV, I. I. 1940. "The Physiological Bases of Winter Hardiness in Cultivated Plants." Seljhozgiz, Leningrad. (*Herbage Abstr.* **8**: 214-223, 1940.)

TUMANOV, I. I., and BORODIN, I. N. 1930. Untersuchungen über die Kälteresistenz von Winterkulturen durch direktes Gefrieren und indirekte Methoden. *Phytopathol. Z.* **1**: 575-604.

TUMANOV, I. I., BORODINA, I. N., and OLEINIKOVA, T. V. 1935. The role of snow cover in wintering crops (trans. title). *Bull. Appl. Botan. Genet. Plant Breeding Ser.* **3**, No. **6**: 1-57. (*Biol. Abstr.* **11**: 9333, 1937.)

TUTTLE, G. M. 1919. Induced changes in reserve materials in evergreen herbaceous leaves. *Ann. Botany* (*London*) **33**: 201-209.

TUTTLE, G. M. 1921. Reserve food materials in vegetative tissues. *Botan. Gaz.* **71**: 146-151.

TYSDAL, H. M. 1933. Influence of light, temperature, and soil moisture on the hardening process in alfalfa. *J. Agr. Research* **46**: 483-515.

TYSDAL, H. M. 1934. Determination of hardiness in alfalfa varieties by their enzymatic responses. *J. Agr. Research* **48**: 219-240.

TYSDAL, H. M., and PIETERS, A. J. 1934. Cold resistance of three species of lespedeza compared to that of alfalfa, red clover, and crown vetch. *J. Am. Soc. Agron.* **26**: 923-928.

TYSDAL, H. M., and SALMON, S. C. 1926. Viscosity and winter hardiness in the small grains. *J. Am. Soc. Agron.* **18**: 1099-1100.

ULLRICH, H. 1941. Über Strukturänderungen beim Gefrieren von Gelen. *Kolloid-Z.* **96**: 348-353.

ULLRICH, H. 1943. Biologische Kältewirkungen und plasmatische Frostresistenz (Unter besonderer Berücksichtigung der Pflanzen). *Protoplasma* **38**: 165-183.

ULLRICH, H., and MÄDE, A. 1940. Studien über die Ursachen der Frostresistenz. II. Untersuchungen über den Temperaturverlauf beim Gefrieren von Blättern und Vergleichsobjekten. *Planta* **31**: 251-262.

ULMER, W. 1937. Über den Jahresgang der Frosthärte einiger immergrüner Arten der alpinen Stufe, sowie der Zirbe und Fichte. Unter Berücksichtigung von osmotischen Wert, Zuckerspiegel und Wassergehalt. *Jahrb. wiss. Botan.* **84**: 553-592.

URSPRUNG, A. 1933. Über die Beziehungen zwischen der Wasserbilanz und einigen osmotischen Zustandsgrössen. *Ber. schweiz botan. Ges.* **42**: 225-237.

URSPRUNG, A., and BLUM, G. 1916. Über die periodischen Schwankungen des osmotischen Wertes. *Ber. deut. botan. Ges.* **34**: 105-123; Über den Einfluss der Aussenbedingungen auf den osmotischen Wert. *Ibid.* **34**: 123-142.

VAN DOREN, C. A. 1937. Bound water and electrical conductivity as measures of cold resistance in winter wheat. *J. Am. Soc. Agron.* **29**: 392-402.

VAN HALTEREN, P. 1950. Effets d'un choc thermique sur le métabolisme des levures. *Bull. soc. chim. biol.* **32**(7/8): 458-463.

VAN MONS. 1838. Les effets produits par les dernières gelées sur les arbres fruitiers. *Bull. acad. roy. sci. belles lettres Bruxelles* **5**: 83-84.

VASSILJEV, I. M. 1931. Untersuchungen über die Dynamik der Kohlehydrate bei dem Weizen. I. Mitt. Einfluss der Wasserversorgung auf die Umwandlung der Kohlehydrate. *Arch. Pflanzenbau* **7**: 126-146.

VASSILJEV, I. M. 1934. Yarovisation of winter varieties and frost resistance. *Compt. rend. acad. sci. U.R.S.S.* **4**: 158-161.

VASSILJEV, I. M. 1939. Winter wheats as lagging behind the spring varieties in growth intensity when subjected to low temperatures. *Compt. rend. acad. sci. U.R.S.S.* **24**: 85-87.

VASSILIEV, I. M., and VASSILIEV, M. G. 1936. Changes in carbohydrate content of wheat plants during the process of hardening for drought resistance. *Plant. Physiol.* **11**: 115-125.

VERDUIN, J., and LOOMIS, W. E. 1944. Absorption of carbon dioxide by maize. *Plant Physiol.* **19**: 278-293.

VETUHOVA, A. 1936. Depression of photosynthesis with fall of temperature as an indicator of relative frost resistance of plants. *Zbirnik Prac. Agrofiziol.* **1**: 140-154. (*Herbage Abstr.* **8**: 1790, 1938.)

VETUHOVA, A. 1936a. Winter hardiness of winter wheat during winter in relation to phasic development of plants. *Zbirnik Prac. Agrofiziol.* **2**: 83-102. (*Herbage Abstr.* **8**: 1861, 1938.)

VETUHOVA, A. 1938. On the internal factors of resistance to frost in winter plants. *Z. Inst. Botan. Akad. Nauk. U.R.S.S.* No. **18-19** (26-27): 57-59. (*Herbage Abstr.* **9**: 633, 1939.)

VETUHOVA, A. 1939. Chemical treatment of winter wheat seed as a measure to increase frost resistance. *Compt. rend. acad. sci. U.R.S.S.* **24**: 605-608.

VETUHOVA, A. 1939a. Colloidal changes in plants of winter wheat in relation to the dynamics of frost resistance. *Kolloid-Z.* **4**: 511-521. (*Herbage Abstr.* **10**: 173, 1940.)

VOGEL, A. 1820. Ueber die Veränderung welche einige Stoffe des organischen Reichs beim Gefrieren erleiden. *Ann. Physik* **64**: 167-171.

VOIGTLÄNDER, H. 1909. Unterkühlung und Kältetod der Pflanzen. *Beitr. Biol. Pflanz.* **9**: 359-414.

VONDRACK, J. 1926. Changes in the composition of frozen beets. *Intern. Sugar. J.* **28**: 149-151. (*Biol. Abstr.* **1**: 311.)

VON USLAR, J. 1794. "Fragmente neuer Pflanzenkunde," pp. 1-188. Vieweg, Braunschweig.

VOUK, V. 1923. Die Probleme der Biologie der Thermen. *Intern. Rev. Hydrobiol.* **11**: 89-99.

VROLI, G., and DE VRIESE, W. H. 1839. Nouvelles expériences sur l'élévation de température du spadice d'une Colocasia odora (Caladium odorum) faites au Jardin Botanique d'Amsterdam. *Ann. sci. nat.* [2] **11**: 65-85.

WADLEIGH, C. H., GAUCH, H. G., and DAVIES, V. 1943. The trend of starch reserves in bean plants before and after irrigation of a saline soil. *Proc. Am. Soc. Hort. Sci.* **43**: 201-209.

WAGGONER, P. E., and SHAW, R. H. 1953. Temperature of potato and tomato leaves. *Plant Physiol.* **27**(4): 710-724.

WAHRY, E. 1936. Permeabilitätsstudien an Hippuris. *Jahrb. wiss. Botan.* **83**: 657-705.

WALDRON, L. R. 1932. Frost injury to spring wheat with a consideration of drought resistance. *J. Am. Soc. Agron.* **23**: 625-637.

WALLACE, T. 1926. An experiment on the winterkilling of vegetable crops in market gardens. *J. Pomol. Hort. Sci.* **5**: 205-209. (*Biol. Abstr.* **2**: 2679, 1928.)

WALTER, H. 1924. Plasmaquellung und Wachstum. *Z. Botan.* **16**: 353-417.

WALTER, H. 1926. Die Anpassungen der Pflanzen an Wassermangel. *Naturw. u. Landwirtsch.* **9**: 115 pp.

WALTER, H. 1929. Plasmaquellung und assimilation. *Protoplasma* **6**: 113-156.

WALTER, H. 1929. Die osmotischen Werte und die Kälteschäden unserer wintergrünen Pflanzen während der Winterperiode 1929. *Ber. deut. botan. Ges.* **47**: 338-348.

WALTER, H. 1931. "Hydratur der Pflanze und ihre physiologisch-ökologische Bedeutung." Fischer, Jena.

WALTER, H. 1936. Tabellen zur Berechnung des osmotischen Wertes von Pflanzenpressäften, Zuckerlösungen und einigen Salzlösungen. *Ber. deut. botan. Ges.* **54**: 328-339.

WALTER, H. 1949. Über die Assimilation und Atmung der Pflanzen im Winter bei tiefen Temperaturen. *Ber. deut. botan. Ges.* **62**: 47-50.

WALTER, H., and WEISMANN, O. 1935. Über die Gefrierpunkte und osmotischen Werte lebender und tote pflanzlicher Gewebe. *Jahrb. wiss. Botan.* **82**: 273-310.

WARMING, E. 1909. "Oecology of Plants," p. 23. Oxford, New York.

WARTENBERG, H. 1929. Zur Biologie der Kartoffel. III. Über die Wirkung der Kalidüngung auf die Frostempfindlichkeit der Kartoffelpflanze. *Arb. biol. Reichsanstalt Land. u. Forstwirtsch. Berlin-Dahlem* **17**: 377-384.

WARTENBURG, H. 1933. Kälte und Hitze als Todesursache der Pflanze und als Ursache von Pflanzenkrankheiten. "Sorauer's Handbuch der Pflanzenkrankheiten" Vol. 1, 6th ed. pp. 475-592. Parey, Berlin.

WARTENBURG, H. 1941. Untersuchungen über den Kältetod der Pflanze. *Landwirtsch. Jahrb.* **90**: 247.

WATANABE, M. 1953. Effect of heat application upon the pollen viability of Japanese black pine and Japanese red pine. *J. Japan. Forestry Soc.* **35**(3): 248-251.

WEBER, F. 1926. Hitzeresistenz funktionierender Schliesszellen. *Planta* **1**: 553-557.

WEBER, F. 1926a. Hitzeresistenz funktionierender Stomata-Nebenzellen. *Planta* **2**: 669-677.

WEBER, F. 1909. Untersuchungen über die Wandlungen des Stärke- und Fettgehaltes der Pflanzen, insbesondere der Bäume. *Sitzber. Akad. Wiss. Wien Math. naturw. Kl. Abt. I* **118**: 967-1031.

WEBER, F. 1930. Permeabilität der Stomata-Zellen. *Protoplasma* **10**: 608-612.

WEBER, F. 1931. Harnstoff-Permeabilität ungleich alter Spirogyra-Zellen. *Protoplasma* **12**: 129-140.

WEBER, F. 1935. Review of Kessler (1935). *Protoplasma* **24**: 631.

WEBER, F., and HOHENEGGER, H. 1923. Reversible Viscositätserhöhung des Protoplasmas bei Kälte. *Ber. deut. botan. Ges.* **41**: 198-204.

WEHMER, C. 1904. Über die Lebensdauer eingetrockneter Pilzkulturen. *Ber. deut. botan. Ges.* **22**: 476-478.

WEIBEL, R. O., and QUISENBERRY, K. S. 1941. Field versus controlled freezing as a measure of cold resistance of winter wheat varieties. *J. Am. Soc. Agron.* **33**: 336-343.

WEIMER, J. L. 1929. Some factors involved in the winterkilling of alfalfa. *J. Agr. Research* **39**: 263-283.

WEISMANN, O. 1938. Eine theoretische und experimentelle Kritik der "Bound Water Theorie." *Protoplasma* **31**: 27-68.

WERK, O. 1954. Untersuchungen zum Dürreeffekt. 2. Über den Kalium- und Calciumgehalt feucht und trocken gezogener Pflanzen. *Flora* **141**: 312-355.

WEST, F. L., and EDLEFSEN, N. E. 1917. The freezing of fruit buds. *Utah Agr. Expt. Sta. Bull.* **151**: 1-24.

WEST, F. L., and EDLEFSEN, N. E. 1921. Freezing of fruit buds. *J. Agr. Research* **20**: 655-662.

WHITESIDE, A. G. O. 1941. Effect of soil drought on wheat plants. *Sci. Agr.* **21**: 320-334.

WHITMAN, W. C. 1941. Seasonal changes in bound water content of some prairie grasses. *Botan. Gaz.* **103**: 38-63.

WHYTE-STEVENS, R. H. 1937. Some cellular changes in celery during freezing and frost hardening. *Proc. Am. Soc. Hort. Sci.* **34**: 570-576.

WIEGAND, K. M. 1906. Some studies regarding the biology of buds and twigs in winter. *Botan. Gaz.* **41**: 373-424.

WIEGAND, K. M. 1906a. The occurrence of ice in plant tissue. *Plant World* **9**: 25-39, 107.

WIEGAND, K. M. 1906b. The passage of water from the plant cell during freezing. *Plant World* **9**: 107-118.

WIGHT, W. 1933. Radial growth of the xylem and the starch reserves of *Pinus sylvestris*. *New Phytologist* **32**: 77-96.

WILHELM, A. F. 1935. Untersuchungen über die Kälteresistenz winterfester Kulturpflanzen unter besonderer Berücksichtigung des Einflusses verschiedener Mineralsalzernährung und des N-Stoffwechsels. *Phytopathol. Z.* **8**: 111-156.

WILHELM, A. F. 1935a. Untersuchungen über das Verhalten sogennanter nicht eisbeständiger Kulturpflanzen bei niederen-Temperaturen, unter besonderer Berücksichtigung des Einflusses verschiedener Mineralsalzernährung und des N-Stoffwechsels. *Phytopathol. Z.* **8**: 337-362.

WILHELM, A. F. 1936. Studien über die Bedeutung der lipoide, insbesondere der Phosphatide, für die Frostresistenz der Pflanzen. *Phytopathol. Z.* **8**: 225-236.

WILLARD, C. J. 1922. Root reserves of alfalfa with special reference to time of cutting on yield. *J. Am. Soc. Agron.* **22**: 595-602.

WILLARD, C. J. 1930. Root reserves of alfalfa with special reference to time of cutting and yield. *J. Am. Soc. Agron.* **22**: 595-602.

WILLDENOW, D. C. 1805. "The Principles of Botany and of Vegetable Physiology," pp. 244-248. Edinburgh.

WILNER, J. 1952. A study of desiccation in relation to winter injury. *Sci. Agr.* **32**: 651-658.

WILSON, B. H. 1929. The relation of hardiness and maturity in the apple. *Proc. Am. Soc. Hort. Sci.* **26**: 199-202.

WILSON, B. H. 1930. The relation of maturity in the apple to relative winter injury. *Sci. Agr.* **10**: 598-606.

WINKLER, A. 1913. Über den Einfluss der Aussenbedingungen auf die Kälteresistenz ausdauernder Gewächse. *Jahrb. wiss. Botan.* **52**: 467-506.

WOHACK, F. 1930. Zur Frostschutzwirkung der Kalisalze. *Ernähr. Pflanze* **26**: 318-319. (*Biol. Abstr.* **5**: 27205, 1931.)

WOLFF, C. J. DE. 1926. Die Saccharosebildung in Kartoffeln während des Trocknens. *Biochem. Z.* **176**: 225-245. (*Biol. Abstr.* **1**: 6519.)

WOODROOF, J. G. 1940. Theory of food freezing. *Chronica Botan.* **6**: 148-150.

WORLEY, C. L. 1937. Carbohydrate changes within the needles of *Pinus ponderosa* and *Pseudotseuga taxifolia*. *Plant Physiol.* **12**: 755-770.

WORZELLA, W. W. 1932. Root development in hardy and non-hardy winter wheat varieties. *J. Am. Soc. Agron.* **24**: 626-637.

WORZELLA, W. W. 1935. Inheritance of cold resistance in winter wheat with preliminary studies on the technic of artificial freezing tests. *J. Agr. Research* **50**: 625-635.

WORZELLA, W. W. 1942. Inheritance and interrelationship of components of quality, cold resistance, and morphological characters in wheat hybrids. *J. Agr. Research* **65**: 501-522.

WORZELLA, W. W., and CUTLER, G. H. 1941. Factors affecting cold resistance in winter wheat. *J. Am. Soc. Agron.* **33**: 221-230.

WRIGHT, R. C. 1927. Freezing injury to potatoes. *U.S. Dept. Agr. Tech. Bull.* **27**: 1-23.

WRIGHT, R. C. 1932. Some physiological studies of potatoes in storage. *J. Agr. Research* **45**: 543-555.

WRIGHT, S. G. 1890. The relation of low temperature to the growth of wheat. *Agr. Sci.* **4**: 337-344.

YASUDA, S. 1926. On the winter-hardiness of barley. I. On the relation between the winterhardiness and the monosaccharose content. *J. Sci. Agr. Soc.* **288**: 486-493. (*Biol. Abstr.* **4**: 3832, 1930.)

YASUDA, S. 1927. On the winter-hardiness of barley. II. Effect of potassium salts. *J. Sci. Agr. Soc.* **295**: 273-281. (*Biol. Abstr.* **4**: 3833, 1930.)

YASUDA, S. 1929. On the physiology of barley under snow at Morioka. *Proc. Crop. Sci. Soc. Japan* **4**: 41-50 (*Biol. Abstr.* **5**: 27206, 1931.)

ZACHAROWA, T. M. 1926. Über den Einfluss niedriger Temperaturen auf die Pflanzen. *Jahrb. wiss. Botan.* **65**: 61-87.

ZELLER, O. 1951. Über Assimilation und Atmung der Pflanzen im Winter bei tiefen Temperaturen. *Planta* **39**: 500-526.

ZIMPFER, P. E. 1938. The effect of certain variables on the freezing point depression of plant tissues. 15th Annual Meeting of the American Society for Plant Physiology, Richmond, Virginia.

ZOBL, K. 1950. Ueber die Beziehungen zwischen chemischer Zusammensetzung von Pilzsporen und ihrem Verhalten gegen Erhitzen. *Sydowia.* **4**(1/6): 175-184.

Index